Trailer Life's
RV
Repair &
Maintenance
Manual

D1452311

OTHER BOOKS BY TRAILER LIFE

Secrets of Successful RVing
John Thompson and the Editors of *Trailer Life* magazine

The RVer's encyclopedia. Here in one handy book are all the facts you need to know to buy, maintain, and enjoy camping trailers, campers, motorhomes, trailers, and van conversions, including rental information.
7¼ × 9¼, 309 pages
$12.95 cover price   ISBN: 0-934798-03-6

RX for RV Performance & Mileage
John Geraghty and Bill Estes

In 32 chapters, this book covers everything an owner must know about how an engine (particularly a V-8) works, vehicle maintenance, propane and diesel as alternative fuels, eliminating engine "ping," improving exhaust systems and fuel economy, and much more.
7¾ × 9¼, 359 pages
$14.95 cover price   ISBN: 0-934798-08-0

Rider's Complete Guide to Motorcycle Touring
Dick Blom & the Editors of *Trailer Life* magazine

This guide brings you the tips and techniques that will make your tours worry-free—whether you're day tripping or touring from coast to coast. You'll find out how to buy a touring motorcycle that fits your needs—and your budget—and how to maintain your motorcycle on and off the road. Hundreds of photos (including sixteen pages in full color!) and drawings.
7½ × 9½, 207 pages
$12.95 cover price   ISBN: 0-934798-02-8

These books are available at fine bookstores everywhere. Or, you may order directly from Trailer Life. For each book ordered, simply send us the name of the book, the cover price, plus $2 per book for shipping and handling (California residents please add 6½% sales tax). Mail to:

Trailer Life, PO Box 4500, Agoura, CA 91301

You may call our Customer Service representatives if you wish to charge your order or if you want more information. Phone, toll-free, Monday through Friday, 7:30 A.M. to 6:00 P.M.; Saturday, 7:30 A.M. to 12:30 P.M. Pacific Time, **1-800-423-5061**. In California call **1-800-382-3455**.

Trailer Life's

RV Repair & Maintenance Manual

By John Thompson
and the Editors of Trailer Life

Editor in Charge: Patrick J. Flaherty
Technical Editor: Bill Estes

Published by Trailer Life Publishing Co., Inc.
29901 Agoura Road, Agoura, California 91301

Book Division
TL Enterprises, Inc.

Richard Rouse
President

Ted Binder
Vice President/General Manager

Bill Estes
Vice President/Technical Editor

Michael Schneider
Publisher, Book Division

Rena Copperman
General Manager, Book Division

Cindy Lang
Assistant Manager, Book Division

Composition by: Publisher's Typography
(A Division of TL Enterprises, Inc.)
Book Design: Jim Doolan

Published by TL Enterprises, Inc.
29901 Agoura Road, Agoura, California 91301

Copyright © 1980 by TL Enterprises, Inc. Sixth impression, 1986. All rights reserved. Reproduction of this work, in whole or in part, without written permission of the publisher, is prohibited.

ISBN 0-934798-00-1

Printed in the United States of America

10 9 8 7

Foreword

Over the years, I've logged hundreds of thousands of miles in recreational vehicles — and I've loved every minute and mile of it.

But don't think for one moment that all my travels were trouble-free. Because I've faced more mechanical problems than I care to remember, and I've wasted more time and money in RV service centers than I care to admit.

As a result, I know from hard experience that RVers have long needed a comprehensive and authoritative technical guide that would show them how to service every system found in their RVs — and thus cut down on the costly emergencies that plague us all. With the publication of Trailer Life's *RV Repair & Maintenance Manual*, the need for such a do-it-yourself reference work has been admirably filled — and I just couldn't be prouder of the job our people have done with it.

Which leaves little to add, except that I hope this new book will save you time, trouble and money in the years ahead, and serve to heighten your enjoyment of the wonderful life we live on wheels.

Art Rouse
Chairman of the Board

Table of Contents

Chapter One

Getting Ready

01.01 PUTTING YOUR MIND INTO REPAIRS.

If you're a typical RVer, you didn't buy this book because you want to while away hours underneath your RV. Instead, your motive was 180 degrees different; you hope that owning this manual will keep you out from under your rig — and away from big repair bills.

Both objectives can be easily achieved if you'll faithfully follow the instructions to be found here, and if you'll read this brief chapter *before* you move on. Because this is where we're going to tell you that the number-one secret of good mechanics lives in their minds, not in their toolboxes . . . and their secret is this:

IDENTIFY THE PROBLEM, THEN
ELEVATE YOUR THINKING ABOVE
THE LEVEL OF THE PROBLEM.

Whether known as "grease monkeys," service engineers or technicians, mechanics can be separated into "The Effectives" or "Those You Wish You Never Met" — all depending on how well they understand and apply the "identify and elevate" principle. Certainly there's no point in maligning ineffective people; but emulating the reasons why other people succeed will give *us* a chance to excel, as well. So let's apply this foundation philosophy to itself and see what it really means.

Remember the joke about the doctor who was elated over his perfect surgical repair, even though the patient died from his efforts? Obviously, this practitioner was caught in the energy of the problem — and oblivious to the total entity on which he was working. Said another way, he understood the mechanics perfectly, and he made an expert repair; but because he couldn't elevate his thinking to include the system which encompassed the malfunction, the results were inevitably ineffective.

Rising above the level of the problem means expanding your perception of things. To use a ridiculously simple example, suppose your reading lamp fails to work and you trace the problem to a defective light socket. Now you understand the problem and you know what to do; but if you don't stop to remember that the lamp is only one part of a vaster electrical system, you may get the last shock of your life.

A more likely occurrence, for an RVer, would be trailer brake pads that keep wearing out. There's a simple diagnosis and cure, but unless you're able to enlarge your vision and picture the brake pads as only a piece in a whole sequence of events, you'll never correct the reason why the pads keep wearing out. That omission could some day prove as serious as the consequences to the doctor's patient!

Yes, the technique is simple — ridiculously so. And you can easily see how it becomes more functional as you progress into more complex malfunctions. Yet there is something very seductive about a problem. As a case in point, remember the last time your awareness was tightly focused on a dilemma or an argument? The parameters of the problem set up an almost magnetic barrier and confined the mind to an enclosed area. That's often what's really meant by the phrase, "closed minded," and that's precisely why an arbitrator is often useful in settling a disagreement; the arbitrator isn't locked into the tunnel-vision that keeps the participants from seeing the total picture.

Becoming intrigued by a mechanical malfunction, or angry with it, or in any way emotional about it, creates this very same enclosed space which is very difficult to surmount. So you must cross over the barriers if you want to be an effective repair or maintenance do-it-yourselfer.

"See the problem, then move into an awareness of the whole." Engrave this motto on your toolbox and use it every time you use this manual, and you'll soon be a hard mechanic to fault.

01.02 STAYING WITH THE FLOW.

Another way of seeing our "identify and elevate" principle is through the *idea of systems* which is taught to any first-year physics student — and even to medical or law or almost any other kind of student. Here's how that works:

Every single thing, whether it be this page, the water pump on your rig or our solar system, is only part of a much vaster system — a cog in a greater wheel or an integral part of the whole. You can go on from here to see that reality consists of systems within systems within systems — so imagining the ultimate system is about as difficult as visualizing infinity. Fortunately, though, we only have to deal with a few systems here — a limited reality — but the broader thoughts are fun on a warm, clear night when you're lying under the stars thinking about your place in the universe.

Does this mind-game really relate to fixing your RV? You bet it does — and in a very big way. For once the student grasps the concept of systems, he moves on to thoughts about equilibrium, and this is something that your run-of-the-mill big-bill low-performance mechanic doesn't bother to recognize, even though he's confronted with it every day.

Everything, but everything, always seeks a state of equilibrium wherein its own force is met by an equal and opposite force. Water runs downhill seeking this equilibrium; the stars describe a specific pattern of travel seeking equilibrium, and the engine that drives your RV is driven by an explosion which is seeking equilibrium.

Regardless of how theoretical this concept may sound, it is absolutely the most functional and practical way to approach your repairs. Simply realize that whenever a part is "running wild" or acting abnormally, it is *seeking* equilibrium in a non-functional, or even destructive, manner. When something is not moving, it has found equilibrium. Hold this concept of systems, equilibrium and flow in mind and you'll soon find yourself extraordinarily adept at discovering problems and clearing malfunctions.

01.03 KEEPING RECORDS.

Moving onto a less cerebral level, you'll find that people who operate large numbers of vehicles have two primary objectives: (1) To keep those rigs on the road, and (2) To keep their repair bills down. Because these goals are identical with our own, we can benefit from understanding that fleet operators achieve their purposes through good records and prompt action, so let these mottos be your guide.

Keeping good records should be simple for you, too, because you're only dealing with one rig. The problem most people encounter here is consistency; for the records to be useful, you must keep them on a regular basis.

The kinds of records you want are obviously based upon the type, size and complexity of your RV. The engines in motorhomes and tow vehicles need separate records, and any book on auto or truck mechanics will give you ideas on doing this. With RV systems and appliances, the most useful records consist of keeping tabs on when things are repaired or maintained. In other words, use a separate page for everything mechanical aboard your rig and record exactly when you clean, adjust, replace a part, overhaul, etc.

The benefits which accrue from this kind of accountancy should be evident. To use the example cited earlier, let's say you're about to replace some worn brake pads and you notice that even though the last replacement was many months ago, only 4,000 miles have elapsed. Now you're alerted to a new dimension of the problem, and perhaps through some simple troubleshooting

"beyond the level of the problem" you'll discover something which can be cured before it becomes expensive.

Keeping accurate records means saving every repair invoice when you have the pros do your work. And it also means asking the service establishment to itemize every part they install, rather than simply giving you a list of illegible stock numbers. Admittedly, this is a pain to the busy service manager — but it's your money and your safety we're talking about, so don't take "no" for an answer.

01.04 HOW THIS BOOK IS ORGANIZED.

The service manual situation in most industries, not just in RVs, is often deficient. The usual situation is that manufacturers may truly understand their product, but they fail to communicate their knowledge clearly. Outside (independently written) service manuals either directly reprint this literature, thereby compounding confusion, or their authors don't really understand that the do-it-yourselfer may also need some very basic information in order to comprehend the repair.

The problem thus boils down to clarity and completeness. These two words are the theme of this volume and, while no book can pretend to cover everything, we've tried in each instance to give you a basic grasp of how each system and accessory works. From this platform of knowledge you can often figure things out for yourself when the specific malfunction isn't detailed.

Some instructions and explanations must necessarily be generalized, because there are configurational differences between different brands. This means that you must be alert to find, for instance, that the adjustment screw you're looking for is on the left side of a knob in one model and the right in another. Stay flexible in your thinking and you won't get lost.

01.05 THE COMPLETE TOOLBOX.

As any mechanic will tell you, you can never have enough tools. "Gadgeteering" can even become a preoccupation wherein you "absolutely need" every single device which hits the market. For most of us, though, a simple toolbox is really the best, and many tools can be made to perform diverse duties when you find that something is lacking. The fundamental assortment consists of the items illustrated in Figure 1, together with battery jumper cables. Additional tools are mentioned throughout the text, so let your budget — and your interest in mechanics — guide your collection.

Optional items you'll want to consider include a

tube of graphite (for lubricating locks), a good rust inhibitor and lubricant (e.g., WD-40), and 100 feet of 500-pound test nylon rope. The rope doesn't have any specific purpose, but our experience is that it has unlimited uses.

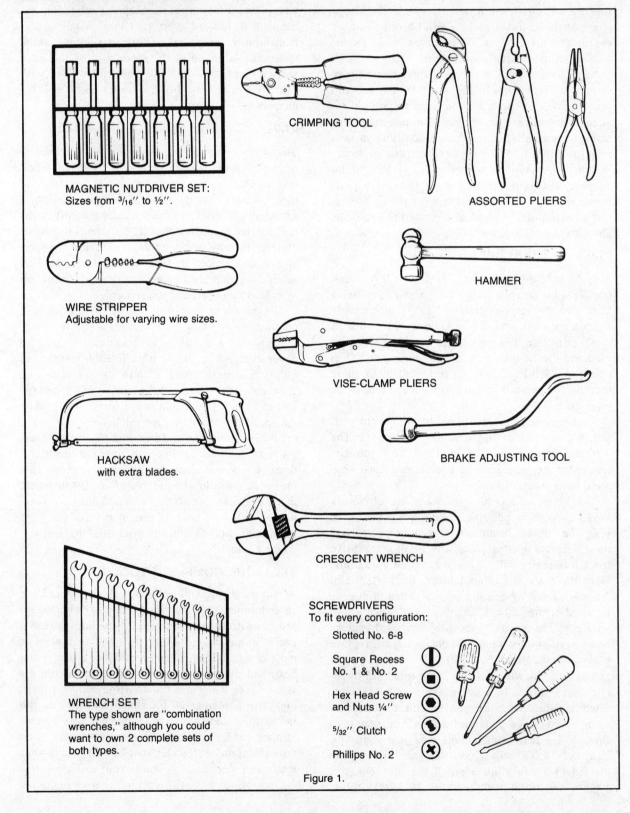

MAGNETIC NUTDRIVER SET:
Sizes from 3/16" to 1/2".

CRIMPING TOOL

ASSORTED PLIERS

WIRE STRIPPER
Adjustable for varying wire sizes.

HAMMER

VISE-CLAMP PLIERS

HACKSAW
with extra blades.

BRAKE ADJUSTING TOOL

CRESCENT WRENCH

WRENCH SET
The type shown are "combination wrenches," although you could want to own 2 complete sets of both types.

SCREWDRIVERS
To fit every configuration:

Slotted No. 6-8

Square Recess
No. 1 & No. 2

Hex Head Screw
and Nuts 1/4"

5/32" Clutch

Phillips No. 2

Figure 1.

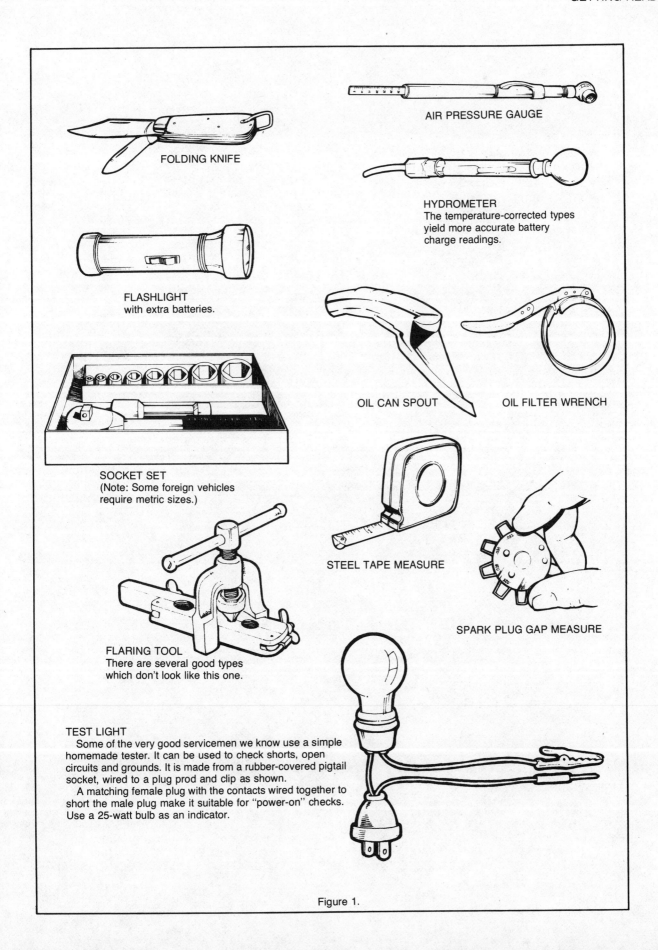

FOLDING KNIFE

AIR PRESSURE GAUGE

HYDROMETER
The temperature-corrected types
yield more accurate battery
charge readings.

FLASHLIGHT
with extra batteries.

OIL CAN SPOUT

OIL FILTER WRENCH

SOCKET SET
(Note: Some foreign vehicles
require metric sizes.)

STEEL TAPE MEASURE

SPARK PLUG GAP MEASURE

FLARING TOOL
There are several good types
which don't look like this one.

TEST LIGHT
Some of the very good servicemen we know use a simple
homemade tester. It can be used to check shorts, open
circuits and grounds. It is made from a rubber-covered pigtail
socket, wired to a plug prod and clip as shown.
A matching female plug with the contacts wired together to
short the male plug make it suitable for "power-on" checks.
Use a 25-watt bulb as an indicator.

Figure 1.

Chapter Two

Trailer Brakes

Most states have laws that require travel trailers weighing over 1,500 pounds to be equipped with their own brakes. Here's the reasoning:

Tow vehicle brakes are rated according to torque, heat capacity and drum loading (the weight of the vehicle divided by the drum area). The average car drum loading of about 15 pounds per square inch is more than ample for safe stopping. But if your vehicle weighs 3,500 pounds, and you add a 2,500-pound travel trailer without brakes of its own, the automobile's brake drum loading jumps to over 25 pounds per square inch. This substantially exceeds the brakes' safety capacity by adding to the overall stopping distance.

One purpose of independent trailer brakes, then, is to provide combined vehicles with stopping times and distances comparable to that of the tow vehicle alone. The other use for independent brakes is to give you instant control over a trailer that begins dancing behind you to its own rhythm!

Assuming that you begin with trouble-free trailer brakes, keeping them safe becomes your responsibility. But this can easily be accomplished through good driving habits, routine inspections, proper maintenance and prompt repair of damage.

02.01   HOW TRAILER BRAKES WORK.

The problem of understanding trailer brakes is made simple by the fact that they haven't changed much since the glory days of America's covered wagons. The principle involved is still the application of pressure on a moving portion of the wheel to create a friction-drag. If this drag is in harmony with the stopping effort of the tow vehicle, and if it is applied uniformly to each wheel, a smooth and straight stop follows. It's easy to see that a lack of uniformity would cause the trailer to swerve toward the more potent brake. And should the trailer brakes exert more or less stopping power than the tow vehicle, this inequality leads to either the trailer stopping the car or the car brakes doing too much of the job. Each of these possibilities is dangerous.

Figure 1 depicts the features which are common to most trailer brakes, regardless of the method used to actuate them.

Two shoes, labeled "A," consist of a metal base to which is attached a covering of hard asbestos or other frictional material called the brake pads. This assembly is stationary. The brake drum, shown partially cut away and labeled "B," revolves with the wheel around the shoes when the trailer is in motion. Under running conditions, the shoes are "at rest" in a contracted position — held by the retractor springs (shown separately in

the top drawing and properly attached in the bottom drawing).

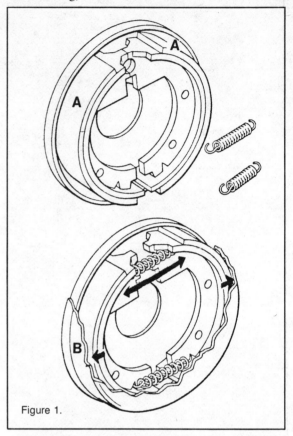

Figure 1.

If you're getting the idea that trailer and automobile brakes are similar, you couldn't be more right. (In some cases the parts are even interchangeable.) The real difference occurs in the way trailer brakes are actuated, but you'll find this easy to understand. And to prove it, let's take a look at the electrically actuated brakes first.

02.02   ELECTRIC BRAKES — HOW THEY WORK.

Most travel trailers have electric brakes. This is partly because the electrics employ an existing energy source (the tow vehicle's 12-volt system) and are more economical to manufacture and install. They are also good brakes.

Electrics employ electromagnets which are attached to a mechanical brake shoe operating mechanism. When it is energized, the magnet is attracted to the armature — a smooth steel plate which rotates with the wheel drum (Figure 2). As the armature continues to revolve, the magnet tries to move with it in the same direction (Figure 3).

This pull on the magnet forces the activating arm to push the leading brake shoe against the drum. Giving the magnet more electricity makes it grip the armature tighter, and as it tries harder to move in the direction of travel, the brake shoe pushes against the drum with greater force.

Cutting off the electric supply stops the magnet's attraction and lets the springs hold the shoes away from the drum.

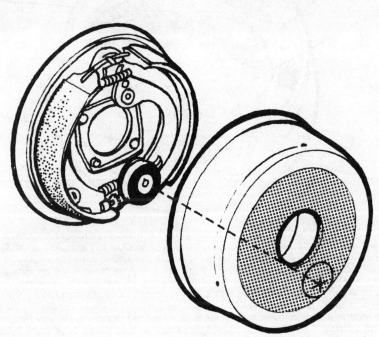

Figure 2. An electric brake showing the drum separated from the braking mechanism. The shaded area inside the drum is the armature, and the broken line indicates where the spot magnet will contact the armature when the brakes are actuated. (Illustration courtesy of Warner Electric Brake and Clutch Company.)

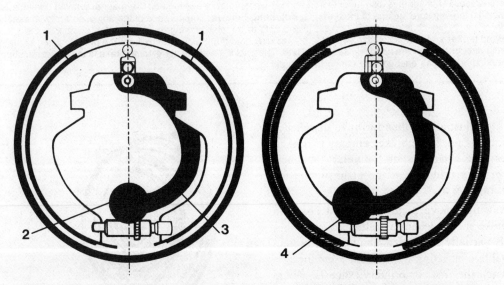

Figure 3. The electric brake in a relaxed (left drawing) and activated (right drawing) position. The outermost circle represents the brake drum. When in a relaxed (non-functioning) position, there is a gap between the brake shoes (1) and the drum, and the magnet (2) is in a centered position. The magnet is attached to a lever (3) whose function is to force the shoe against the drum when the magnet is energized. (4) shows the position of the magnet as it is energized and attracted to the moving armature. This movement causes the lever to push the brake shoes against the drum. (Illustration courtesy of Dico Company, Incorporated.)

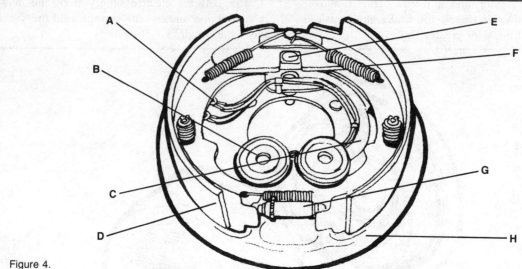

Figure 4.

A. Electric Terminals. An electric brake is easily wired for service, with two wires requiring connection to the magnet lead wires projecting from the backing plate of the brake, or to terminal connectors in the backing plate. **B. Magnet Assembly.** Electromagnets are the means by which an electric brake is actuated. Whether one or two magnets are used, or whether the magnets are small spot magnets (as illustrated) or the large annular type magnet, the principle is the same. Current is applied to the electromagnet, the magnetic force draws the magnet against the armature surface of the brake drum, operating the actuating lever in the direction in which the drum is turning. **C. Actuating Lever.** The actuating lever in the illustration is a lever arm which turns an actuating cam wedged between the brake shoes. In Warner Electric's largest brake the actuating lever is a large annular magnet which is connected directly to the independent cams between the shoes. **D. Shoes and Linings.** As is true of all drum-type brakes, electric brakes have brake lining material of varying characteristics, either bonded or riveted to a pair of shoes or a single brake band. **E. Actuating Cam.** The actuating lever turns the actuating cam, forcing the primary shoe (or band and lining) out against the inside of the brake drum. Through the adjusting screw the force of the primary shoe moves the secondary shoe into contact with the brake drum. **F. Springs.** Shoe return spring and adjuster springs are designed to respond quickly to a decrease in current to the magnet, decreasing the outward pressure of the brake shoes or if all current is removed from the magnet, restoring all components to their inactive position. The magnet is also mounted on springs whose purpose is to keep the magnet running continuously, but lightly against the armature surface of the drum. **G. Adjusting Screws.** The purpose of the adjusting screw is to adjust the brake for wear. In two-shoe adjustable brakes, it also acts to transfer braking forces from the primary to the secondary shoe. Band brakes and non-adjustable two-shoe brakes distribute the braking forces from the primary lining to the secondary lining directly through the band. **H. Backing Plate.** The backing plate of the electric brake is the structural support for the tremendous stresses encountered during trailer braking.

While the illustrations thus far have depicted a single spot magnet, some brakes employ two. And still others use a circular or "annular" magnet. But the braking principle is the same with each type (Figures 4 & 5).

The drawings above picture the most common type of brake shoe mechanics, called *uni servo* because it is partially self-energizing. In this system an adjustable connecting mechanism joins the two shoes. When the first, or primary, shoe is moved into position against the drum, it is dragged in the direction of travel. The distance which it can actually move is limited, but that movement is transmitted through the connecting mechanism to the secondary shoe, pulling it against the drum also. In this way the brake is both externally and internally actuated.

Because electrics depend upon the magnet firm-

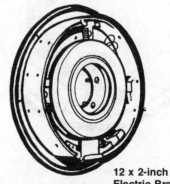

Figure 5.

12 x 2-inch Electric Brake
For trailer axles rated for a maximum of 5,200 lbs. load.

ly grasping the armature, it's important that the armature plates be clean, dry and undamaged. (The plate itself could theoretically last for an incredibly long time, but it must be cared for.) Faulty grease seals can easily be the cause of magnets not adhering to the armature, which results in a loss of braking ability on that wheel. Check and replace these seals frequently. Also, dirt and sand can work between the magnet and armature to seriously score the armature surface. A thorough checkup and cleansing after being exposed to these conditions can be preventative, but if damage does occur it's no great hassle to replace most armatures (see Section 02.24).

Other wearing surfaces should also be checked with greater frequency after mountainous driving, exposure to abrasives or whenever braking has been excessive. Brake linings should be replaced whenever they get close to the degree of wear specified by their manufacturer, as poor linings will yield anywhere from poor to extremely grabby braking, and the drums should frequently be visually inspected for excessive scoring. Also, it's both inexpensive and a very good idea to replace subsidiary parts such as retractor springs at the same time you reline your brakes. Experts caution that both sets of brake linings on an axle should be replaced at the same time, even if only one set is badly worn (if this is the case, you'll want to find out why they're wearing unevenly).

Also important in keeping repair bills down are frequent and thorough brake and bearing inspections. Your owner's manual will tell you how often to inspect, but experts advise doing it more frequently than most manuals suggest. Especially after hard driving conditions (such as encountered in mountains, deserts or wind storms), a look inside can pay big dividends. Even after a trailer has sat unused for a long time, a quick inspection may reveal a little problem that is working itself into a big expense.

02.03 SERVICING TRAILER BRAKES: THE STEP-BY-STEP PROCEDURE.

Many trailerists choose to let the pros do all the servicing work simply because having the equipment and facilities already set up is a big timesaver. Surprisingly, though, doing the work yourself is not difficult. Greasy, perhaps, but comprehendible.

The biggest problem with doing your own work has historically been the availability of parts. Even the larger service establishments complain that many brake manufacturers are slow on delivery, so it's worthwhile to keep your own inventory of the following items: adjuster, shoe return and hold-down spring assemblies, grease seals, magnet kits and bearing cotter pins. And if you want to be really thorough, you can also carry extra wheel bearings and linings. In some locations (especially small towns), even professionals can't get parts without special-ordering them, so having your own supply gives you a decided advantage.

The only tools you really need are pliers and a screwdriver, but $10 to $15 will buy you a Universal Brake Spring Plier and an adjusting tool which will make the job even easier (see Figure 6). Other necessities are plenty of clean news-

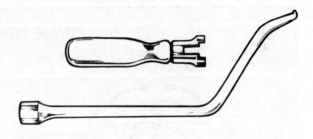

Figure 6.

papers, shop cloths and a generous supply of a good hand cleaner.

For the sake of cleanliness, you may also wish to tape some clear plastic to these pages so you can follow along without covering the illustrations with greasy fingerprints.

Before actually starting, study the diagrams in Figures 7, 8 and 9 to acquaint yourself with what you'll be discovering as you progress.

The drawings illustrating each of the following steps are necessarily generalized; they are based upon an actual servicing of Kelsey-Hayes spot magnet brakes because these are similar to most trailer installations. It's a good idea to consult the service manual for your specific brakes, as well.

Elevating the trailer wheels is an important pre-service step, as you must be absolutely certain the job is secure. Both as a convenience and for safety, we strongly recommend that you use a jack stand to keep the trailer elevated (Figure 10).

Finally, it's an excellent idea to service only one wheel and brake set at a time. This way, if you get lost in the reassembly process you'll have an intact model to consult.

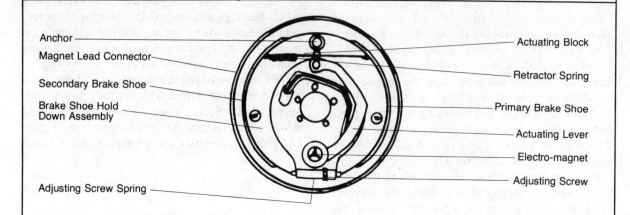

ELECTRIC BRAKE PARTS IDENTIFICATION

Anchor

Magnet Lead Connector

Secondary Brake Shoe

Brake Shoe Hold
Down Assembly

Adjusting Screw Spring

Actuating Block

Retractor Spring

Primary Brake Shoe

Actuating Lever

Electro-magnet

Adjusting Screw

BRAKE IDENTIFICATION

High Anchor
Single Retractor Spring

High Anchor
Dual Retractor Spring

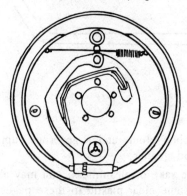

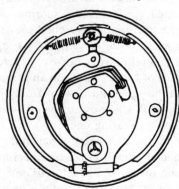

SHOE AND LINING IDENTIFICATION

Note: 7¼ x 1¼-inch
brakes use same
size primary &
secondary shoes.

PRIMARY

PRIMARY

SECONDARY

L.H. Brake

R.H. Brake

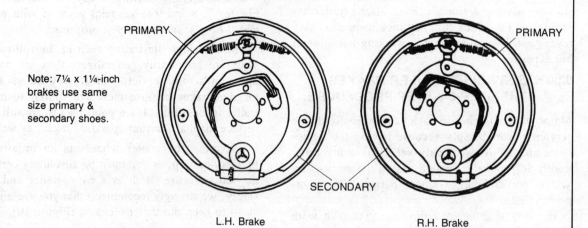

Figure 7.

Figure 8.

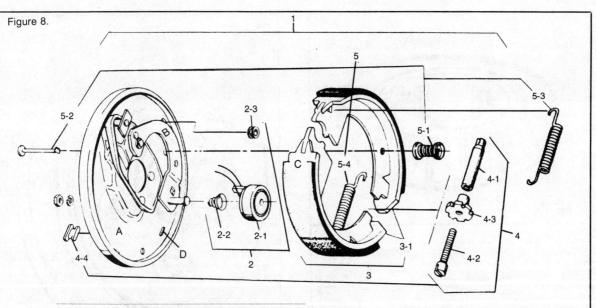

Item	Description
1	Brake Assembly, Right Hand
	Brake Assembly, Left Hand
2	Magnet Accessory Kit
2-1	Magnet
2-2	Spring
2-3	Grommet
3	Shoe Accessory Kit
3-1	Shoe Assembly, R.H. or L.H. (Spring Accessory Kit, Item 5, Included)
4	Adjuster Accessory Kit
4-1	Sleeve, Adjuster
4-2	Screw
4-3	Nut
4-4	Plug
5	Spring Accessory Kit
5-1	Shoe Hold-Down Spring Ass'y.
5-2	Pin
5-3	Shoe Return Spring
5-4	Adjuster Spring

A Backing Plate
B Lever Assembly
C Shoe and Lining Assembly
D Brake Adjustment Hole

10 X 2 SPOT MAGNET
WHEEL BRAKE ASSEMBLY
Right Hand Shown

(Courtesy Warner Electric Brake and Clutch Co.)

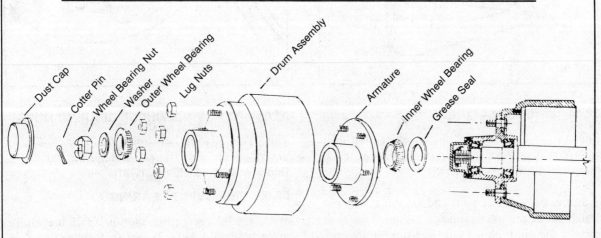

Exploded view of wheel bearing and drum assemblies.

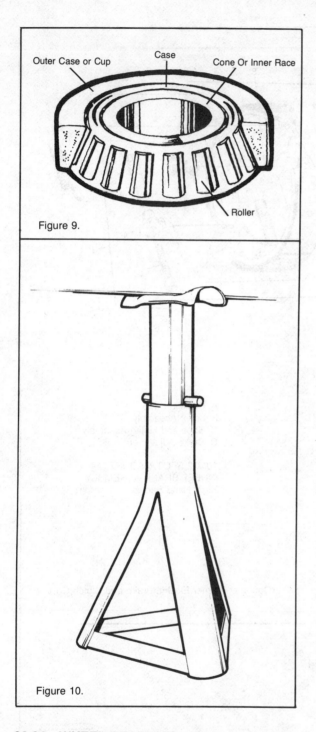

Figure 9.

Figure 10.

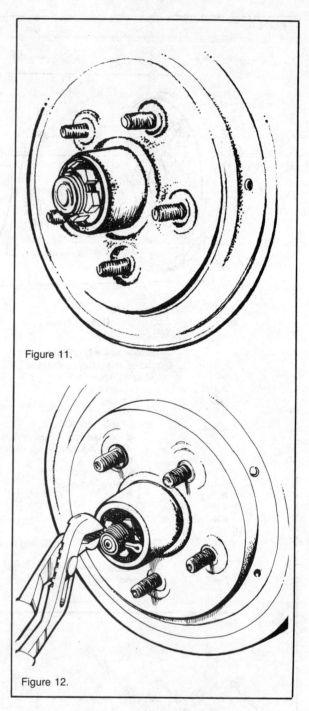

Figure 11.

Figure 12.

02.04   WHEEL BEARINGS.

Remove the tire. Pull off the wheel bearing dust cap. You'll now see the serrated outer edge of the wheel bearing nut (Figure 11).

Straighten out the open end of the cotter pin which holds the nut in place. (Notice how both ends of the pin keep the nut from turning by resting between the outer ridges of the nut.) Now remove the cotter pin (Figure 12).

02.05   REMOVING WHEEL BEARING NUTS.

The wheel bearing nut should be loose enough to unscrew with your fingers. Behind the nut you'll find a washer which simply lifts out.

02.06   REMOVING BEARINGS.

With a slight wiggling motion, pull the entire drum assembly toward you an inch or so, then push it back into its original position. This action will loosen the outer bearing enough so that you

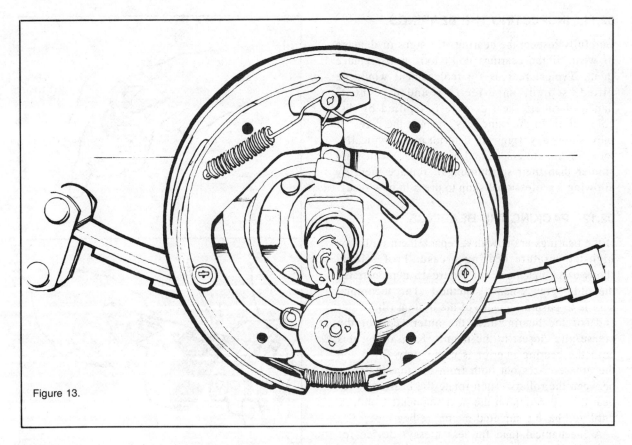

Figure 13.

can reach in, remove it and place it on a clean surface.

CAUTION: Don't pull the drum assembly so far toward you that the outer bearing drops out onto the pavement, as it is easily damaged.

02.07 REMOVING DRUM ASSEMBLY.

Remove the drum assembly and place it outer-side-up on clean newspapers. Now the braking mechanism is exposed (Figure 13).

02.08 REMOVING INNER WHEEL BEARING.

To remove the inner wheel bearing, run a wooden shaft through the spindle hole so that it contacts the back of the inner grease seal. (Using a metal instrument is inadvisable, as it could damage the bearing.) Tap the shaft to dislodge the seal. If the inner bearing does not come out on its own at this point, simply reach in, remove it and put it on the same clean surface as the outer bearing.

02.09 CLEANING THE BEARINGS.

Using parts-cleaning solvent (most general solvents such as gasoline leave a dangerous coating of residue), meticulously clean the bearings inside and out — washers, nuts, dust cap and spindle. Be sure you flush every last molecule of the old grease pack from the bearing interior. Put these

clean parts on clean cloths to dry. It's a good idea to lay another clean cloth loosely over them to keep out airborne contaminants.

02.10 CLEANING THE HUB INTERIOR.

With the same attention to detail, clean out the hub interior, being careful about keeping grease away from the drum or armature (Figure 14).

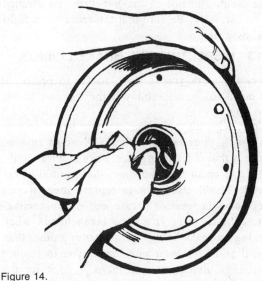

Figure 14.

02.11 INSPECTING THE BEARINGS.

Carefully inspect the bearings for signs of damage or wear. If the bearings don't look new, replace them. Typical reasons for replacement would be pitted, scored, imperfectly rounded or heat-damaged rollers (heat damage is typified by discoloration). In the same way, inspect the races. If they show any signs of deterioration (typically, look for minute cracks and worn areas, which are shinier than their surroundings), replace them by allowing a professional shop to press in new races.

02.12 PACKING THE BEARINGS.

If the bearings are now dry, repack them with new high-temperature bearing grease. Professional shops use a machine, but Figure 15 demonstrates the old "greasy-hand" method. The technique here is to push a segment of the bottom (the wider end) of the bearing into the outer edge of the grease pile closest to the thumb. Keep doing this until the bearing interior is completely filled and the grease oozes out both from the top and from between the rollers. Then rotate the bearing to repeat this operation on the next segment. Continue until you have completed the entire bearing.

A mechanical (and far less messy) device for replacing bearings is marketed by the Sta-Lube people of Compton, California (Figure 16). This gadget simply requires insertion of the bearing between two metal columns, a twist of the cylinder and — *presto!* — repacked bearings. It even comes packaged with a sample of an excellent hand cleaner which you'll definitely be grateful for in a few more minutes. But while you still have grease on your fingers, go ahead and rub some on the interior of the hub that you cleaned out so carefully. Be sure that the races get a light coat, as well.

02.13 INSPECTING THE BRAKE LININGS.

Cover the work you've done so far to protect it and put is aside; reassembly is the last step in our servicing.

Now, wipe all the grease off your hands so you can touch your brake linings. A good rule of thumb is that if the linings are worn down to within 1/32 of an inch of the shoe, they should be replaced. You'll also want to replace them if you detect uneven wear or grease and oil contamination. (This is why you need clean hands when working on brake linings.) If something other than normal and even wear does cause you to replace the linings, don't just stop there — look for the cause of this abnormality. Also, remember to re-

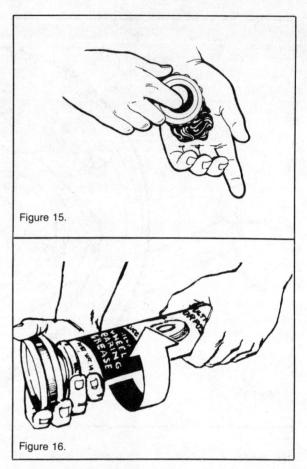

Figure 15.

Figure 16.

place all the brake linings in wheels on the same axle at the same time. Never just replace one set, as this will automatically yield uneven braking.

02.14 REMOVING SHOE RETURN SPRINGS.

To install new shoes and linings, the first step is to remove the two shoe return springs, using either your brake tool or pliers (preferably locking type). CAUTION: Be very careful about removing and installing all springs because they are under tension and can easily snap out of your grip (Figure 17).

02.15 REMOVING SHOE HOLD-DOWN SPRINGS.

The shoe hold-down springs come out in a special way. First, reaching behind the brake assembly, grasp the hold-down spring's center pin with your fingers, so it won't move when you turn the spring retainer. Then, grasping the spring retainer head (also called a hold-down cup) on the front of the brake assembly with your pliers or tool, push inward and turn 90 degrees in either direction, in order to align the rectangular head of the pin with the slot in the cup (Figures 18 and 19).

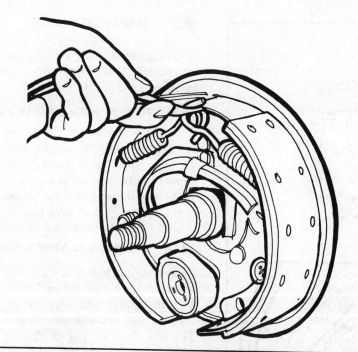

Figure 17.

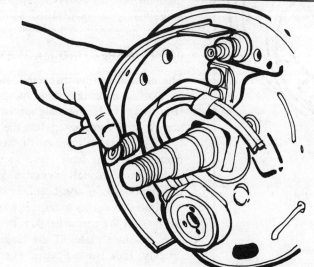

Figure 18.

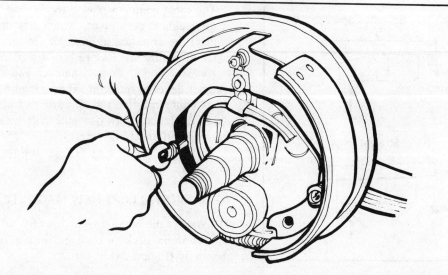

Figure 19.

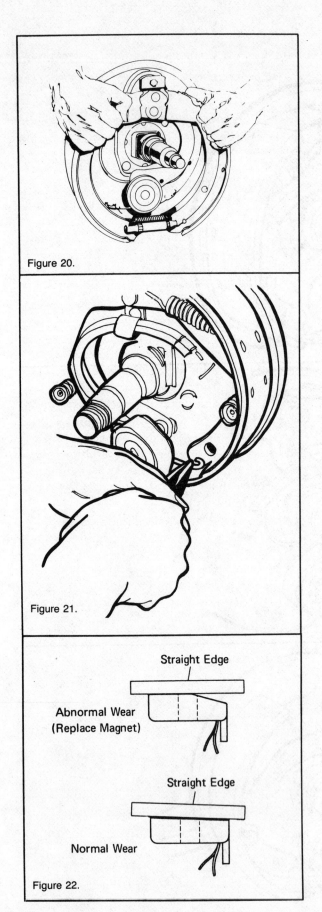

Figure 20.

Figure 21.

Straight Edge

Abnormal Wear
(Replace Magnet)

Straight Edge

Normal Wear

Figure 22.

02.16   REMOVING SHOES.

If the shoes don't come out easily at this point, simply grasp them close to the top, pull them apart and remove them along with the adjuster and adjuster spring as a unit (Figure 20).

02.17   REMOVING ADJUSTER AND SPRING.

Disengage the adjuster and adjuster spring (Figure 21) and carefully inspect them, along with all the other small parts you've taken off. If you're going to reuse any of these parts, clean them thoroughly. Make sure that the adjuster (new or old) works smoothly, and give it a very light application of a manufacturer-recommended lubricant.

02.18   INSTALLING NEW SHOES.

Remembering that the shoe labeled "primary" leads, and the "secondary" shoe trails, install an adjuster spring and adjuster on the new shoes (making sure the adjuster nut is on the left side). The new shoes are put on by simply reversing the dismantling procedure. But first carry out the magnet inspection detailed below, as replacing a magnet may require that the shoes be off.

02.19   INSPECTING MAGNETS.

The magnet can be inspected without disassembly by placing a straight edge on the rubbing surface (Figure 22). If the magnet is flat all the way across, it is rubbing against the armature correctly. If there is still plenty of wear on it (i.e., the friction element isn't close to wearing through), and if there is not excessive scoring from contaminants, you needn't replace it.

Figure 23 shows a magnet which has worn down so far that the screw heads rub against and damage the armature plate. If the magnet is wearing unevenly, look for the cause, correct it and put on a new magnet.

The most common reason for uneven wear is a worn magnet lever pivot, which lets the magnet contact the armature at an angle. In this case, replace the entire lever assembly as well.

As with brake shoes, whatever you do to one magnet, lever or retractor spring, you must also do to its counterpart on the opposite end of the same axle. Replacing only one side will yield uneven braking and unsafe driving.

To install a new magnet, just follow this easy procedure:

02.20   INSTALLING NEW MAGNETS.

Disconnect the magnet lead wires by pulling them out of their sockets on the front of the brake assembly (Figure 24).

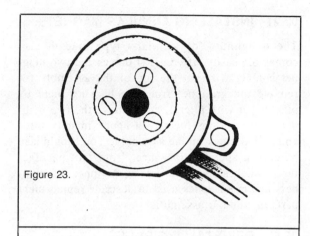

Figure 23.

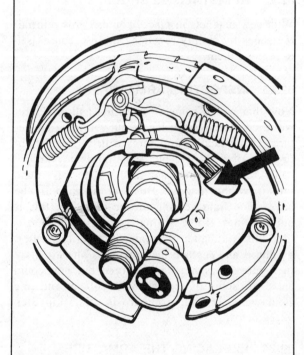

Figure 24.

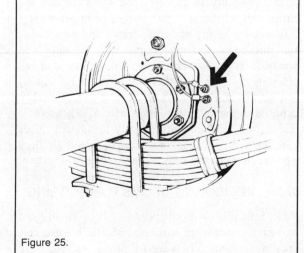

Figure 25.

Some brakes have these wires running through a hole in the backing plate, and you have to reach behind the brake and cut or detach them (Figure 25). In the latter case, if a grommet holds the wires in the backing plate hole, you'll remove it with pliers before pulling the wires through. If you also measure the straight-line distance along the wire between magnet and grommet after you've pulled the grommet, you'll be able to correctly position a new grommet on the new magnet lead wires.

If you're going to remove the lever arm, you'll notice it is held in place at only one point. Carefully remove the clip which keeps it in position. Slide the lever off its stud and place it on a clean surface (Figure 26).

The magnet can often be replaced with the lever arm either in position or removed. On Kelseys, you must first remove the little spring clip from the positioning stud (Figure 27), and the magnet lifts right off its mount. On others, there is a detent ring within the magnet assembly — but it will easily slip off the stud when you pull the magnet toward you with a rocking motion. Note how the follow-up spring is positioned behind the magnet and replace it with a new one. Sometimes these springs are wider on one end than the other, and they must be replaced exactly as you found them (usually with the wider end toward you). The purpose of this spring is to keep the magnet in even contact with the armature.

Slip on the new magnets using the new clip which comes with your magnet kit. (You may have to squeeze this with pliers until it fits snugly in place.) Reinstall the lever mechanism if you removed it. Route the magnet lead wires properly (look at your other brake if you've forgotten how they should go), then clean the receptacle and plug in the terminals, using your pliers to get a firm grip on the leads. If you had to cut the wires, reconnect them with a good crimp connector or by soldering them, but in both cases, wrap your connections in electrical tape and tape the wires securely to the axle. Protecting these connections or maintaining clean receptacles is very important, as contamination can decrease the voltage reaching the brake and cause uneven braking.

If after removing the drum assembly you're surprised by the sight of two magnets or a huge doughnut-shaped magnet, don't be concerned. The twin-spot magnets come off in much the same way as a single, and a brief inspection will reveal the details (see Figure 28).

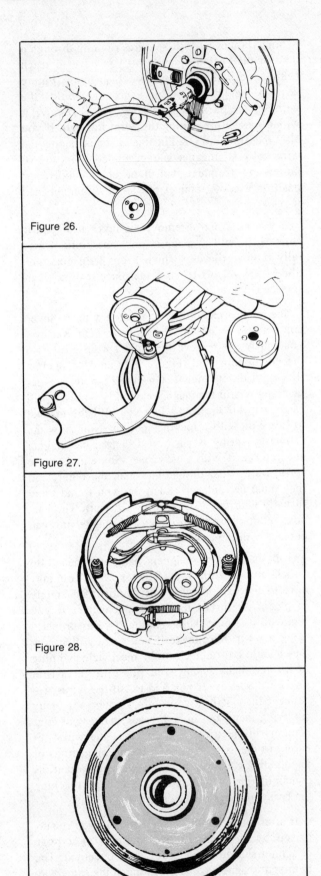

Figure 26.

Figure 27.

Figure 28.

Figure 29.

02.21 INSTALLING ANNULAR MAGNETS.

The doughnut- (or annular-) type magnet also comes off easily, if you first detach the two magnet contact wires at the top of the assembly (or remove the grommet from the backing plate by pinching it with pliers), and remove the two magnet return springs located at approximately three and nine o'clock on the assembly. You should also procure a specification sheet from the manufacturer which shows you how to decipher the numbers and color codes used to describe replacement parts on annular assemblies.

02.22 REINSTALLING SHOES.

With new magnets in place, you can now reinstall the shoes by simply reversing the procedure used to remove them.

02.23 INSPECTING ARMATURES.

Now that we've come to the drum and armature, we're on the downhill leg of our servicing adventure. Theoretically, armatures will last for the entire life of a trailer, but sometimes they do get badly scored by dirt and sand which are ground into it by the magnet. Don't be alarmed if you have some light scoring on the armature; this is quite normal. If the scoring is excessive, however (and this is a matter of judgment rather than rule), go ahead and replace the armature. The armature in Figure 29 is not badly scored but you could clean off some of the rust with solvent and fine steel wool. If your armature is OK, skip Step 02.24 below.

02.24 REPLACING THE ARMATURE.

Replacing an armature should be relatively simple. If the assembly is unicast, you must replace the entire unit. If the armature is riveted in place, just drill out the rivets and use screws and nuts to install the new armature. Fortunately, if only one armature is badly scored, you need not also replace its mate on the other end of the axle. But do inspect the other armatures, as they were probably exposed to the same contaminants. Also, carefully inspect the magnets which apply to the armatures you replace, because the chances are high they have been damaged also.

02.25 INSPECTING DRUMS FOR SCORING.

Next, take a look at your drums. They should not be heavily scored or worn and should have a dull gray appearance. In case of heavy scoring, the cause is often found to be continimants imbedded in the lining, loose lining rivets, or linings which have worn down so far that the rivets rub on the drum.

02.26   INSPECTING FOR OUT-OF-ROUND DRUMS.

Also look at your drums for signs of their being out-of-round. Often, this is evidenced by an area which appears different from the rest of the drum, as though the brake shoe was not fully contacting that one spot. In cases of damaged or out-of-round drums, take them to a professional; correctional procedures here require lathes and measuring devices which are far too expensive for individual ownership.

After drums have been rebored or turned, and reinstalled, be sure to adjust your brakes. You may find that the linings no longer fit their drums, in which case you can have linings ground to size. If, on the other hand, you can't adjust the brakes to contact the drum, an often-used solution is to place a shim between the linings and the shoe.

02.27   INSPECTING DRUM ASSEMBLY BOLTS.

When everything else about the drum assembly looks OK, check the bolts which mount it to the hub. Loose bolts are quite hazardous because they could shear apart during a hard brake application.

02.28   GETTING IT ALL TOGETHER — REINSTALLING INNER BEARINGS.

Now we're ready to reassemble everything. The first step is to literally "get our bearings."

Laying the drum inside-up, insert the inner bearing and place a new grease seal lightly in place, making sure that it is seated evenly and not cocked at an angle. Never reuse an old seal, as the danger of grease leaking out onto the brake armature and lining is too high. Carefully place a block of smooth, hardwood on top of the seal and tap it with a hammer to drive the seal evenly into place (Figure 30).

Move the block to a new position with each tap so you get an even sealing. Note in Figure 31 that the properly inserted grease seal is well below flush.

02.29   REINSTALLING DRUM ASSEMBLY.

Reinstall the drum assembly onto its thoroughly clean spindle and push it as far back as it will go;

the drum should completely cover the shoes.

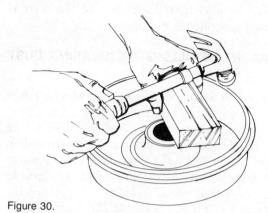

Figure 30.

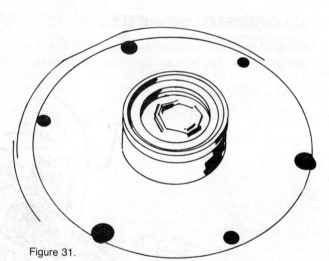

Figure 31.

02.30   REINSTALLING BEARING NUT.

While slowly rotating the wheel counterclockwise, screw the bearing nut with pliers until it is just snug; don't tighten it (Figure 32).

Stop spinning the wheel; loosen the nut and re-tighten it with your fingers only. When it is snug again, back it off about one-quarter turn (overly tight nuts and dry rollers are primary causes of bearing failure).

Reinstall the cotter pin, making sure the head and tail are secure between the ridges of the nut, and bend the portion of the tail nearest you so that it wraps over the end of the spindle. The other end can either be clipped or bent back out of the way.

02.31   TESTING THE REASSEMBLY.

Spin the wheel again. It should spin freely. If it doesn't find out why. If the shoes are tight against the drum, back them off with the adjusting screw and try spinning the wheel again. (See Figure 33 below.) The purpose of this test is to be sure everything is installed correctly, and that there is nothing jamming the bearing.

02.32   REINSTALLING THE BEARING DUST COVER.

Replace the bearing dust-cap. If it slides on rather than screwing, you may have to give it a few taps; but be very careful not to dent it. When you're rolling, the cap spins but the nut underneath it doesn't, so a dent that contacts the nut will quickly become a hole. As the purpose of the cap is to keep out contaminants, including water, definitely use a new one if it looks at all like it can't do the job any longer.

02.33   REINSTALLING WHEELS.

Reinstall the wheel and tire and tighten the nuts to specifications. Do be sure to check them again after you've driven 40 to 50 miles, as loose wheel lugs can cause noteworthy damage.

02.34   ADJUSTING THE BRAKES.

Your last chore is adjusting the brakes. To do this, remove the adjustment plug in the rear of the brake assembly and insert an adjusting tool (or a screwdriver) until it contacts the adjuster screw. Spin the wheel and turn the screw until the wheel drags significantly. (Usually a downward motion of your tool will tighten the shoes and an upward motion will loosen.) Then back it off until you reach the precise point where the wheel turns freely (Figure 33).

02.35   THE FINAL STEP.

Remember that hand cleaner we spoke of? Now is the time to use it — before you pat yourself on the back for a job well done.

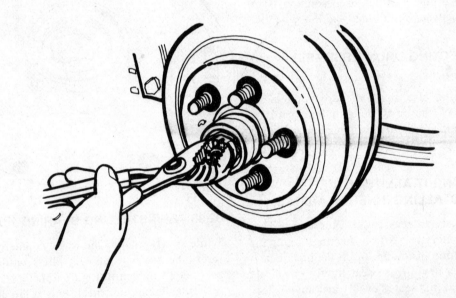

Figure 32.

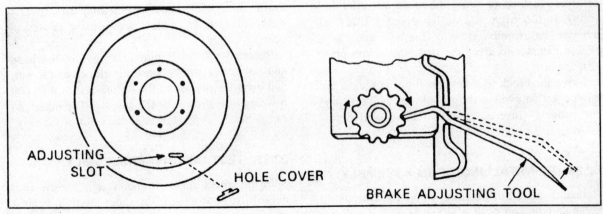

ADJUSTING SLOT

HOLE COVER

BRAKE ADJUSTING TOOL

Figure 33.

Chapter Three

Electric Brake Circuitry and Controllers

The electrical braking circuit passes from the tow vehicle's battery through a controller located in the driving compartment, a selective resistor, a connector linking tow car and trailer, the brake magnet, and is then grounded back at the battery (see Figure 1). Depending upon the particular system, the power connection may be made at some convenient point other than the battery, but that doesn't alter the function of each part of the whole system.

Many controllers allow the driver to adjust or operate the trailer braking system without operating the tow vehicle brakes; this option is called manual controlling. When the trailer brakes are activated solely be applying the tow vehicle brakes, it is called automatic. The two functions can also be operated simultaneously.

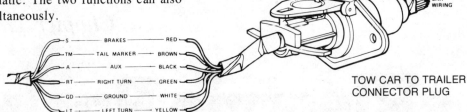

Figure 1.

03.01 CONTROLLER TYPES AND HOW THEY WORK.

The most prevalent type of controller has both hydraulic and electrical functioning, but this doesn't necessarily imply that they are superior, as a good case can easily be made for the all-electric type.

Electrohydraulic controllers (Figure 2) are connected to the trailer brakes via electrical wiring, and to the tow vehicle's master brake cylinder by a hydraulic line (Figure 3).

When the tow vehicle's brakes are applied, hydraulic pressure is simultaneously transmitted to the controller. Within the controller, this pressure moves an electrical contact along a wire-wound resistor coil. Current passes through the resistor and travels to the brake magnet. As more brake pressure is applied, the hydraulic pressure increases and the contact rides farther down the resistor, allowing more electricity to flow to the trailer brakes.

Controllers may also have an adjustment mechanism for determining how much hydraulic fluid displacement is necessary for moving the electrical contact. This lets you manipulate the braking system's sensitivity to accommodate varying load weights and driving conditions. Most controllers of this type use an arm or lever for operating the electrical contact manually, thus enabling the driver to use the trailer brakes alone.

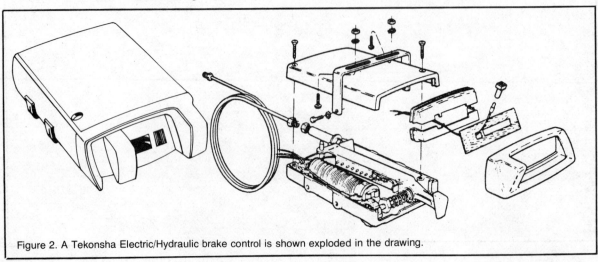

Figure 2. A Tekonsha Electric/Hydraulic brake control is shown exploded in the drawing.

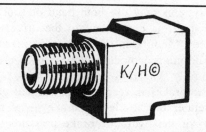

Figure 3. This Kelsey-Hayes Tee fitting penetrates the tow vehicle's master cylinder, tying the vehicle's hydraulic brake system to an electric/hydraulic trailer brake controller.

Another type of trailer brake actuator mounts directly on the tow vehicle's brake pedal. As the driver's foot moves the brake pedal, the trailer brakes are automatically and synchronistically brought into play through an all-electric system (Figure 4).

Figure 4.

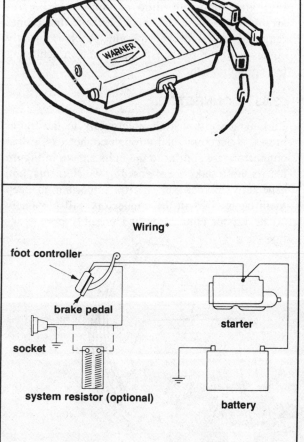

Wiring*

foot controller

brake pedal

socket

starter

system resistor (optional)

battery

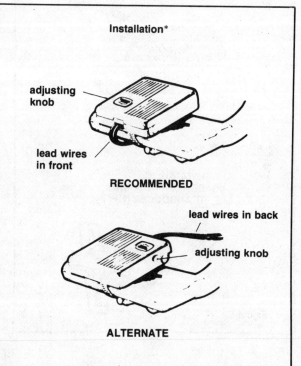

Installation*

adjusting knob

lead wires in front

RECOMMENDED

lead wires in back

adjusting knob

ALTERNATE

Mount the controller on the brake pedal as shown above. Tighten controller securely to the pedal with the clamp provided. Insert the connector end of the hookup wire segment into a matching connector extending from the controller. An electrical socket that mates with the trailer power cable is to be installed in the rear of the towing vehicle. Run wire from the socket, under the towing vehicle, and through the firewall to attach to the controller.

*Actual installation instructions included in kit. Above is offered for example only.

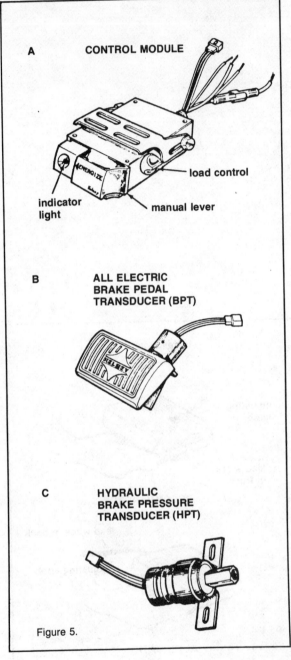

A   CONTROL MODULE

load control

indicator
light

manual lever

B   ALL ELECTRIC
BRAKE PEDAL
TRANSDUCER (BPT)

C   HYDRAULIC
BRAKE PRESSURE
TRANSDUCER (HPT)

Figure 5.

Some systems may use both hand or foot control, whichever is convenient to the driver. The new Kelsey Modulator IV (Figure 5) is an example. The control module (A) is engineered to provide a fully synchronized signal to two, four or six electric brakes in response to a signal generated by either the all-electric brake pedal transducer (B) or the hydraulic brake pressure transducer (C).

The Sure Stop, formerly made by VSI and now manufactured by Trailer Equipment Supply Company, is another type of electric controller. This device is wired to, and activated by, the tow vehicle's stoplight switch. The intensity of electricity reaching the trailer is adjusted through a rheostat, and simply pushing a button actuates the trailer brakes independently (Figure 6).

03.02   VARIABLE RESISTORS.

Beyond the controller, trailer braking power can also be adjusted through a selective resistor. These devices (Figure 7) modulate a quantity of electricity which passes through the circuit from controller to brakes. They are often mounted on the tow vehicle's fire wall and are adjustable — either through a movable slide or simple wiring rearrangements — to let you operate in the proper range of trailer brake strength. A chart usually comes with the resistor to guide you in achieving the optimum setting.

03.03   CONNECTORS.

Linking the tow vehicle electrically to the trailer brakes is accomplished through connectors. (Most connectors are similar to the units shown in Figure 8.) As these links are exposed to the elements, and especially to road splash, it's important to keep them clean. Dirt in the connectors will obviously create a poor connection and possibly poor braking.

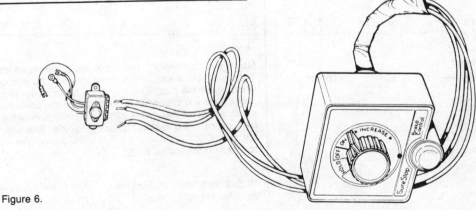

Figure 6.

03.04 BREAKAWAY SWITCH SYSTEM.

An additional safety component found on all-electric trailer brake systems is the breakaway switch. This device is simply a plug-type 12-volt connector, one end of which is secured to the two vehicles by a lanyard (Figures 9 and 10). If the trailer should break loose, the switch is opened and the trailer brakes are immediately actuated. Power comes from a separate battery housed in the trailer itself, and there is no connection with the tow vehicle's power supply. (On trailers which can be positioned by hand, it's a good idea to hold the breakaway switch lanyard so you can yank it just in case the trailer gets away from you.)

Another device which combines both breakaway switch and tow car to trailer electrical connections in one unit is pictured in Figure 11.

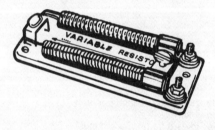

Figure 7. The exact amperage which passes between the electric/hydraulic controller and trailer brakes can be modulated by an adjustable resistor. This model, made by Tekonsha, has a simple thumb screw adjustment which lets you compensate for varying trailer loads to reduce grabbing and to achieve smoother stopping control.

Figure 8. Typical car-to-trailer connectors used in electric braking systems. The top model has a heavy-duty metal casing and accepts up to six circuits, while the lower model is a molded inline connector. Most connectors of these types are interchangeable with equivalent models made by other manufacturers. For example, either side of these Tekonsha connectors will plug into corresponding Berg, Pollak or Cole-Hersee models.

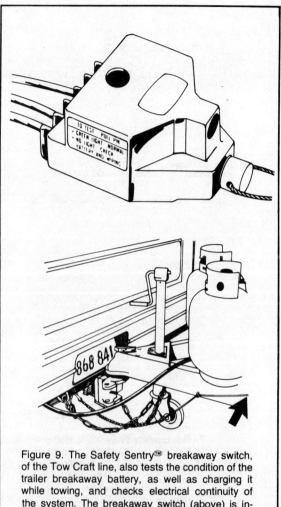

Figure 9. The Safety Sentry™ breakaway switch, of the Tow Craft line, also tests the condition of the trailer breakaway battery, as well as charging it while towing, and checks electrical continuity of the system. The breakaway switch (above) is installed on the trailer near the arrow (below).

The breakaway system is obviously a vital safety link and thus deserves frequent checkups, both at home and in transit.

The special braking battery is easy to check in the conventional manner (see Section 08.08), and every tool kit should have at least a hydrometer for doing this. The actual functioning of the system can be "field tested" by pulling the pin (do this on level ground!) and gently attempting to drive forward. The resistance offered by a well-functioning system will be obvious.

A more accurate check of the breakaway system is made by wiring an ammeter in series between the breakaway switch and the trailer brakes. Pulling the pin on the breakaway switch should cause the ammeter to immediately register. If it doesn't, the problem is often found to be only dirty contacts or a discharged battery. Check the ammeter first, though; failure to connect it securely will also cause an absence of reading.

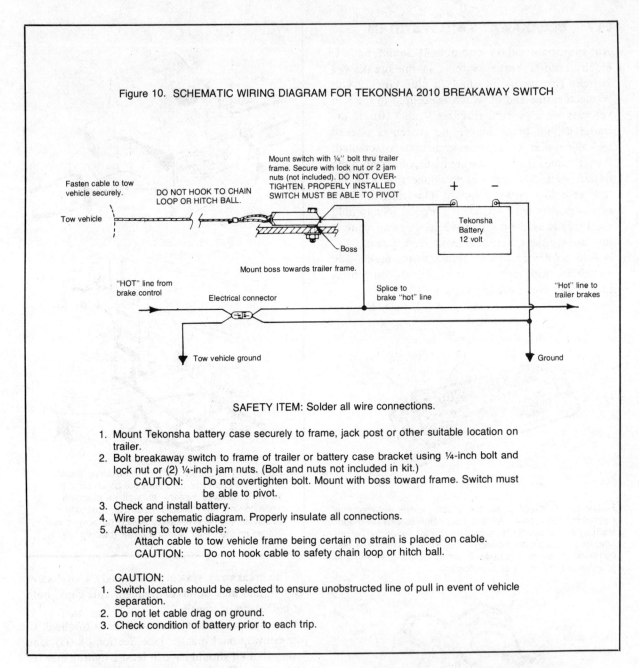

Figure 10. SCHEMATIC WIRING DIAGRAM FOR TEKONSHA 2010 BREAKAWAY SWITCH

SAFETY ITEM: Solder all wire connections.

1. Mount Tekonsha battery case securely to frame, jack post or other suitable location on trailer.
2. Bolt breakaway switch to frame of trailer or battery case bracket using ¼-inch bolt and lock nut or (2) ¼-inch jam nuts. (Bolt and nuts not included in kit.)
   CAUTION: Do not overtighten bolt. Mount with boss toward frame. Switch must be able to pivot.
3. Check and install battery.
4. Wire per schematic diagram. Properly insulate all connections.
5. Attaching to tow vehicle:
   Attach cable to tow vehicle frame being certain no strain is placed on cable.
   CAUTION: Do not hook cable to safety chain loop or hitch ball.

CAUTION:
1. Switch location should be selected to ensure unobstructed line of pull in event of vehicle separation.
2. Do not let cable drag on ground.
3. Check condition of battery prior to each trip.

03.05   TESTING CONTROLLERS.

Electric controllers should be given routine checks, but this doesn't require opening them up (actually servicing a controller yourself is not recommended by manufacturers and may void the warranty if it is still in effect).

One important test measures the controller's modulation, i.e., how smoothly it increases or decreases the flow of electric current. An erratic or uneven output can be a source of grabbing brakes. To make the test, simply connect an ammeter as shown in Figure 12, being very careful to wire in the .5 ohm resistor. Then operate your controller

with smooth movements and watch the ammeter dial; it should move smoothly, also. If it registers unevenly or not at all, it's likely that the problem lies in the resistor coil, and a burned-out coil is obvious when you look at it.

An alternate way to test the controller actually tests the whole braking electrical system. To do this, hook up the trailer and the wire running from the controller to the trailer brakes. As in the previous test, operating the controller should cause the ammeter needle to move smoothly. Also, check the value of the reading you're getting. Your owner's manual will show you which numbers should be registering on the ammeter; variations from these can signal a problem.

03.06   CHECKING LINKAGES AND WIRING.

While you're looking at the controller, feel the hydraulic line connection for leakage. Also, visually inspect the whole length of tubing for kinks, weak spots or any other irregularities. Then have someone observe the taillights as you activate the brakes both by foot pedal and controller. They should operate in each instance.

All electrical wiring should also be checked to catch wear, loose or corroded connections or impending damage before a problem leaves you roaring down the highway with no trailer brakes. Specifically, pay attention to connections which can be jarred loose by road vibrations. And don't forget to check soldered connections, too, as it's possible, even on a new rig, to get an incomplete solder.

Although you probably won't have occasion to change this configuration, keep in mind that electric brakes must be wired in parallel, and good quality insulated crimp-type connectors should be used (Figure 13).

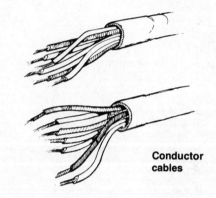

Conductor cables

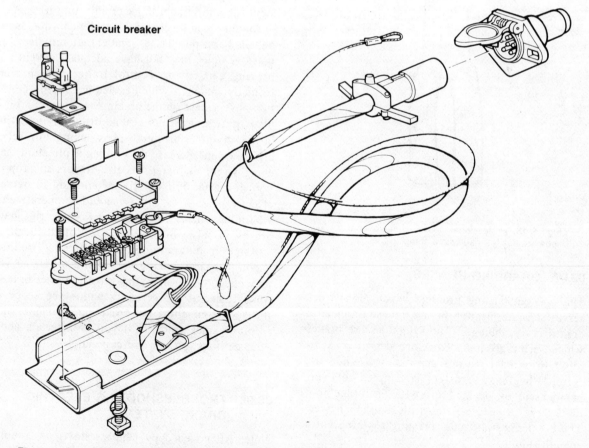

Circuit breaker

Figure 11. Sure-Stop's combined harness and breakaway assemblies

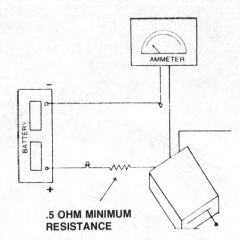

.5 OHM MINIMUM
RESISTANCE

Figure 12. How to use an ammeter to check the modulation of an electric controller.

Figure 13. Professional quality crimped connections are easily made with a crimping tool.

03.07   GRABBING BRAKES.

The one outstanding problem which always deserves separate mention in any treatise on electric brakes is "grabbing." The symptoms are brakes which seemingly jump from one degree of actuation to a much harder application. When the "grab" begins, the driver is tempted to overcompensate by backing off with the brake foot until there is suddenly too little braking power. These extremes alternate, creating anything but a smooth stop.

Mechanics and service managers have been wrestling with this problem for a long time and have finally reached the conclusion that the situation is simply inherent in the design of some electrics. This opinion seems to be seconded by a government-funded report written by the National Highway Safety Research Institute which says that, regardless of their otherwise admirable performance, "electric brakes have been found historically to have a propensity for erratic behavior. The basic high gain of the device, as well as the use of two friction surfaces (magnet-to-drum, in addition to lining-to-drum) are the primary sources of the problem."

Additionally, changing trailer load weights and driving conditions mean that you seldom have a system which delivers just the right amperage flow to the magnets. Also, dirt and water (especially salt water), as well as uneven battery output, can mean an unstable flow of electricity — and brakes which pull erratically. But all servicepeople agree that a well-aligned and maintained brake system will be much less prone to these problems.

Often, it's found that the variable resistor is not wired to provide resistance commensurate with the trailer weight being towed, and this can definitely produce grabbing. Because this device is out of sight, people seldom think of adjusting it.

Another non-mechanical problem is that many people have purchased smaller automobiles, but these vehicles may not have adequate weight and braking capacity to control trailers which were formally matched with heavier cars. This condition is very hard on the braking system — and it is also quite dangerous. In addition to installing larger diameter trailer brakes, using uni servo brakes would increase the braking application, and using larger diameter wheel cylinders in proportion to master cylinder size would add to overall effectiveness. Also, brakes should be operative on all trailer wheels (e.g., some two-axle rigs have brakes on only two wheels instead of all four).

Aside from grabbing, the following troubleshooting charts detail some of the problems you may encounter in operating electric trailer brakes. Most remedies are certainly within the scope of the do-it-yourselfer, but brakes are too important to play games with. So if you're uncertain about your abilities, go to a professional.

03.08   TROUBLESHOOTING ELECTRIC BRAKE SYSTEMS.

Note: All boxed copy which follows on troubleshooting electrical circuits appears courtesy of Kelsey-Hayes Company.

TROUBLESHOOTING ELECTRICAL CIRCUITS

ELECTRICAL CIRCUITS

1. No current flow apparent (will result in no brakes).
   a. Check for proper wiring of the electrical circuit.
   b. Be sure all connections are clean, dry and tight — especially at tow car-to-trailer connector plug.
   c. Check the controller resistor coil.
2. Minimum and maximum readings too high (will result in excessive and grabby brakes — possible controller burnout).
   a. Short in wiring. Carefully check circuit for frayed insulation, etc.
   b. Short in brakes. Remove the magnet terminal components from the brake backing plates and inspect for evidence of shorting. Remove magnet assemblies and check for worn leads. Bench check for internal shorts. Replace if necessary.
   c. Stoplights connected in brake circuit.
3. Minimum and maximum readings too low (will result in insufficient brakes).
   a. Poor circuit connections or inadequate ground.
   b. Open circuit in at least one magnet. Check the current flow in each brake. If there is no current flow through either of the magnets, check the magnet leads and bench check magnet.
   c. Brakes wired in series. Recheck tow car circuit.
4. No modulation — only maximum current available (will result in grabby brakes).
   a. Check for burned out controller resistor coil.
5. Intermittent current flow (will cause intermittent or possible surging brakes). Intermittent current flow is usually caused by attempts to ground through the trailer hitch. It may also be caused by a magnet lead which is partially severed causing intermittent contact with every wheel revolution. Another cause may be a broken or frayed wire at any point in the system. To locate the cause of this intermittent current flow you may have to install your ammeter or test light at the controller and have an assistant observe under actual driving conditions.

PROBLEM: NO BRAKES

Probable Cause	Remedy
Open Circuit	Check for broken wires, loose connections, improper grounding, faulty connector plug between car and trailer, etc.
Improperly Wired or Inoperative Controller	Rewire controller. Check controller operation.
Poor Brake Adjustment	Adjust brakes.
Selective Resistor Defective	Check resistor for loose connections.
Worn or Defective Magnet	Replace magnets.
Short Circuit	Check electrical circuit.

PROBLEM: INTERMITTENT OR SURGING BRAKES

Probable Cause	Remedy
Out-of-Round Drums	Rebore drums if more than .015-inch out of round.
Inadequate Trailer Ground	Check for proper grounding. (Note: A ground through trailer hitch is inadequate.)
Broken Magnet Lead Wires	Bench check magnets. Replace if necessary.
Loose Wheel Bearings	Check and adjust bearings.

PROBLEM: WEAK BRAKES

Probable Cause	Remedy
Poor Connections	Check that all connections are clean and tight.
Poor Ground	Do not depend upon grounding through the trailer hitch.
Short Circuit	Check electrical circuit.
Selective Resistor Setting Incorrect	Check for proper setting to avoid too much resistance.
Worn or Defective Magnets	Replace magnets.
Poor Brake Adjustment	Adjust brakes.
Backing Plate Bent	Check backing plate and flange. Correct if necessary.
Greasy Lining	Check for worn or damaged grease seals. Replace if necessary. Make sure bearings are packed with high-grade bearing grease, not cup grease or chassis lubricant.
Excessive Load on Trailer	Check to be sure your trailer is not under-braked. Too much weight will result in lack of torque, fade, poor performance. Also, be sure to have brakes on every axle — one set of brakes cannot be expected to handle the weight on two axles.
Using Trailer Brakes Only	Use of trailer brakes only can cause early fade or loss of friction due to excessive heat.
Inadequate Gauge of Wire	See wiring recommendations.

TROUBLESHOOTING MECHANICAL COMPONENTS

PROBLEM: GRABBY OR LOCKING BRAKES

Probable Cause	Remedy
Flanges Improperly Installed	Check flange location. Refer to axle manufacturer.
Grease on Lining	Check for contamination. Replace seals and lining.
Controller Not Modulating	Disconnect red wire on controller. Road test for braking modulation. If modulation is OK, check red wire. Bench check controller — replace if necessary.
Improper Lining	Be sure replacement lining is genuine K-H lining. Replace, if necessary.
No Selective Resistor	A selective resistor is required when brakes have greater power than is necessary for the weight on the axle. Install selective resistor when necessary.
Loose Parts in Brakes	Check for loose rivets, broken springs, etc., jammed in brakes.
Rust in Armature Plate and/or Brake Drums	Caused by non-use. Usually corrected by normal continued use.

PROBLEM: NOISY BRAKES

Probable Cause	Remedy
Lining Worn to Rivets	Check and replace shoe lining.
Loose Parts — Rivets, Broken Springs, etc.	Check and repair.
Flange Improperly Located, Bent Backing Plate	Check and repair if necessary.
Grease on Lining	Check and replace if necessary.
Improper Bearing Adjustment	Check linings and replace if necessary. Check for worn or damaged bearings. Replace if necessary.
Poor Adjustment	A certain amount of noise is normal when the brake releases. Proper adjustment will minimize this noise.

PROBLEM: STOP LIGHTS OR TURN-SIGNALS INOPERATIVE

Probable Cause	Remedy
Incorrectly Wired	See instructions. Rewire if necessary.
Controller Stoplight Switch Improperly Adjusted	Adjust controller stoplight switch.

PROBLEM: DRAGGING BRAKES

Probable Cause	Remedy
Brakes Adjusted Incorrectly	Check brake adjustment.
Electrical Defect in Controller	Insufficient gap between controller contractor strip and coil may cause brakes to be on continuously. Correct condition.
Hydraulic Defect in Controller	Too high a residual pressure in the tow car hydraulic system or a gummed up controller cylinder may cause the controller to be held "on" slightly. Check and repair.
Flanges Improperly Installed	Refer to axle manufacturer.
Badly Corroded Brake Assemblies	Check brake assemblies for severe corrosion. Check to be sure magnet levers operate freely. Clean and lubricate brake assemblies.
Weak or Broken Shoe Return Springs	Check and replace if necessary.

Chapter Four

Hydraulic Trailer Brakes

Hydraulic brakes stop a trailer in much the same way that electrics do — brake shoes creating a friction drag on the revolving wheel drums. But now the electromagnet and armature are unnecessary and the brake assembly looks much like standard automotive brakes. And instead of an electric wire leading to each brake, a hydraulic line supplies the actuating energy as it does on an automobile.

The major application for hydraulic brakes on recreational trailers is with small units, especially boat trailers, because electric brakes would be incapacitated by submersion in water. Some small rental units also use hydraulic systems, as customers would be unlikely to have the tow vehicle portion of the electrical setup. In both cases the preferred hydraulic actuation is called surge.

04.01   SURGE ACTUATION.

The heart of a surge actuating mechanism is contained in a special type of tongue coupler which accepts a conventional ball hitch (Figures 1 and 2). As the tow vehicle brakes and decelerates, the trailer, wanting to continue at the original speed, pushes against a device within the coupler. This device moves and actuates a master cylinder, which in turn applies the trailer brakes in proportion to the amount of braking being exerted by the tow vehicle.

It's easy to visualize that backing a trailer would also apply the same force to the coupler and actuate the brakes. For this reason, brakes which are not self-energizing are usually preferred with surge actuation. In some of these brakes, the primary shoe continues to resist backing, while the effect of the secondary shoe is mechanically minimized. Other brakes intended for surge activation go a step further and provide a mechanical lockout device to block brake operation. If this device is manually operated, you must remember to re-engage your brakes before moving forward again or you'll find yourself brakeless! (Figure 3 illustrates a brake which automatically disengages in reverse.)

Critics of surge cite the slight delay between the tow vehicle and trailer brake application which is inherent in the system. They also complain that once you are unable to operate trailer brakes independently, you can't correct sway in the conventional way. And, of course, if the tow vehicle brakes fail, you're without "whoaing" ability all around. The facts behind these criticisms are accurate, but in reality surge braking performs admirably and safely when it is used on compatible equipment. Even the manufacturers, though, warn against using surge on rigs which are substantial enough to require load distributing hitches. The spring bars and drain hookup to the trailer frame limit movement of the surge systems.

Hydraulic brakes on trailers are so similar to automotive hydraulic brakes that good maintenance information is readily available. For this reason it would only be redundant to go into detailed troubleshooting information here. Interestingly enough, service managers report that the biggest problem with hydraulics arise from poor

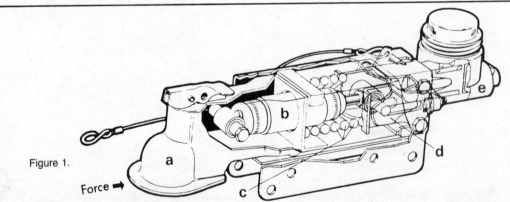

Figure 1.

Force ➡

Cutaway view of Bendix's Sur-Act III hydraulic surge actuator. As the tow vehicle brakes are applied, force in the direction of the arrow is transmitted through the coupler (a). The coupler is thus moved back toward the trailer, compressing the shock absorber (b), and then the coil spring (c). The shock absorber and spring are there to dampen brake activation and assure that the brakes don't unnecessarily grab during non-braking driving maneuvers. The rear of the spring (c) pushes the push-rod (d), which applies force to the master cylinder (e). The master cylinder is connected to each brake via a hydraulic line, and the change in fluid pressure within the cylinder actuates the brakes. The breakaway cable connection can be seen extending to the left of the coupler. If vehicle and trailer are separated, tension on the cable moves a ratchet which will cause the brakes to lock into stopping position.

Figure 2. HOW THE ATWOOD HYDRAULIC SURGE BRAKE SYSTEM OPERATES

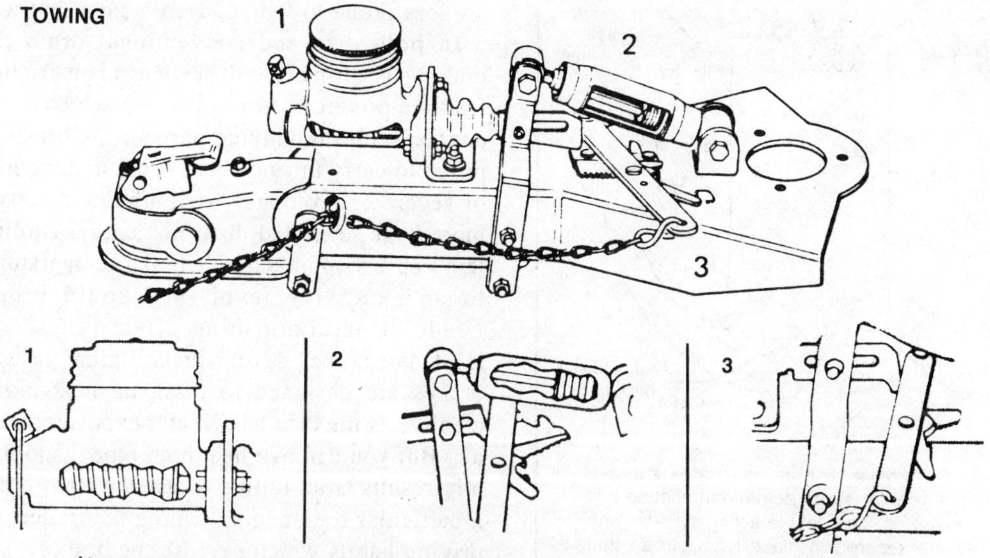

TOWING

At constant speed, master brake cylinder (1) has plunger in free position; no pressure on trailer wheel brake cylinders. Shock absorber (2) prevents intermittent application of trailer brakes during stopping and when towing on rough roads. If trailer uncouples under way, breakaway lever (3) is pulled forward by chain attached to car, setting trailer brakes.

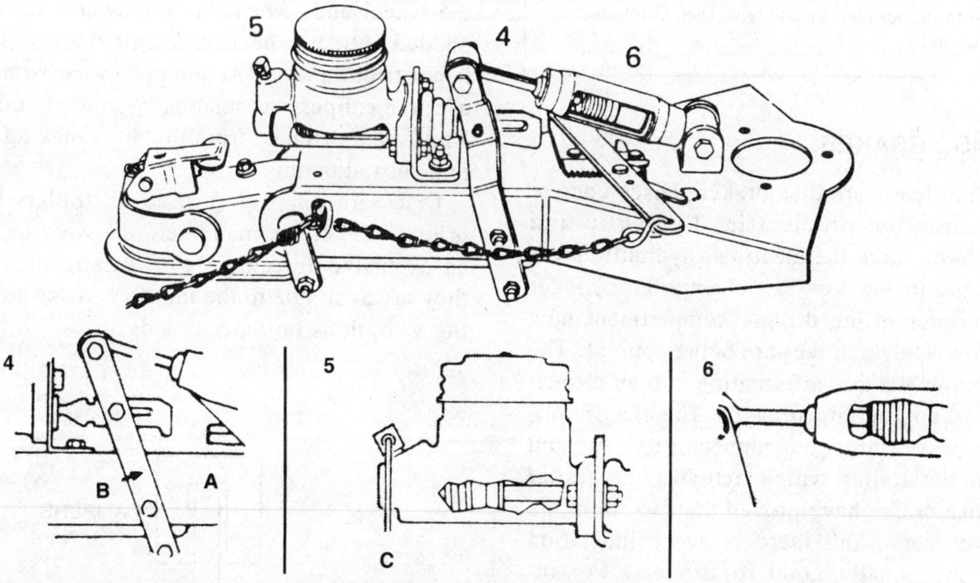

As car slows (4), trailer tongue (A) moves forward applying pressure through linkage (B) to master cylinder (5), in direct proportion to car braking. Pressure is transmitted to wheel brakes through brake lines (C). Shock absorber (6) assures smooth, even application of brakes. Atwood brakes require no connections to car's electrical or hydraulic systems, need no batteries. Fully self-contained.

installation. Otherwise, most of the hydraulics they see merely need routine work.

One word of caution when servicing hydraulic brakes: Be absolutely sure to bleed the system according to the manufacturer's directions every time you open it. Failing to do this leaves a very dangerous pocket of air in the line.

Additionally, hydraulic fluid levels should be frequently monitored and the cause of any sudden change in reservoir contents must be immediately investigated. The formula is easy: No fluid means no brakes.

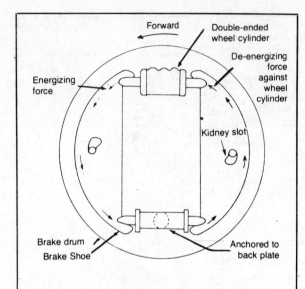

Figure 3. The above diagram illustrates a brake which is practical for surge actuation because it is not self-energizing. The double acting cylinder with the shoes are secured in place by a pin so that each half acts independently. The shoes are mounted on a carrying plate that contains two kidney-shaped slots. When the wheels are reversed, the brake shoes start turning with the drum, but the mounting pins fall into the kidney slots to release the pressure on the shoes and provide free backing. (Courtesy of Dico Company, Incorporated.)

04.02   DISC BRAKES.

Last, but not least, are disc brakes. Discs operate on a combination of electric, hydraulic and vacuum power. Like the electrics, hydraulic pressure changes in the tow vehicle master cylinder tell a controller in the driving compartment how hard the tow vehicle brakes are being applied. The controller converts this information into an electrical signal of appropriate strength. The electric impulse then passes through a connector to a vacuum system in the trailer which actuates the trailer brakes. Disc brakes have proved their worth in the automotive arena, and there is every indication that they are equally good for trailers. For instance, some interesting test data published by the Society of Automotive Engineers, Incorporated (the familiar SAE group), showed that, among other advantages, disc brakes were less sensitive to premature lockup or wheel skid (and skidding wheels yield up to a 40% loss in braking force). The report also stated that discs were less bothered by dirt, dust and water than servo-drum brakes and that "coupled with a compatible actuating and control device, (they) can give the best controlled and balanced braking of a trailer and towing ve-

hicle combination of any type of foundation brake."

Industry proponents also state that disc brakes are less prone to fading. Here's how that works:

In both disc and conventional drum design, braking is ultimately dependent upon friction and friction produces heat. The air which comes in contact with the moving parts of the brake is supposed to carry this heat away, but under conditions of severe or prolonged hard braking there may be more heat generated than this natural cooling system can accommodate. If brake temperatures rise to an excessive level they could produce a "fade," or diminishing effectiveness. At the least, hot brakes devour brake linings faster. Disc brakes are designed to dissipate heat more efficiently, as the disc has greater exposure to cooling air. But you can overheat both types, and this usually results from failing to use the right brakes for a particular trailer, overloading the trailer, or poor driving habits which overuse the brakes.

Disc brakes use the same principle of friction but they apply it differently. Figure 4 is a sketch which shows the large steel disc from which the system derives its name. This disc revolves with the wheel and, when the brakes are actuated, the padded calipers squeeze against the disc to establish a friction drag. As the pads wear from normal use, the calipers automatically adjust to maintain a "relaxed" distance from the disc, making the system self-adjusting.

Discs are not widely used on trailers because, prior to 1978, the manufacturers were locked into an exclusive agreement with Airstream. Now that they are available to the industry, discs are appearing as options on other brands.

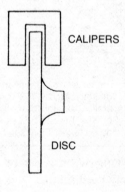

Figure 4.

Chapter Five

Trailer Hitches

Most hitch maintenance or repair problems really aren't equipment troubles at all, but relate to incorrect usage, an improperly loaded trailer or poor driving habits. In fact, so little maintenance is required that it's little wonder that so many RVers forget about doing it. Nevertheless, trailer hitches are an obviously vital connection whose incorrect functioning or failure spells D-A-N-G-E-R.

05.01   WEIGHT CARRYING HITCHES.

Weight carrying hitches are basic connections for light trailers, with a tongue weight of 200 pounds generally considered maximum. As the name implies, weight carrying hitches simply attach to the underside of the tow vehicle and all of the tongue weight is concentrated upon the ball mount and attachment point (Figure 1). In effect, this focus of weight means that the vehicle's rear axle supports the trailer and, on the road, a seesaw movement develops wherein some of the tow vehicle weight is transferred from the front axle to the rear. With a light trailer, the added weight on the tow vehicle rear axle is negligible. With a heavy trailer (tongue weight over 200 pounds), the effect becomes exaggerated and leads to vehicle oversteering problems and trailer sway or yaw.

As might be suspected, maintenance of weight carrying hitches is minimal. Cleanliness and inspections for tight connections, soundness of the metal and proper attachment just about covers everything. But do remember that these hitches are sensitive to some of the incorrect installation problems enumerated in Section 05.03.

05.02   WEIGHT DISTRIBUTING HITCHES.

Weight distributing hitches very simply use multiple attachment points beneath the tow vehicle and trailer to distribute the trailer tongue weight over the several axles of both vehicles. Because of their effect, some people refer to these devices as load equalizer hitches, but regardless of the name the results are the same.

Beyond the ball mount, weight distribution hitches are composed of a tow bar, which is welded or bolted to the vehicle frame, and the spring bar assembly, which is the key element in distributing the tongue weight through its leverage action (see Figure 2). It is this latter effect which, when properly used, inhibits sway and other motion-related problems. "Properly used" is the key in this case, and according to manufacturers it includes proper installation.

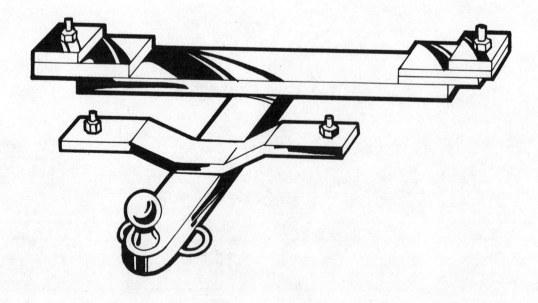

Figure 1.

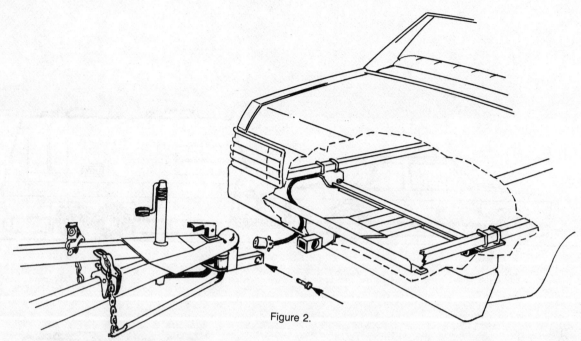

Figure 2.

05.03   HITCH MAINTENANCE AND TROUBLESHOOTING.

The following is a roundup of the most common sources of troubles encountered in normal trailer hitch usage:

[1] *Improper ball mount angle.* The device to which the hitch ball is bolted, and to which the spring bars are attached, is called the ball mount (Figure 3). Ball mounts are welded or bolted to the shank. The shank fits into the receiver box attached to the tow vehicle. Shanks are held in place with a steel pin.

Both the angle and height of attachment of the ball mount are variable, thus there are two directions in which errors can occur — and occur they do.

Figure 4 illustrates three potential car/trailer attitudes. The top drawing depicts the result of a properly positioned ball mount, while the middle and lower drawings show two common errors.

The center drawing in Figure 4 illustrates what happens when the height of the ball mount is correct — but the angle is wrong. Because the spring bar tips are too close to the trailer frame, insufficient tension on the bars does not permit them to carry the weight they should be carrying, and the vehicle's rear axle is overloaded. That's why the car's tail is sagging. When this occurs, many trailerists think that they must add auxiliary springs, air shocks or air bags; but these "remedies" only exaggerate the seesaw action referred to in Section 05.01 by lightening the front axle load and forcing the vehicle's rear axle to carry even more weight.

To prevent improper ball mount angle and the resultant towing problems, you must first be sure that the loaded car is level *before* the trailer is hitched. After hitching, spring bars should be adjusted to maintain level car and trailer attitudes, and air should not be added to shocks or air bags. If the car cannot be leveled by adjusting the spring bar tension, you may suspect that the ball mount angle is incorrect and/or that the spring bars are overloaded.

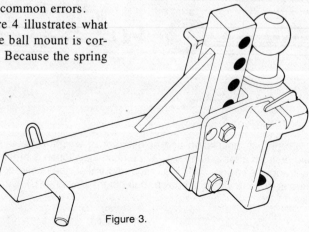

Figure 3.

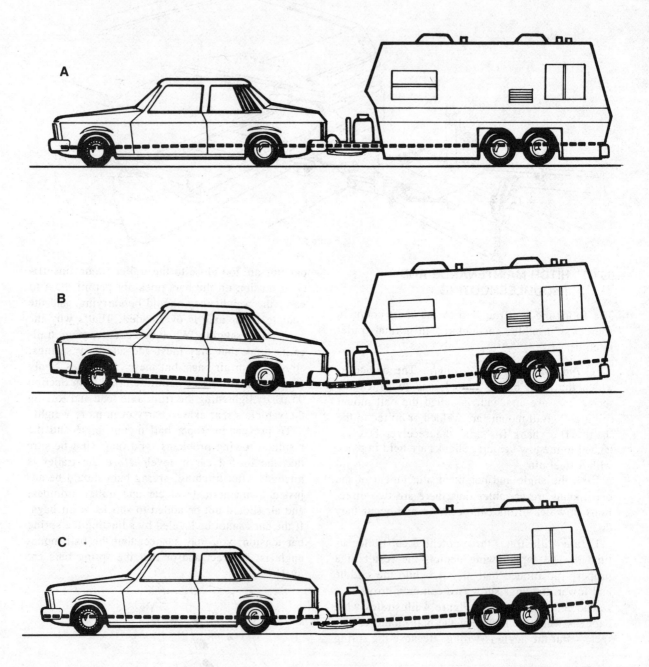

Figure 4. With proper installation and adjustment of weight-distributing (equalizer) hitch, car and trailer should be level after loading (A). When hitch installation is proper but spring bars are too light or ball-mount angle is wrong, car's rear sags and trailer goes nose-down (B). When car is level but trailer attitude is nose-down or tail-down, ball height is wrong (C). Car-trailer attitudes exaggerated for emphasis.

[2] *Improper ball height.* The position of the ball mount on the shank determines the ball height, which in turn dictates the attitude of the trailer in comparison to that of the car. Ideally, both should be level when fully loaded. If the ball position is too high, the car may be level while the trailer has a tail-down attitude (a common cause of tail dragging scrapes in driveways).

By itself, improper ball height doesn't always lead to improper operation of the hitch. However, misguided adjustments — especially when the condition is in combination with an improper ball mount angle — can lead to serious problems.

To determine if the ball is at the proper height, follow this simple procedure: (1) Park car and trailer on absolutely flat pavement. (2) Unhitch. (3) Adjust the tongue jack so the trailer frame is parallel to the pavement. (4) Measure the distance from the pavement to the inside of the trailer coupler (socket). (5) Proper ball height, with vehicle loaded and level, should measure about ½ inch more than the distance from the pavement to the inside of the coupler.

[3] *Improper spring bar adjustment.* If the ball height and ball mount angle are correct, the next check is the adjustment of the spring bars (or, how many chain links are under tension). This adjustment determines how well the hitch distributes the tongue weight, and the method used to achieve proper tensioning is simple:

Start with the unhitched car and trailer in a level attitude. Now hitch up again and note the level of both components. If the ball height seems improper, and it's impractical to get it changed immediately, adjust the spring bars so the car is level again. If, though, the car was sagging under its own load before hitching, attempting to level it with the spring bars only adds the car's trunk weight to the spring bars and results in an overloaded hitch. When this maladjustment is allowed to exist, the spring bar tips are cinched up close to the frame brackets and, in tight turns, the frame brackets can be ripped right off the trailer frame. The minimum number of chain links between the tip of the spring bar and the frame bracket attachment point should be four.

If cinching up the spring bars to the minimum number of links remaining under tension does not properly level the vehicle and trailer, either the ball mount angle is improper or the bars are not heavy enough.

[4] *Faulty hitch installation.* To limit the possibilities of poor installation, the trend in recent times has been toward bolted rather than welded-in-place hitch platforms or assemblies (the under-car parts). Even though a good welding job is every bit as strong as a bolt-on, the popularity of the latter method came about because it can be prefabricated to fit a specific vehicle, and the hitch can be easily removed. Welded installations, on the other hand, are somewhat customized by the installer and this leaves more room for error.

The points to look for when inspecting your hitch installation are these: broken welds or loose bolts; hitch members that are not attached to the strongest section of the car frame; positioning of the tow bar too close to the gas tank (a minimum clearance is about ¼ inch); cross members of adequate size (see manufacturer's specifications); and, in some hitches, a gusset in the ball mount which is not attached either too high or too low (again, see the manufacturer's instructions).

In some cases, the absence of diagonal bracing can critically affect riding comfort. Many trailerists complain of the pitching motion that occurs on some concrete highways — a fore/aft jerking which has been loosely defined as "freeway buck." It's actually the regular seams in the highway which instigate this motion and, in cases where these jolts are magnified by significant distances between trailer and tow vehicle axles, the rhythmic motion can become quite intense.

Contributing to the pitching in many cases is the flexing of the vehicle cross members to which the hitch platform is attached. These cross members may be moving only a fraction of an inch in response to the road shocks, but the action magnifies the effect upon passengers in the tow vehicle. For this reason, some manufacturers prefer diagonal braces originating at the hitch box (at the bumper) and angling forward at 45 degrees to suitable attachment points (Figure 5). This won't usually solve freeway buck, but it may substantially reduce the effect.

A hitch which has been transferred from one vehicle to another may present problems because it will not attach in a way that takes advantage of its strengths. Even if the hitch "almost" fits correctly, it must virtually be redesigned to fit the new vehicle. When this happens, you're depending on the person doing the installation and slip-shod workmanship may occur.

[5] *Overloaded hitch.* Most hitch platforms today are rated for tongue load maximums of 1,000 to 1,200 pounds, so they are rarely insufficient — assuming proper installation. But spring bars are an entirely different story, and too many installations include spring bars of incorrect size.

This is a particularly prevalent problem when owners change trailer sizes but retain the old hitching assemblies.

When spring bars are inadequate for the trailer weight, they are often incapable of correcting rear-end sag. When the owner erroneously guesses that he now needs air shocks and inflates them to compensate for the spring bar inadequacy, he's left with exaggerated seesaw action — unloading of the front wheels and the resultant oversteer. A good rule to remember is that if the car sags *before* the trailer is hitched, air shocks or air bags are indeed in order. If these compensating devices are not used, the spring bars must be rated to handle the maximum gross hitch weight (with trailer loaded), plus the car trunk weight. Of course, there's no need for shocks or bags if the loaded vehicle is level before hitching.

The opposite error is springs rated in excess of the weight to be handled. This stiffens the coupling between tow vehicle and trailer and can stiffen your ride. Optimally, spring bars should be rated no more than about 250 pounds above loaded trailer hitch weight.

A good formula for determining correct spring bar ratings is this one, from Reese Products Company:

$$MGHL = TW + CTL$$
(maximum gross hitch load = tongue weight plus car trunk load)

[6] *Safety chains*. The variety of chains attached in different ways serves to underline the lack of uniformity in controlling codes. A system that appears to have merit, and has been adopted by several states, specifies that each of two required safety chains be rated to carry the entire weight of the trailer. Also, this preferred ruling specifies that the attachment to the car and trailer must be stronger than the chain's breaking point.

Correctly positioned, safety chains should cross each other to form an "X" under the ball mount. They should contain enough slack to prevent binding during turns, but not enough to allow the jack post to hit the ground. Chain attachments should be to steel members of the hitch, or to special eyes welded to the hitch for that purpose.

If, as often happens, the safety chains are welded to the trailer coupler, the welded link can become brittle and break under stress. The preferable attachment is to run a steel loop through the end link and weld both ends of the loop to the coupler.

[7] *Improperly adjusted sway control*. Like collision insurance, you don't need a good sway con-

trol device until it's too late to buy it. And with an improperly adjusted control unit, some of your insurance coverage is canceled.

With the Reese Strait-Line sway control unit, it's very important to make sure that the brackets are fully seated on the cams when the car and trailer are tracking straight ahead. The easiest way to assure this condition is to drive the rig forward while aiming at a specific object. Check the seating of the brackets on the cams and, if they're not fully seated, loosen the bracket attachment bolts and tap the bracket with a hammer in the proper direction. Also, be sure that the nut and bolt are secure and that they allow the arm to move freely. If friction creates an irritating noise, dab a little petroleum jelly or the special Reese lubricant on the points of metal contact.

Electronic sway controls offer a control box in the driving compartment which is tied to a sensor within the trailer and a command relay near the hitch. The electronic nature of these units render them highly sensitive, but they are best not opened for repair by RVers.

With friction-type sway controls, proper adjustment is basically a seat-of-the-pants determination. A small amount of sway under moderate conditions can mean a potential accident, should conditions get severe. With a friction device, the driver should be able to detect resistance while turning corners at low speeds. It should be barely detectable — not actually stiff, which would accelerate tire wear. Check for wear of friction surfaces and replace them when worn. Also, be sure that the sliding bar remains free of grease and oil.

[8] *Wiring*. Trailer electrical connectors and their method of attachment are an area of divergent opinion among installers. Practicality, though, should be the rule; the connector should be designed for its purpose and offer protection from water and dirt. Connectors should also be mounted in a position where they are secure from damage by rear-end drag or accidental back-ups into dirt, etc. The electrical contacts should be treated occasionally with a dry-type corrosion protector, such as the spray sold in electrical equipment stores for cleaning TV channel selector contacts. Lubricants such as petroleum jelly, which collect dirt, should never be used. Corroded contacts should be wire-brushed before the corrosion protector is applied.

[9] *Visual inspection*. Beyond the specifics discussed, many trailer attachment problems can be discovered and cured simply by looking at what's

happening. Worn, loose or dirty parts should be immediately corrected, and the integrity of this important system should be maintained in high order at all times.

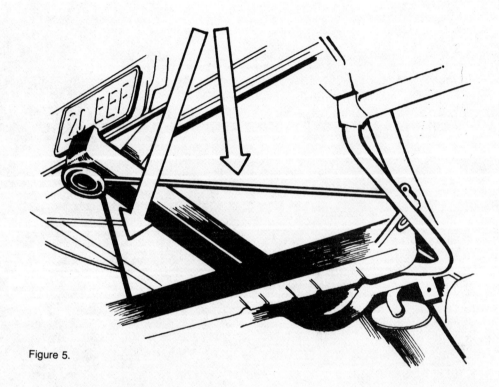

Figure 5.

05.04 FIFTH WHEEL HITCHES

Fifth wheel trailers utilize a different style of hitch and, although they come in a variety of makes, they require little maintenance.

A not too infrequent complaint is that the hitch begins tearing free from the truck bed, but this problem is directly related to poor installation. Fifth wheel hitches should be securely anchored to the more stable frame, and never to the truck bed by itself.

Lubrication is another key to hitch longevity. The platen should periodically be treated with a manufacturer-approved compound to prevent undue friction. And as it is directly exposed to the elements when the trailer is detached, frequently inspect this area for dirt accumulation; clean and re-lubricate when appropriate.

An alternative to lubrication with some units is a teflon-like friction-free disc, but these do not totally eliminate the recommended lubrication requirement.

Chapter Six

Tires

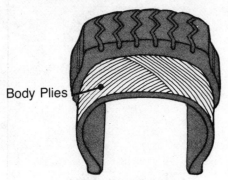

FIGURE 1. DIAGONAL (BIAS)

Body Plies

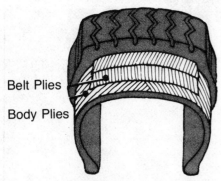

FIGURE 2. BELTED BIAS

Belt Plies
Body Plies

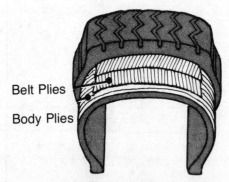

FIGURE 3. RADIAL

Belt Plies
Body Plies

AUTHOR'S NOTE: Much of the material in this chapter is taken from professional publications of the Rubber Manufacturer's Association and the Tire Industry Safety Council. It's not generally a good practice to let industry people write material which is intended to be unbiased, but in this case there was little point in altering what is a clear and well-prepared presentation. And readers will also benefit from knowing that the data presented here represents the best thinking from all of the major tire manufacturers.

Tires are one of the few RV components which let you measure the consequences of abuse on a progressive basis. Appliances usually hide degenerative processes until the moment of total breakdown, but you can literally watch bad things happening to tires and, if you're alert, you can change what you're doing wrong.

The first and most obvious decision about tires is selecting the correct replacements for your rig. That doesn't necessarily mean just duplicating what the RV manufacturer supplied, so let's begin by taking a closer look at tire construction.

Principal tire constructions are as follows:

06.01 DIAGONAL (BIAS) TIRES.

These may have two, four or more body plies which cross at an angle of approximately 35 degrees to the center line of the tread, giving strength to both sidewall and tread. Alternate plies extend in opposite directions (Figure 1).

06.02 BELTED BIAS TIRES.

These have a body similar to that of bias tires, plus two or more ''belts'' under the tread. This construction gives strength to the sidewall and greater stability to the tread. The belts reduce tread movement during contact with the road, thus improving tread life (Figure 2).

06.03 RADIAL TIRES.

A major difference between the construction of a radial tire and a bias-ply tire is the direction in which the ply cords are built into the tire. In a bias-ply tire, the cords run at an angle from bead to bead. In a radial tire, the cords run substantially perpendicular across the tire from bead to bead. Radial tires have belt plies, which run circumferentially around the tire, under the tread; they constrict the radial ply cords and give rigidity to the tread. This construction gives greater strength to the tread area and flexibility to the sidewall. The belts restrict tread movement during contact with the road, thus improving tread life (Figure 3).

06.04 HOW TO READ SIDEWALL MARKINGS.

All the vital statistics about a tire appear on the sidewall (Figure 4).

(1) Size marking (see Section 06.05).

(2) All tires which have "radial" construction must bear that designation on their sidewall.

(3) The letter identifies the load and inflation limits for a specific type of service (see Section 06.06).

(4) This indicates the tire's load limits and maximum cold inflation. For normal operation, follow the pressure recommendations in the owner's manual or on the instruction sticker in the vehicle.

(5) This indicates the tire ply composition and materials used.

(6) The letters D.O.T. certify compliance with Department of Transportation tire safety standards. Adjacent to these is a tire identification or serial number. The first two characters identify size, type and date of manufacture.

(7) Tires must be marked either "tubeless" or "tube-type."

M/S — Any combination of the letters M and S indicate the tire meets the RMA definition for a mud and snow tire.

06.05 WHAT TIRE SIZE DESIGNATIONS MEAN.

Several systems of tire size designation are used by the industry.

NUMERIC:

6.45 — 14, for example

The numeric designation shown above represents the oldest type of system. The first number (6.45) refers to the approximate cross section width of an inflated tire in inches. The second number (14) is the rim diameter.

ALPHA NUMERIC:

F	R	78	14
Indicates Load/Size Relationship	Radial	Height-to-Width Ratio	Rim Diameter in Inches

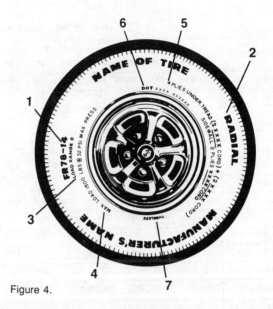

Figure 4.

In the alpha numeric size designation in this illustration, the first letter designates the load/size relationship. The lower the letter, the smaller the size and load-carrying capability of a tire at a given inflation pressure. "R" indicates the tire's approximate section height-to-width ratio ("78" means that the tire is 78% as high as it is wide). The second number indicates the rim size in inches ("14" indicates the tire fits a 14-inch rim).

An alpha numeric tire that does not have an "R" in the designation is not a radial-ply tire.

METRIC:

195R14

Metric uses a three-digit number, e.g., to indicate the approximate cross section in millimeters, followed by "R" for radial, and "14" for the rim diameter in inches.

"P" SERIES:

P	155/	80	R	13
Identifies Passenger Car Tire	Section Width in Millimeters	Height-to-Width Ratio	Identifies Tire Construction: R if radial; B if belted; D if diagonal (Bias)	Rim Diameter in Inches

This is the newest type of tire identification, based on international standards. Each of the components involved in tire size identification shown above may vary according to the section width, height-to-width ratio, construction and rim diameter of the tire.

TIRE SIZE	Load Limits (pounds per tire) at various cold inflation pressures																	
	15	20	25	30	35	40	45	50	55	60	65	70	75	80	85	90	95	100
4.80-8	260	310	350	390(A)	430	465	495	530	560	**590B**	615	645	670	695	720	**745(C)**		
4.80-12	345	410	465	520	570	615	660	700	740	**780(B)**	815	855	890	920	955			
5.30-12	395	465	530	590	645	700	745	795	**840(B)**	885	925	970	1010	**1045(C)**				
5.70-8	355	420	480	530	580	630	675	**715(B)**	760	800	835	875	**910(C)**	945	980	1010	1045	**1075(D)**
6.90-9	500	**590(A)**	670	750	820	**885(B)**	950	1010	1065	**1120(C)**	1175	1225	1280	1325	**1375(D)**	1420	1470	**1510(E)**
6.90-12	595	705	805	895	980	**1060(B)**	1135	1205	1275	**1345(C)**								
6.50-10	530	625	715	795	870	940	1010	1070	1135	**1190(C)**	1250	1305	1360	1410	1460	1510	1560	**1605(E)**
7.00-10	645	760	865	965	1055	1140	1225	1300	1375	1445	1515	1585	**1650(D)**	1710	1775	**1835(E)**		
7.50-10	695	820	935	1040	1135	1230	1315	1400	1480	1560	1635	1705	1775	1845	1910	**1975(E)**		
16.5x6.5-8	335	**395(A)**	450	495	540	580	**620(B)**	660	695	730	765	**795(C)**	825	855	885	**915(D)**		
20.5x8.0-10	565	660	750	830	**905(B)**	975	1040	**1105(C)**	1165	1225	1280	**1330(D)**	1385	1435	1485	**1535(E)**		
18.5x8.5-8	480	565	630	705	**770(B)**	830	885	**940(C)**										
23.5x8.5-12	675	795	900	995	**1085(B)**	1165	1245	**1320(C)**										

TRAILER TIRE LOAD RATINGS FOR NORMAL HIGHWAY SERVICE

Note: 1. Letters in parentheses indicate Load Range for which **Bold Face** Loads are maximum. (See Load Range – Ply Rating Conversion Table)

LOAD RANGE – PLY RATING CONVERSION TABLE

Load Range	Replaces Ply Rating
A	2
B	4
C	6
D	8
E	10
F	12
G	14

06.06 BALANCING LOAD AND INFLATION.

The load that any tire can carry depends upon several variables. These include the tire size, the load range (or ply rating) of the tire and the inflation pressure. Refer to the vehicle manufacturer's recommendations in the owner's manual or placard affixed to the vehicle for tire information. Also, check the load and inflation tables in this section to be certain that you have adequate tire load capacity.

Proper inflation is the most important requirement for maximum tire safety and mileage. Correct inflation provides proper sidewall deflection and safe operating temperature for the tires. Underinflation, on the other hand, creates excessive heat, lowers load carrying capacity, seriously reduces tire life and can cause premature tire failure.

The sidewall bulge which is characteristic of radial tires makes it impossible to visually determine whether radial tires are properly inflated, as dramatized in the following drawings. The tire on the right is 33% underinflated. As a result, it will run hotter, wear faster and/or unevenly, adversely affect vehicle handling and may fail in service. Radial tire pressure *must* be regularly checked with a reliable air gauge (See Section 06.07 regarding inflating procedures and Figure 5).

Most trailer tires require higher inflation pressures than passenger car tires, a fact not generally known by service personnel. Bleeding air from the trailer tires in a misguided attempt to match trailer tire inflation pressures to the lower inflation pressures of passenger car tires may result in underinflation, causing fast and uneven tread wear, trailer instability at high speeds and extreme heat build-up, which can result in tire failure.

When loading a car and any kind of trailer, make an axle-by-axle check of maximum permissible tire loads as marked on the tire sidewall. Distribute the load in both vehicles to prevent overloading the tires on any axle or wheel position, and remember to include the weight of the driver and passengers.

If passenger tires are used on a trailer, only 91% of the maximum-rated load marked on the tire sidewall is permissible, and such tires must be inflated to the maximum rated inflation. Also remember that some of the weight of the loaded trailer transfers to the rear axle of the towing vehicle, thus reducing the payload that can safely be placed in, or on top of, the towing vehicle. Load leveling hitch devices will distribute the hitch load equally to the front and rear axles of the towing vehicle.

The only sure way to prevent overload is to weigh, axle-by-axle, the fully loaded vehicles on reliable platform weigh scales. Divide each loaded axle weight by the number of tires on that axle. If the actual per-tire load exceeds the per-tire load capacity (as marked on tire sidewall) for tires on that axle, reduce your load to within the tire load capacity. If you can't reduce the load, replace the tires with some that will adequately carry the load. It may also be necessary to replace the wheels with heavy-duty wheels.

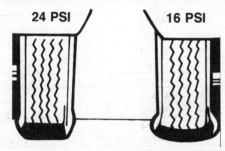

24 PSI   **16 PSI**

Figure 5. The tire on the right is 33% under-inflated. As a result, it will run hotter, wear faster and/or unevenly, adversely affect vehicle handling and may fail in service. Radial tire pressure must be checked regularly with a reliable air gauge.

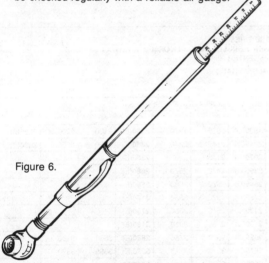

Figure 6.

06.07   HOW TO INFLATE TIRES.

A limited study by the National Bureau of Standards shows that gas station gauges may be off from two to four psi or more. Our own experience with gasoline station gauges tends toward the "or more." As inflation is so important to good tire safety and longevity, RVers are well-advised to carry their own reliable handheld pressure gauge (Figure 6).

Check the air pressure when the tire is cold, that is, when the vehicle has been driven less than one mile at moderate speed. This is important because inflation tables list cold pressures and you're only guessing when you measure a hot tire.

Never "bleed" or reduce air pressure when tires are hot from driving. A hot tire at or below recommended cold inflation pressure is dangerously underinflated.

Figure 7. DIAGRAMMATIC ILLUSTRATIONS OF TIRE IN VARIOUS STATES OF INFLATION (Exaggerated Views)*

UNDERINFLATION

TREAD CONTACT WITH ROAD

Causes excessive tire deflection and heat buildup, running the risk of failure. It also causes excessive wear on outer tread ribs.

OVERINFLATION

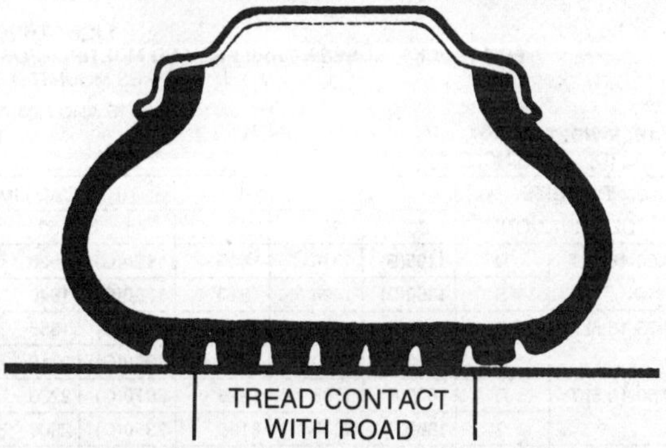

TREAD CONTACT WITH ROAD

Causes tires to ride hard and makes them more vulnerable to impact damage and weakening of the tire body.

PROPER INFLATION

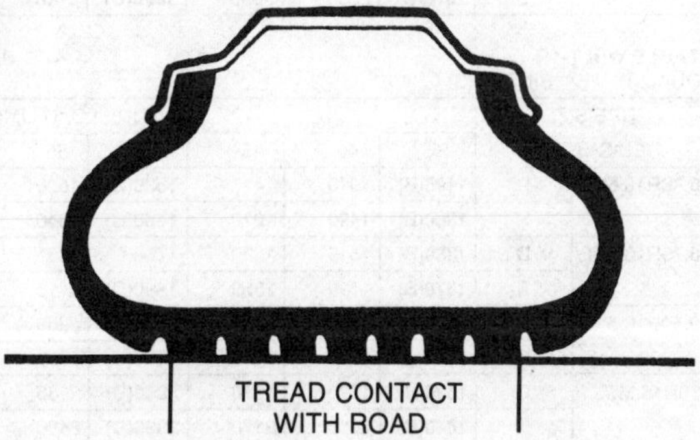

TREAD CONTACT WITH ROAD

The correct profile for full contact with the road which results in optimum tire performance.

*Because radial ply tires have a characteristic bulge in the sidewall even when properly inflated, it is impossible to visually determine the degree of inflation. Use a reliable air gauge to check inflation pressure.

SPECIAL TRAILER TIRE LOAD RATINGS FOR NORMAL HIGHWAY SERVICE

TIRE SIZE	Load Limits (pounds per tire) at various cold inflation pressures										
	15	20	25	30	35	40	45	50	55	60	65
6.00-13 ST	570	675	765	855	**935(B)**	1010	1080	**1150(C)**			
6.50-13 ST	650	770	875	975	**1065(B)**	1150	1235	**1315(C)**			
7.00-13 ST	715	845	965	1075	**1175(B)**	1270	1360	**1450(C)**			
6.45-14 ST	630	745	850	945	**1035(B)**	1120	1200	**1275(C)**			
7.35-14 ST	755	895	1020	1135	**1245(B)**	1345	1440	**1530(C)**			
7.75-14 ST	830	980	1120	1245	**1365(B)**	1475	1580	**1680(C)**			
8.25-14 ST	895	1060	1210	1345	**1470(B)**	1590	1705	**1815(C)**			
8.55-14 ST	980	1155	1320	1465	**1605(B)**	1735	1860	**1975(C)**			
6.85-15 ST	690	815	925	1030	**1130(B)**	1220	1310	**1390(C)**			
7.35-15 ST	780	920	1050	1170	**1280(B)**	1385	1480	**1575(C)**			
7.75-15 ST	830	985	1120	1245	**1365(B)**	1475	1580	**1680(C)**			
8.25-15 ST	905	1070	1220	1355	**1485(B)**	1615	1720	**1825(C)**			
8.55-15 ST	990	1170	1330	1480	**1620(B)**	1755	1880	**2000(C)**	2115	2225	**2330(D)**
8.85-15 ST	1035	1220	1390	1550	**1695(B)**	1835	1965	**2090(C)**			

Note: 1. Letters in parentheses indicate Load Range for which **Bold Face** loads are maximum. (See Load Range – Ply Rating Conversion Table)

LIGHT TRUCK WIDE BASE TIRES
FOR TRUCKS, BUSSES, TRAILERS AND MULTIPURPOSE PASSENGER VEHICLES USED IN NORMAL HIGHWAY SERVICE
TIRES MOUNTED ON 15° DROP CENTER RIMS

TIRE AND RIM ASSOCIATION STANDARD
BIAS PLY

TABLE WBLT-1B
DUAL (D)   SINGLE (S)

TIRE SIZE DESIGNATION		TIRE LOAD LIMITS AT VARIOUS COLD INFLATION PRESSURES											
		30	35	40	45	50	55	60	65	70	75	80	85	90
8.00-16.5LT	D	**1195(B)**	1310	1415	**1520(C)**	1620	1710	**1800(D)**	1885	1970	**2050(E)**	2130	2200	**2280(F)**
	S	**1360(B)**	1490	1610	**1730(C)**	1840	1945	**2045(D)**	2145	2240	**2330(E)**	2420	2500	**2590(F)**
8.75-16.5LT	D	**1380(B)**	1515	1630	**1750(C)**	1855	1970	**2070(D)**	2175	2260	**2360(E)**			
	S	**1570(B)**	1720	1850	**1990(C)**	2110	2240	**2350(D)**	2470	2570	**2680(E)**			
9.50-16.5LT	D	**1635(B)**	1785	1925	**2070(C)**	2200	2330	**2445(D)**	2570	2685	**2790(E)**			
	S	**1860(B)**	2030	2190	**2350(C)**	2500	2650	**2780(D)**	2920	3050	**3170(E)**			
10-16.5LT	D	**1620(B)**	1770	1910	**2050(C)**	2180	2310	**2420(D)**	2540	2650	**2760(E)**			
	S	**1840(B)**	2010	2170	**2330(C)**	2480	2620	**2750(D)**	2885	3010	**3135(E)**			
10-17.5LT	D	1680	1840	1990	**2135(C)**	2270	2400	**2525(D)**	2650	2765	**2880(E)**	2990	3100	**3200(F)**
	S	1910	2095	2265	**2425(C)**	2580	2730	**2870(D)**	3010	3140	**3270(E)**	3395	3520	**3640(F)**
12-16.5LT	D	**2090(C)**	2280	2460	**2640(D)**	2810	2970	**3120(E)**	3275	3420	**3560(F)**			
	S	**2370(C)**	2590	2800	**3000(D)**	3190	3370	**3550(E)**	3720	3885	**4045(F)**			

TABLE WBLT-1R   **RADIAL PLY**
DUAL (D)   SINGLE (S)

TIRE SIZE DESIGNATION		TIRE LOAD LIMITS AT VARIOUS COLD INFLATION PRESSURES											
		35	40	45	50	55	60	65	70	75	80	85	90	95
8.00R16.5LT	D	**1195(B)**	1310	1415	**1520(C)**	1620	1710	**1800(D)**	1885	1970	**2050(E)**	2130	2200	**2280(F)**
	S	**1360(B)**	1490	1610	**1730(C)**	1840	1945	**2045(D)**	2145	2240	**2330(E)**	2420	2500	**2590(F)**
8.75R16.5LT	D	**1380(B)**	1515	1630	**1750(C)**	1855	1970	**2070(D)**	2175	2260	**2360(E)**			
	S	**1570(B)**	1720	1850	**1990(C)**	2110	2240	**2350(D)**	2470	2570	**2680(E)**			
9.50R16.5LT	D	**1635(B)**	1785	1925	**2070(C)**	2200	2330	**2445(D)**	2570	2685	**2790(E)**			
	S	**1860(B)**	2030	2190	**2350(C)**	2500	2650	**2780(D)**	2920	3050	**3170(E)**			
10R16.5LT	D	**1620(B)**	1770	1910	**2050(C)**	2180	2310	**2420(D)**	2540	2650	**2760(E)**			
	S	**1840(B)**	2010	2170	**2330(C)**	2480	2620	**2750(D)**	2885	3010	**3135(E)**			
10R17.5LT	D	1680	1840	1990	**2135(C)**	2270	2400	**2525(D)**	2650	2765	**2880(E)**	2990	3100	**3200(F)**
	S	1910	2095	2265	**2425(C)**	2580	2730	**2870(D)**	3010	3140	**3270(E)**	3395	3520	**3640(F)**
12R16.5LT	D	**2090(C)**	2280	2460	**2640(D)**	2810	2970	**3120(E)**	3275	3420	**3560(F)**			
	S	**2370(C)**	2590	2800	**3000(D)**	3190	3370	**3550(E)**	3720	3885	**4045(F)**			

NOTE: Letters in parentheses denote Load Range for which Bold Face Loads are maximum.

BIAS AND RADIAL PLY TIRES USED ON PASSENGER CARS AND STATION WAGONS
TIRE AND RIM ASSOCIATION STANDARD
TABLE PC-7 — REFER TO GENERAL DATA TABLES FOR SPECIFIC TIRE SIZE DESIGNATIONS

ALPHA DESIGNATION	LOAD RANGE	TIRE LOAD LIMITS AT VARIOUS COLD INFLATION PRESSURES												
		16	18	20	22	24	26	28	30	32	34	36	38	40
A, AR	B	720	770	810	860	900	940	980	1020	1060				
	C	720	770	810	860	900	940	980	1020	1060	1090	1130		
	D	720	770	810	860	900	940	980	1020	1060	1090	1130	1160	1200
B, BR	B	780	840	890	930	980	1030	1070	1110	1150				
	C	780	840	890	930	980	1030	1070	1110	1150	1190	1230		
	D	780	840	890	930	980	1030	1070	1110	1150	1190	1230	1270	1300
C, CR	B	840	890	950	1000	1050	1100	1140	1190	1230				
	C	840	890	950	1000	1050	1100	1140	1190	1230	1270	1320		
	D	840	890	950	1000	1050	1100	1140	1190	1230	1270	1320	1360	1400
D, DR	B	890	950	1010	1070	1120	1170	1220	1270	1320				
	C	890	950	1010	1070	1120	1170	1220	1270	1320	1360	1410		
	D	890	950	1010	1070	1120	1170	1220	1270	1320	1360	1410	1450	1490
E, ER	B	950	1010	1070	1130	1190	1240	1300	1350	1400				
	C	950	1010	1070	1130	1190	1240	1300	1350	1400	1440	1490		
	D	950	1010	1070	1130	1190	1240	1300	1350	1400	1440	1490	1540	1580
F, FR	B	1020	1090	1160	1220	1280	1340	1400	1450	1500				
	C	1020	1090	1160	1220	1280	1340	1400	1450	1500	1550	1610		
	D	1020	1090	1160	1220	1280	1340	1400	1450	1500	1550	1610	1650	1700
G, GR	B	1100	1180	1250	1310	1380	1440	1500	1560	1620				
	C	1100	1180	1250	1310	1380	1440	1500	1560	1620	1680	1730		
	D	1100	1180	1250	1310	1380	1440	1500	1560	1620	1680	1730	1780	1830
H, HR	B	1200	1290	1360	1440	1510	1580	1650	1710	1770				
	C	1200	1290	1360	1440	1510	1580	1650	1710	1770	1830	1890		
	D	1200	1290	1360	1440	1510	1580	1650	1710	1770	1830	1890	1950	2010
J, JR	B	1260	1350	1430	1500	1580	1650	1720	1790	1860				
	C	1260	1350	1430	1500	1580	1650	1720	1790	1860	1920	1980		
	D	1260	1350	1430	1500	1580	1650	1720	1790	1860	1920	1980	2040	2100
K, KR	B	1290	1380	1460	1540	1620	1690	1770	1830	1900				
	C	1290	1380	1460	1540	1620	1690	1770	1830	1900	1970	2030		
	D	1290	1380	1460	1540	1620	1690	1770	1830	1900	1970	2030	2090	2150
L, LR	B	1340	1430	1520	1600	1680	1750	1830	1900	1970				
	C	1340	1430	1520	1600	1680	1750	1830	1900	1970	2040	2100		
	D	1340	1430	1520	1600	1680	1750	1830	1900	1970	2040	2100	2170	2230
M, MR	B	1420	1520	1610	1700	1780	1860	1940	2020	2090				
	C	1420	1520	1610	1700	1780	1860	1940	2020	2090	2160	2230		
	D	1420	1520	1610	1700	1780	1860	1940	2020	2090	2160	2230	2300	2370
N, NR	B	1500	1600	1700	1790	1880	1970	2050	2130	2210				
	C	1500	1600	1700	1790	1880	1970	2050	2130	2210	2280	2360		
	D	1500	1600	1700	1790	1880	1970	2050	2130	2210	2280	2360	2430	2500

NOTES 1: Minimum inflation pressures are to be as indicated in the table for the various tire loads.

2: Increased inflation pressures:

a) Inflation pressures may be increased above those indicated in table when recommended by car manufacturer for optimum stability and handling but not to exceed 32 psi for Load Range B, 36 psi for Load Range C and 40 psi for Load Range D tires.

b) For sustained high speed driving over 75 mph, cold inflation pressures must be increased a minimum of 4 psi above that applicable for the tire load but not to exceed 32 psi for Load Range B, 36 psi for Load Range C and 40 psi for Load Range D tires. Where the required increase cannot be made without exceeding the maximum allowable inflation pressure, speed must be limited to 75 mph.

Table A / **LIGHT TRUCK TIRES**
FOR TRUCKS, BUSSES, TRAILERS AND MULTIPURPOSE PASSENGER VEHICLES USED IN NORMAL HIGHWAY SERVICE
TABLE LT-1B
DUAL (D)   SINGLE (S)

TIRE SIZE DESIGNATION		TIRE LOAD LIMITS AT VARIOUS COLD INFLATION PRESSURES														
		30	35	40	45	50	55	60	65	70	75	80	85	90	95	100
6.00-16LT	D	990	1080	1170	**1255**(C)	1330	1410	**1480**(D)	1560	1620	**1690**(E)					
	S	1130	1230	1330	**1430**(C)	1520	1600	**1690**(D)	1770	1850	**1920**(E)					
6.50-16LT	D	1120	1225	1320	**1420**(C)	1500	1590	**1670**(D)	1750	1830	**1900**(E)					
	S	1270	1390	1500	**1610**(C)	1710	1800	**1900**(D)	1990	2080	**2160**(E)					
6.70-15LT	D	1060	1170	1265	**1355**(C)	1440	1520	**1600**(D)	1670	1750	**1820**(E)					
	S	1210	1320	1430	**1530**(C)	1630	1720	**1810**(D)	1900	1980	**2060**(E)					
7.00-13LT	D	880	960	1035	**1110**(C)	1180	1250	**1315**(D)								
	S	1000	1090	1170	**1260**(C)	1340	1420	**1490**(D)								
7.00-14LT	D	910	995	1075	**1155**(C)	1225	1300	**1365**(D)	1430	1495	**1555**(E)					
	S	1030	1130	1220	**1310**(C)	1390	1470	**1550**(D)	1620	1700	**1770**(E)					
7.00-15LT	D	1190	1310	1420	**1520**(C)	1620	1715	**1800**(D)	1870	1960	**2040**(E)					
	S	1350	1480	1610	**1720**(C)	1830	1940	**2040**(D)	2130	2220	**2320**(E)					
7.00-16LT	D	1260	1365	1475	**1580**(C)	1685	1780	**1870**(D)	1960	2040	**2130**(E)					
	S	1430	1560	1680	**1800**(C)	1910	2030	**2130**(D)	2240	2330	**2430**(E)					
7.10-15LT	D	1160	1270	1370	**1470**(C)	1570	1660	**1740**(D)	1830	1910	**1990**(E)					
	S	1320	1440	1560	**1670**(C)	1780	1880	**1970**(D)	2070	2160	**2250**(E)					
7.50-15LT	D	1370	1500	1620	1735	1850	1965	**2060**(D)	2160	2250	**2350**(E)					
	S	1560	1710	1840	1980	2100	2220	**2330**(D)	2450	2560	**2660**(E)					
7.50-16LT	D	1430	1565	1690	**1815**(C)	1930	2040	**2140**(D)	2245	2345	**2440**(E)					
	S	1620	1770	1930	**2060**(C)	2190	2310	**2440**(D)	2560	2670	**2780**(E)					
8.25-16LT	D	1740	1900	**2050**(C)	2200	**2340**(D)	2480	**2600**(E)	2730	2850	**2970**(F)	3080	3195	**3300**(G)		
	S	1980	2160	**2330**(C)	2500	**2660**(D)	2820	**2960**(E)	3105	3240	**3370**(F)	3500	3630	**3750**(G)		
9.00-16LT	D	1980	2165	**2340**(C)	2505	**2665**(D)	2820	**2965**(E)	3080	3245	**3380**(F)	3505	3635	**3760**(G)		
	S	2250	2460	**2660**(C)	2850	**3030**(D)	3210	**3370**(E)	3535	3690	**3840**(F)	3985	4130	**4275**(G)		

Note: Letters in parentheses denote Load Range for which Bold Face Loads are maximum.

Tire Size	Ply and Load Range	Max. Cap. (Lbs.)	Tire Load Capacity at Various Cold Inflation Pressures (Lbs. Per Square Inch)						
			30	35	40	45	50	55	60
Used as Singles									
8-17.5	6-C	2075	1640	1790	1940	2075	—	—	—
8-17.5	8-D	2455	1640	1790	1940	2075	2205	2335	2455
Used as Duals									
8-17.5	6-C	1820	1445	1575	1700	1820	—	—	—
8-17.5	8-D	2155	1445	1575	1700	1820	1935	2050	2155

Tire Size	Ply and Load Range	Max. Cap. (Lbs.)	Tire Load Capacity at Various Cold Inflation Pressures (Lbs. Per Square Inch)												
			50	55	60	65	70	75	80	85	90	95	100	105	110
Used as Singles															
8-19.5	8-D	2800	2110	2270	2410	2540	2680	2800							
Used as Duals															
8-19.5	8-D	2460	2110	2230	2350	2460	—	—							
Used as Singles															
8-19.5	10-E	3170	2110	2270	2410	2540	2680	2800	2930	3060	3170				
Used as Duals															
8-19.5	10-E	2780	2110	2230	2350	2460	2570	2680	2780	—	—				
Used as Singles															
8R-19.5	10-E	3170		2110	2270	2410	2540	2680	2800	2930	3060	3170			
Used as Duals															
8R-19.5	10-E	2780	1990	2110	2230	2350	2460	2570	2680	2780	—	—			
Used as Singles															
8R-19.5	12-F	3500		2110	2270	2410	2540	2680	2800	2930	3060	3170	3280	3400	3500
Used as Duals															
8R-19.5	12-F	3070	1990	2110	2230	2350	2460	2570	2680	2780	2880	2980	3070		

NOTE: For special operating conditions, cold inflation pressures may be increased up to 10 psi above those indicated in the table with no increase in loads. For sustained high speed driving over 60 mph, cold inflation pressures must be increased 10 psi above those specified in the table for the load being carried.

RECREATIONAL AND TRAILER TIRE LOAD RATINGS FOR NORMAL HIGHWAY SERVICE
FOR DIAGONAL (BIAS) AND BELTED BIAS LIGHT TRUCK TIRES USED AS SINGLES

TIRE SIZE	Load Limits (pounds per tire) at various cold inflation pressures														
	30	35	40	45	50	55	60	65	70	75	80	85	90	95	100
Tires Used on 5° Tapered Rims															
6.00-16 LT	1130	1230	1330	**1430(C)**	1520	1600	**1690(D)**	1770	1850	**1920(E)**					
6.50-16 LT	1270	1390	1500	**1610(C)**	1710	1800	**1900(D)**	1990	2080	**2160(E)**					
6.70-15 LT	1210	1320	1430	**1530(C)**	1630	1720	**1810(D)**	1900	1980	**2060(E)**					
7.00-13 LT	1000	1090	1170	**1260(C)**	1340	1420	**1490(D)**								
7.00-14 LT	1030	1130	1220	**1310(C)**	1390	1470	**1550(D)**	1620	1700	**1770(E)**					
7.00-15 LT	1350	1480	1610	**1720(C)**	1830	1940	**2040(D)**	2130	2220	**2320(E)**					
7.00-16 LT	1430	1560	1680	**1800(C)**	1910	2030	**2130(D)**	2240	2330	**2430(E)**					
7.10-15 LT	1320	1440	1560	**1670(C)**	1780	1880	**1970(D)**	2070	2160	**2250(E)**					
7.50-15 LT	1560	1710	1840	1980	2100	2220	**2330(D)**	2450	2560	**2660(E)**					
7.50-16 LT	1620	1770	1930	**2060(C)**	2190	2310	**2440(D)**	2560	2670	**2780(E)**					
8.25-16 LT	1980	2160	2330	2500	**2660(D)**	2820	**2960(D)**	3105	3240	**3370(F)**	3500	3630	**3750(G)**		
9.00-16 LT	2250	2460	2660	2850	**3030(D)**	3210	**3370(D)**	3535	3690	**3840(F)**	3985	4130	**4275(G)**		
7.9-14 LT	**1000(B)**	1090	1180	**1260(C)**	1340	1420	**1490(D)**								
9-15 LT	**1560(B)**	1710	1850	**1980(C)**	2100	2220	**2340(D)**								
10-15 LT	**1760(B)**	1930	2080	**2230(C)**	2370	2510	**2640(D)**								
10-16 LT	**1840(B)**	2010	2170	**2330(C)**	2480	2620	**2750(D)**								
11-14 LT	**1820(B)**	1990	2150	**2300(C)**	2450	2590	**2730(D)**								
11-15 LT	**1900(B)**	2080	2250	**2410(C)**	2560	2710	**2850(D)**								
11-16 LT	**1980(B)**	2160	2330	**2500(C)**	2650	2810	**2950(D)**								
12-15 LT	**2250(B)**	2460	2660	**2850(C)**	3030	3200	**3370(D)**								
E78-14 LT	1140	1240	1340	**1440(C)**	1530	1620	**1710(D)**	1790	1870	**1950(E)**					
G78-14 LT	1260	1380	1490	**1590(C)**											
C78-15 LT	1080	1180	1280	**1370(C)**	1450	1540	**1620(D)**								
G78-15 LT	1310	1430	1550	**1660(C)**	1770	1870	**1960(D)**	2060	2150	**2240(E)**					
H78-15 LT	1440	1580	1710	**1830(C)**	1950	2060	**2170(D)**	2270	2370	**2470(E)**					
L78-15 LT	1600	1750	1900	**2030(C)**	2160	2290	**2400(D)**	2520	2630	**2740(E)**					
F78-16 LT	1270	1400	1510	**1620(C)**	1720	1820	**1910(D)**	2010	2100	**2180(E)**					
H78-16 LT	1510	1650	1780	**1910(C)**	2030	2150	**2260(D)**	2370	2480	**2580(E)**					
L78-16 LT	1670	1820	1970	**2110(C)**	2250	2380	**2500(D)**	2620	2740	**2850(E)**					
Tires Used on 15° Tapered Rims															
7-14.5 LT	1140	1240	1350	1440	1530	1620	1710	1790	**1870(D)**	1940	2020	**2090(E)**	2160	2230	**2300(F)**
8-14.5 LT	1380	1510	1630	1750	1860	1970	2070	2170	2270	2360	2450	**2540(E)**	2620	2710	**2790(F)**
9-14.5 LT	1600	1750	1890	2020	2150	2280	2400	2510	**2620(D)**	2730	2830	**2940(E)**	3040	3130	**3230(F)**
7-17.5 LT	1430	1565	1695	**1815(C)**	1925	2040	**2145(C)**								
8-17.5 LT	1640	1790	1940	**2075(C)**	2205	2335	**2455(D)**	2575	2685	**2795(E)**					
8.00-16.5 LT	**1360(B)**	1490	1610	**1730(C)**	1840	1945	**2045(D)**	2145	2240	**2330(E)**	2420	2500	**2590(F)**		
8.75-16.5 LT	**1570(B)**	1720	1850	**1990(C)**	2110	2240	**2350(D)**	2470	2570	**2680(E)**					
9.50-16.5 LT	**1860(B)**	2030	2190	**2350(C)**	2500	2650	**2780(D)**	2920	3050	**3970(E)**					
10-16.5 LT	**1840(B)**	2010	2170	**2330(C)**	2480	2620	**2750(D)**	2885	3010	**3135(E)**					
10-17.5 LT	1910	2095	2265	**2425(C)**	2580	2730	**2870(D)**	3010	3140	**3270(E)**	3395	3520	**3640(F)**		
12-16.5 LT	**2370(C)**	2590	2800	**3000(D)**	3190	3370	**3550(E)**	3720	3885	**4045(F)**					

NOTES:

1. For load and inflation tables for dual wheels, consult current Tire and Rim Association Yearbook.

2. Letters in parentheses indicate Load Range for which **Bold Face** Loads are maximum. (See Load Range – Ply Rating Conversion Table)

3. For sustained high speed driving, cold inflation pressures **must** be increased 10 psi above that specified in the table above for the load being carried. Where this increase is limited by the maximum rim capacity, speed must be limited or tire load reduced to the limit indicated for 10 psi less inflation.

TIGHTENING REFERENCE

WHEEL STUD NUTS

Models	Nut Type	Thread Size	Torque
M300, M400	Flanged	5/8-18	300-350 Foot-Pounds
M500	Double Lock	See Note	450-500 Foot-Pounds
M600	Double Lock	See Note	450-500 Foot-Pounds

NOTE: Front Wheel and Inner Dual Rear Wheel nut is 3/4-16. Outer Dual Rear Wheel nut is 1-1/8-16.

Increase cold inflation pressure four pounds over that shown in the tables for highway driving over long periods. Do not exceed the limits labeled on the tire sidewall.

Make certain all tire valves and extensions are equipped with valve caps to keep out dirt and moisture. These caps provide a vital second seal to the valve core, as well as keeping out dirt, water, sand, etc., and they protect the core seal from damage and possible air leaks. It is recommended that an entire new valve be installed whenever a tire is replaced.

06.08 MEASURING TIRE TREAD.

Here's something that most people don't realize they can do for themselves. All it requires is a simple gauge device which tells you precisely how much tread is left. Here's how: (Figure 8).

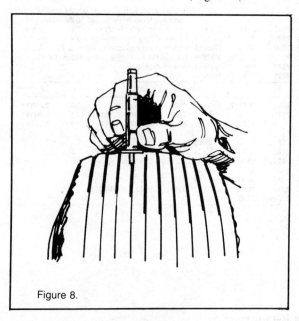

Figure 8.

Check the center groove in three different locations to give an overall reading. The device pictured is typical of most you'll find in auto supply stores; simply depress the indicator pin into the tire groove and the reading will show against the main body of the instrument. The gauge is calibrated in 1/32 inches. If the reading shows 2/32 inches or less (4/32 inches for truck front wheels), the tire is at the danger level.

The Tire Industry Safety Council sells a handy "Recreational Vehicle Tire Kit" which contains a tread depth gauge, a special high pressure tire air gauge calibrated to 120 pounds and a set of four protective metal valve caps. To obtain your kit, write the Tire Industry Safety Council, Box 1801, Washington, DC 20013.

06.09 HOW TO INSPECT TIRES FOR VISIBLE DAMAGE.

(1) Tread worn to the level of the tread wear indicators or when cord or fabric is exposed.

(2) Fabric break or a non-repairable injury.

(3) Cracks, cuts or snags deep enough to expose the body cords.

(4) Any indication of possible separation.

(5) Tire marked "unsafe for highway use," "not for highway use," "for racing purposes only," or "agricultural use only."

(6) Tire punctured by nails or other foreign objects.

(7) Rim bent, cracked, or otherwise damaged.

06.10 ABNORMAL TREAD WEAR.

The uneven tread wear patterns shown here were probably caused by conditions such as wrong inflation pressure, misalignment, improper balance or suspension neglect. These conditions can be avoided or corrected.

Mechanical irregularities often cause abnormal tread wear. Misalignment of front or rear wheels, bent wheels, sprung axle housings, worn bushings and the conditions shown below contribute to uneven and rapid tread wear and should be corrected.

IMPROPER CAMBER
(wheels tilted excessively inward or outward) causes more wear on one side of the tires.

FAULTY OR WORN SHOCK ABSORBERS
cause irregular tire wear and lead to other mechanical irregularities. They can also affect steering and stability and thereby constitute a safety hazard.

FAULTY OR "GRABBING" BRAKES
can cause much the same condition as out-of-balance wheels — flat spots and bald spots.

06.11 HIDDEN TIRE DAMAGE.

Illustrated in the following descriptions and drawings are various types of tire damage, along with explanations of why the tires failed, and how these failures could have been prevented. Damage often occurs sometime before the resulting tire failure. This is frequently difficult for people to understand, but there are several reasons:

PUNCTURES — Undetected punctures cause a slow loss of air which result in excessive heat buildup and lead to serious tire damage, e.g., tread separation, destruction of tire body and blowouts.

IMPACTS — Any tire, even a new one, may be damaged by impact. Determining factors are the size and shape of the object hit, the angle at which it is hit and the force of the impact. Accordingly, damages vary in severity and appearance.

The body of a tire may be damaged by impact with little or no visible exterior indication.

Impact or bruise injuries may cause blowouts or flat tires, but not necessarily at the time an object is struck. The tire may run many miles before failing. The break usually starts on the inside of the tire and is aggravated by the constant flexing of the tire until failure occurs.

Figures 9 and 10 show what often happens when a tire is crushed between a curb or chuckhole and the steel rim of the wheel. The angle at which the object is struck determines the position and shape of the break.

In tubeless tires, impact damage may result in a slow leak (a "slow-out" instead of a blow-out). Investigate any air leakage immediately.

DAMAGE CAUSED BY UNDERINFLATION — Driving on a tire inflated below the minimum recommended level causes the tire to heat excessively. This can lead to tire damage and possibly to tire failure, which may result in vehicle damage

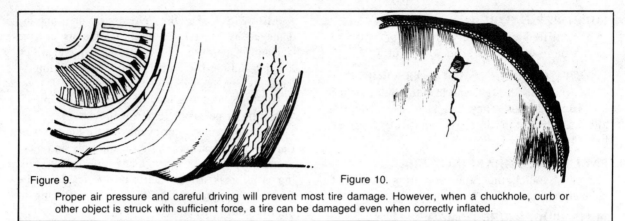

Figure 9.

Figure 10.

Proper air pressure and careful driving will prevent most tire damage. However, when a chuckhole, curb or other object is struck with sufficient force, a tire can be damaged even when correctly inflated.

and/or personal injury. Frequent tire inspection can detect underinflation. To prevent tire damage, always maintain the inflation pressure recommended by the vehicle manufacturer (Figures 11 and 12).

DAMAGE CAUSED BY OVERINFLATION — Overinflation creates stresses in the tire and may result in damage and/or failure due to impacts with road hazards. Never exceed the maximum inflation pressure labeled on the sidewall of the tire.

06.12 TIRE ROTATION.

To realize full tire life potential, tires should be inspected and rotated in accordance with the recommendations in the vehicle owner's manual, if available, or at 6,000- to 8,000-mile intervals. The first such rotation is the most important one in setting the stage for long and even tread wear. In some instances, if irregular wear begins to develop, rotation will be advisable before the recommended mileage interval. Before rotating, though, determine the cause of wear and correct any misalignment, balance or other mechanical problem. Earlier and more frequent rotation may also be desirable due to differences in tread wear between front and rear wheel tires.

If tires of different size or construction (diagonal, belted bias or radial) are mixed on the vehicle, consult your tire dealer for the correct relocation of these tires.

After rotation, adjustment of individual tire air pressure to conform to the tire's new location on the vehicle should be accomplished immediately (Figure 13).

06.13 TIRE REPAIR, MOUNTING AND DEMOUNTING.

While these procedures are almost always accomplished by service personnel, RVers may like to understand the approved techniques — so they may at least watch with a knowing eye. Reprinted here are the procedures advocated by the Rubber Manufacturer's Association:

PUNCTURE REPAIR PROCEDURES
FOR AUTOMOBILE TIRES

Recommended procedures for use by tire dealers and service stations for repairing of all tubeless tires.

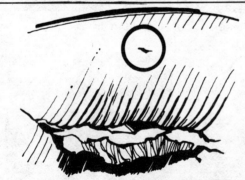

Figure 11. Drawing shows inside view of tire run flat to destruction. Puncture, circled above, caused gradual loss of air pressure which eventually resulted in failure.

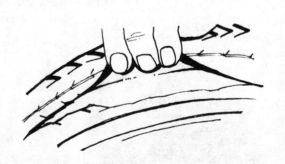

Figure 12. Driving even a short distance on a seriously underinflated or flat tire will result in damage which cannot be repaired.

FIGURE 13.

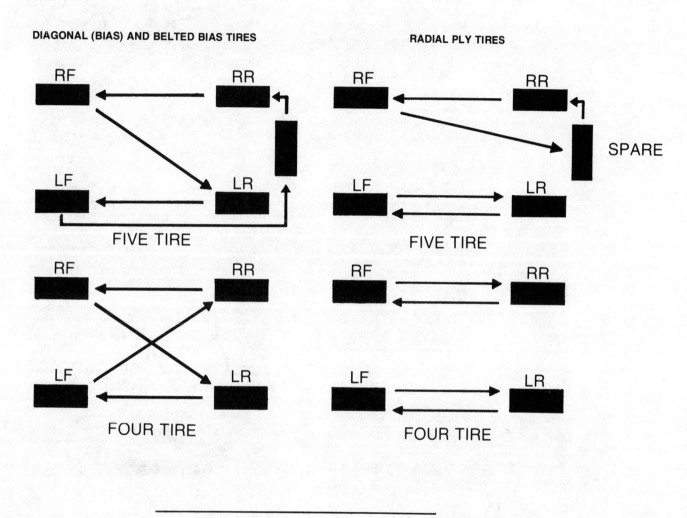

DIAGONAL (BIAS) AND BELTED BIAS TIRES

RADIAL PLY TIRES

FIVE TIRE

FIVE TIRE

FOUR TIRE

FOUR TIRE

SPARE

SNOW TIRE ROTATION

When snow tires are installed, the regular tread tires on the rear should be moved to the front and front tire stored. When snow tires are removed, install stored tires on the rear.
Do not rotate studded tires. Always remount them in original positions.

NOTE: Puncture repairs by dealers or service station personnel should be confined to the tread. Repairs in the sidewall or bead areas and repairs larger than those shown below should be referred to a full-service tire repair facility.

- **NEVER REPAIR TIRES WORN BELOW 1/16 INCH TREAD DEPTH.**

- **NEVER TRY TO REPAIR TIRES WITH TREAD PUNCTURES LARGER THAN 1/4 INCH.**

Tread punctures, nail holes or cuts up to ½ inch must be repaired from the inside of the tire. The repair material used must seal the inner liner and fill the injury to be considered a permanent repair.

Industry-approved repair methods include a combination of plug and patch, chemical or hot vulcanizing patches and head-type plugs — all applied from inside the tire.

If a tire continues to lose air, or has lost all or most of its air pressure, it must be removed from the wheel for complete internal inspection to be sure it is not damaged.

REPAIR PROCEDURES

A. INSPECTION

Before repairing, remove nail or other puncturing object from tire. With tire inflated, apply soap solution to damaged area to determine if air loss is from one or more than one puncture. Unseat the beads and apply approved bead lubricant. Then remove tire from wheel carefully to avoid further damage to the tire, particularly to the bead, and place on spreader.

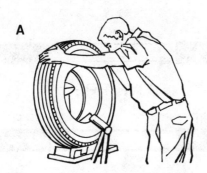

B. PROBING

Probe puncture with blunt, smooth surface awl or other hand probing tool to determine size and direction of injury, making sure no foreign material is left in the injury. Injuries exceeding ¼ inch should not be repaired.

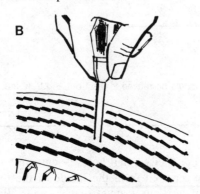

C. INTERNAL EXAMINATION

Bulge tire on spreader, marking the puncture with tire crayon. Inspect for evidence of other damage, e.g., in the bead area. Care should be used not to enlarge the injury.

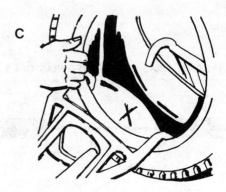

D. CLEANING

Clean punctured area thoroughly with chemical buffer cleaner, covering a slightly larger area than required for patch. This serves to remove dirt, mold lubricants, etc.; also keeps buffing tools clean. Make certain that no loose or frayed wire ends protrude through the liner.

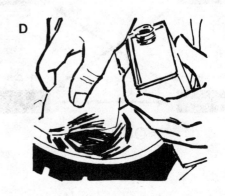

E. BUFFING

Buff cleaned area thoroughly, to a smooth velvet surface (RMA No. 1 buffed texture for chemical, valcanizing repairs, or to RMA No. 3 buffed texture for uncured repairs), taking care not to gouge liner or expose casing fabric. Remove dust from buffing with an approved method.

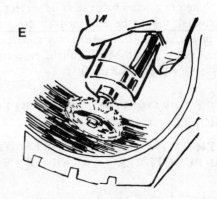

**F. AFTER COMPLETING BASIC PREP-
ARATION, FINISH REPAIR BY SELECTING
ONE OF THE THREE REPAIR METHODS
SHOWN ON THESE TWO PAGES:**

CHEMICAL VULCANIZING REPAIRS

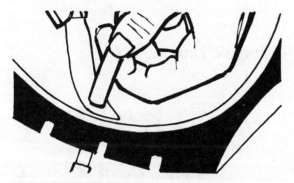

1. FILL INJURY. The injury must be filled with contour conforming material following manufacturer's instructions. Cut off material flush with inner liner.

2. CEMENTING. Always use self-vulcanizing cement recommended by the patch manufacturer. Apply a thin even coating of chemical vulcanizing cement to the prepared and buffed surface. ALLOW TO DRY THOROUGHLY. Keep dirt and other impurities from contaminating the cement remaining in the can.

3. PATCH APPLICATION. Remove backing from non-reinforced patch and center over injury. Stitch down thoroughly with stitching tool, working from center out.

HOT VULCANIZING REPAIRS

1. FILL INJURY. The injury must be filled with contour conforming material following manufacturer's instructions. Cut off material flush with inner liner.

2. CEMENTING. Always use the cement recommended by the patch manufacturer. Apply thin coat of recommended cement to the prepared and buffed surface. ALLOW TO DRY THOROUGHLY.

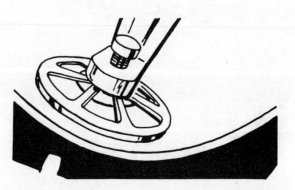

3. PATCH APPLICATION. Apply hot vulcanizing and cure according to manufacturer's recommendations.

HEAD-TYPE PLUG REPAIRS

1. CEMENTING. Always use the cement recommended by the plug manufacturer. Apply a thin coat of chemical vulcanizing cement to the cleaned and buffed surface. ALLOW TO DRY THOROUGHLY.

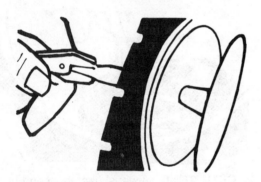

2. PLUG INSERTION. Remove backing from stem and plug head. Pull through according to manufacturer's recommendations.

3. STITCHING. Stitch plug head down firmly with stitching tool, working from center out.

G. FINISHED REPAIR

There are a number of satisfactory methods of repair. Regardless of type of repair used, finished repair should seal the inner liner and fill the injury. After inflating, check finished repair with water or soap solution to assure complete seal.

MOUNTING PROCEDURES

1. MOUNTING: Never mount a tire on a rim that is damaged, or has been repaired by welding or brazing. Be certain that rim flanges and bead ledges (especially hump and radius) are smooth and clean. Remove any oxidized rubber, dried soap solution, rust, heavy paint, etc., with a wire brush. Inspect valve and replace if damaged or deteriorated.

2. Place wheel on changer with narrow bead-ledge up. For your protection, wheel should be **centered** and securely fastened on the changer with the hold-down mechanism.

3. Lubricate sides and bases of tire beads, rim flanges, and bead ledge areas with rubber lubricant approved by the tire manufacturer. Never use antifreeze, silicones, or petroleum-based lubricants.

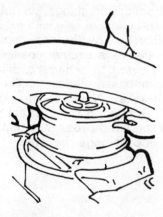

4. Be sure there are no tools, foreign objects, or liquids inside the tire casing. In mounting the tire, push the bottom bead **first** in the well of the wheel, as shown here.

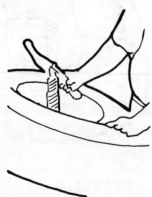

5. Then push the top bead down into the center well of the wheel. Hold the tire in this position while rotating finger runs the bead onto the wheel. Center tire on rim.

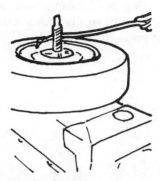

6. Check to be sure the wheel is securely fastened to the changer by the hold-down mechanism. **Use an extension air hose with gauge and clip-on chuck to permit operator to stand clear of tire assembly. Slowly inflate the tire until the beads "pop" onto the bead ledge of the wheel (see special "WARNING" below). Prior to inflating the tire to the recommended pressure, loosen slightly the hold-down cone so that it and the tire assembly can be removed later. Insert valve core and reinflate to recommended inflation.**

WARNING!
NEVER INFLATE BEYOND 40 POUNDS PRESSURE

If beads have not seated by the time pressure reaches 40 pounds, deflate the assembly, reposition the tire on the rim, relubricate and reinflate. After seating beads, adjust inflation to recommended pressure. Allowing air pressure to build beyond 40 pounds during mounting in an attempt to seat the beads is a DANGEROUS PRACTICE and may break a bead (or even the rim) with explosive force resulting in serious injury or death. Inspect both sides of tire to be sure beads are evenly seated. If not, completely deflate tire, unseat beads and repeat entire mounting procedure. If ring-type or other bead-seating device is used, manufacturer's instructions must be followed. In no case should inflation pressure exceed 40 pounds.

DO NOT STAND, LEAN, OR REACH OVER TIRE WHILE INFLATING IT!

DEMOUNTING PROCEDURES

- **Tire changing can be dangerous, and should be done by trained personnel using proper tools and procedures.**

1. DEMOUNTING: Place tire in a horizontal position on changer, as shown here. Be sure that the narrow ledge of the wheel is facing up. Do not drop or throw tire onto the changer. Remove valve core and completely deflate tire.

3. Loosen **both** tire beads from rim flanges. This operation should be done carefully. If the beads do not readily separate from the rim flange, do not force or hammer. Lubricate only with rubber lubricant approved by the tire manufacturer and rotate tire to another position and try again. Never use antifreeze, silicones or petroleum-based lubricants. **The bottom bead breaker should be checked to be sure it is making full contact with the tire. If the bead breaker is bent, it may strike and damage the wheel.**

2. The wheel should be **centered** and securely fastened on the changer with the hold-down mechanism. In this illustration, the hold-down is a cone which the serviceman is placing over the center shaft. Worn or damaged cones should be replaced. **Remove all old balance weights from the rim prior to dismounting to prevent bead tearing from weight clip.**

4. After beads are loosened from rim flanges, the inside of the wheel and both bead areas of the tire should be lubricated again. This makes it easy to remove the tire from the wheel without damage.

5. Use a tire iron to bring the bead of the tire onto the rotating finger of the tire changer. Hold the tire bead in the center wheel well during this operation. Never use a pipe or a make-shift bar.

6. Start the tire changer to remove the top bead from the wheel. Properly lubricated, the bead will slip away from the rim flange of the wheel with ease if the tire bead is held in the center well of the wheel, as shown.

7. Again lubricate the tire beads and bead seat areas of the wheel, including drop-center well of the wheel. This lubrication is necessary to enable the bead of the tire to slip down into the center well.

8. Use tire iron to raise bottom bead and bring it over the rotating finger of the changer. The side of the tire opposite the rotating finger must be down in the center well of the wheel and held in this position by the hip and hand.

06.14 ALIGNMENT AND BALANCE.

Tire/wheel assembly vibration is caused by the rotating assembly being out of balance (Figures 14 and 15). An assembly seriously out-of-balance at the tread will develop a disturbing pounding at highway speeds. When this occurs, you should consult a specialist for a balancing.

Balancing is usually accomplished by attaching lead weights to the wheel rim at precise points as indicated by an electronic balancing mechanism. A balancing generally lasts quite a while, but it can be ruined by tire damage. (The lead weights occasionally come off, so keep a record or drawing of where they belong so you can check them from time to time.)

Wheel alignment should be checked by a qualified shop at least every 10,000 miles, but more frequently if you often drive rough roads or if you've suffered severe tire impact. Misalignment will eventually show up as uneven tire wear, but why wait for that to happen?

06.15 STORING TIRES.

When tires aren't to be used for a time, it's best to take the weight off of them. Put the RV up on jacks and release about 10 pounds from each tire. Also, protect the tires from direct sunshine or excessive heat, even if this means taking them off and storing them inside. (HINT: Tag each tire with it's correct location so you can replace it where it belongs.) Be sure to reinflate each tire to its proper pressure before allowing them to support vehicle weight again.

FIGURE 14. STATIC OUT-OF-BALANCE

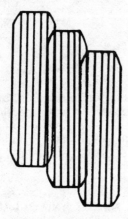

A wheel out of balance when stationary. This causes vertical vibration of the tire/wheel assembly, due to the tendency of the heavier part to remain at the lowest point on the wheel.

FIGURE 15. DYNAMIC OUT-OF-BALANCE

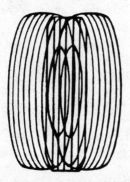

A wheel out of balance when rotating or when the two halves of a wheel act in opposite directions along different planes. The wheel tends to turn inward and outward every ½ revolution.

Chapter Seven

Electrical Systems

Like love, a vehicular electrical system is a many splendored thing — until it fails you or jolts you. It has multiple components joined by confusing bundles of colored wires, and some of these pieces wear out or require periodic replacement. By far the largest gremlins in an RV electrical system, though, are dirt, incorrect wiring and attempting to use the wrong type of battery. We'll start with a brief look at electricity and batteries, and then work into the features of your electrical system.

07.01 WATTS CURRENT?

Amps, as many RVers quickly learn when they run low, are quantities of energy moving through a circuit. Voltage is an electrical pressure which causes energy to move. Higher voltage allows more amps through to do more work. Watts are the rate at which current is working — the power of the current.

Let's take a closer look at what current is all about.

Remember the old picture of an atom from your school books? (Figure 1.) The atom contains particles, some of which have positive charge, and others (the electrons), which are negatively charged. In a stable atom the positive charge equals the negative charge, so everything holds together quite nicely. But if you could reach in and remove just one of the negative electrons, the atom would be unstable — it would now have more positive charge than negative. If you then placed a new electron nearby, the atom would attract and capture that electron in the same way that a magnet attracts paper clips. Now the atom is complete and electrically neutral again.

ATOM
STRUCTURE

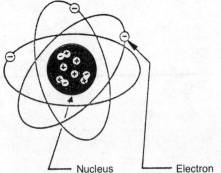

Figure 1.

07.02 CONDUCTIVITY.

A copper (or any other) wire is nothing more than a long collection of atoms. If you removed an electron from an atom at the end of the wire, it would rob an electron from its neighbor, and that neighbor would in turn take one from its neighbor, and on down the wire in a "chain reaction" (Figure 2). Roughly speaking, this is what an electric current is all about. The whole process occurs at such incredible speeds that to us it appears instantaneous.

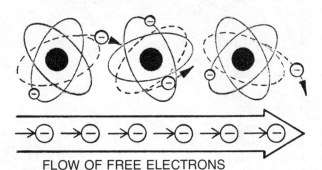

FLOW OF FREE ELECTRONS

Figure 2.

The reason why some materials conduct electricity better than others is simply that they lose their electrons easier. It takes immense energy to remove an electron from rubber, so we use rubberized gloves to insulate our hands when handling potentially hot wires. Copper isn't necessarily the easiest material to remove an electron from (actually, gold is better), but its other properties plus its abundance on the planet make it commercially desirable.

Obviously, no one reaches in and removes electrons from a wire — so there must be another way of starting and maintaining an electric current. In practice, the flow begins when there is a difference in "electrical potential" between one end of the wire and the other. As an illustration, the familiar storage battery makes this happen by chemically creating a difference in potential. In other words, one side of the battery's chemistry produces a situation which is attractive to electrons. If you have trouble visualizing this, just imagine a copper wire connecting the "+" and "−" battery terminals together (don't do this, though, as it's dangerous). In a short time the battery would completely deplete itself — it would be "dead" because the reservoir of extra electrons behind one terminal was attracted along the wire to the terminal which had too few electrons. When a state of neutrality was achieved, the battery would no longer have a charge.

A physicist would quickly point out that this explanation takes many shortcuts and is far from precise. But it does describe the events in a way that is useful to the RV mechanic. And, remembering this simplified discussion will enable you to more fully understand our discussions of batteries, generators and many other electrical problems.

07.03 RESISTANCE.

To understand how appliances and light bulbs fit into this flow, consider this example: When a lamp is placed so that the current must pass through it, it offers resistance to that flow and the electrons have a hard time getting through. All this pushing, shoving and collisions of electrons creates heat — just like a crowd of active people in a confined space — and the heat makes the lamp filament glow. That's how simple a light bulb is. Electric motors use an electric current differently, but it's still the flow of electrons that does the job.

Now let's go back to amps and volts.

We said that amps are a quantity of energy; actually, an amp is an unpronounceable number of electrons moving past any point in the circuit in one second's time. Voltage is a measurement of electrical pressure (called, as you'll remember, potential). When voltage is weak, few electrons will flow along the wire, thus amperage will also be less than if the voltage were high. On a practical level, increase the potential difference in a storage battery and you'll also increase the amps.

Watts, as we now see, is a product of volts and amps. One watt is equal to a current of one ampere driven by a pressure of one volt. This relationship is expressed in a mathematical manner which you'll want to remember:

$$VOLTS \times AMPS = WATTS$$

With this formula you can know, for instance, how many amps you'll need to operate a 25-watt bulb from your RV's 12-volt battery: 25 watts ÷ 12 volts = 2.08 amps. Or, if you want to know the power rating of a 120-volt, 30-ampere generator: 120 x 30 = 3,600 watts.

Incidentally, when we get into larger wattage we simplify by saying kilowatts; one kilowatt is 1,000 watts.

We spoke of "resistance" in connection with the light bulb example, but actually any electric circuit has resistance throughout. The copper wire itself has a certain amount of resistance to the flow of electrons, and a smaller wire will obviously resist a current more than a larger one will. This is why a wire that's too small for the job will get noticeably hot — it's offering too much resistance for the current it's being asked to carry. And as a wire gets hotter, its resistance also increases. In extreme cases, the

wire's insulating wrappings will melt away and leave the wire exposed as a fire or handling hazard.

Resistance is particularly important to RVers because it applies to any circuit which is battery-powered (and also to some campground circuits). To make things easier, resistance is measured in ohms, and one ohm describes a resistance which will allow one ampere of current to flow when one volt of force is applied. Seen mathematically, this relationship is:

$$VOLTS = AMPS \times OHMS$$

Now you can see why wire is rated in ohms — and why it's important to use wire with resistance that is compatible with the job.

$$VOLTS \times AMPS = WATTS$$

$$\frac{WATTS}{AMPS} = VOLTS$$

$$\frac{WATTS}{VOLTS} = AMPS$$

$$AMPS \times OHMS = VOLTS$$

$$\frac{VOLTS}{OHMS} = AMPS$$

$$\frac{VOLTS}{AMPS} = OHMS$$

Just as an aside, you might like to know that each of the terms we've been discussing are named after real people: Alessandro Volta, André Marie Ampère, Geoff Simon Ohm and James Watt. Interestingly, Watt was the Britisher who invented the steam engine. Skeptics were always asking Watt to compare his device with the conventional source of power at that time, horses; so he measured just how much work an average horse could do. His findings were so useful that they have survived and to this day are called "horsepower." More importantly for Mr. Watt, he could then claim with some authority that his steam engines would do just as much work as anywhere between four and 100 horses, depending upon the model. Today both horsepower and watts are used to describe power, and the equation is 746 watts of electrical energy equals one horsepower.

Chapter Eight

Batteries

Amps, when used in connection with batteries, really refer to ampere-hours; the number of amps the battery will deliver in one hour if it yields its entire capacity. A 100-amp battery, for instance, will give its entire 100 amps in one hour, or it will run a 20-amp motor for five hours, or a 40-amp motor for 2½ hours.

A new rating system also offers specific battery information. The first part of the new system specifies a "Cold Amperage Rating," or the battery's starting ability at zero degrees F. The second part specifies a "Reserve Capacity Rating," which indicates the approximate number of minutes an average automobile will operate with lights on should the alternator stop supplying electrical energy.

Far too many users find their batteries depleting too fast and usually the blame is directed at everything except the real causes. In the vast majority of cases, the real reasons behind poor battery performance are incorrect wiring, incorrect battery for the job, bad charging practices and outright abuse or neglect. We'll begin by looking at the types of batteries available.

08.01 HOW AUTOMOTIVE BATTERIES WORK.

Vehicle engines require a very large initial burst of amps to get them started. Battery people call this "cranking draw" because the amps are drawn from the battery to crank the engine. Once the engine is started, however, the recharge begins immediately — so the battery is never drawn down very far. If these batteries are used to run lights and appliances while you're self-contained, they are often drawn to near depletion and the resultant failure is easily predictable. Looking at how a battery functions will explain this.

Chemical bonds store energy, and a battery is an efficient place for these bonds to be broken and the energy released as electric current. In the lead-acid storage battery, which we use in our vehicles and boats, negative and positive electrodes made of lead and lead dioxide, respectively, are in contact with the electrolyte, water and sulfuric acid. As long as the positive and negative electrodes are isolated, nothing happens. When the two terminals are connected, for instance, via the circuitry to a light bulb, electricity can pass between them and the electrolyte and terminals react together. The bonding energy in the electrolyte is broken, and a new compound, lead sulfate, is formed on the battery plates. When nearly all the electrolyte has been broken down, the battery can

no longer deliver a useful current and the plates are then heavily encrusted with lead sulfate.

For those who remember their chemistry, the overall reaction is:

$$Pb + 2HSO4 + 2H + PbO2 \quad 2PbSO4 \rightleftarrows 2H2O$$

(lead + acid + hydrogen + lead oxide $\rightleftarrows$ lead sulfate + water)

The beauty of this accumulator-type battery is that the reaction is reversible (Figure 1). By introducing current from an alternator, for instance, the lead sulfate on the plates combines with the water and the original chemistry is restored. Theoretically, this discharge-charge cycle should be able to go on forever, but, as we know, it doesn't. Batteries do wear out, and when they are incorrectly used they give up astoundingly fast! What happens is that some of the active ingredients on the plates literally wash off and fall to the bottom each time the cell is cycled. This is called shedding. The more shedding that takes place, the greater the fall-off in capacity to hold a charge.

Automotive starting batteries are built with open, porous plates which expose the maximum amount of active material to the electrolyte. Additionally, they often have special channel-type separators between the plates for hastening the circulation. Everything is built for speed, and this is why these batteries are able to deliver big surges of power.

08.02 DEEP-CYCLE BATTERIES.

On the other hand, deep-cycle batteries are built with heavy-duty dense plates (Figure 2). In addition, battery makers such as Gould use interlocking glass fiber separators between the plates to inhibit the active materials from washing off during the discharge-recharge cycle. And because fewer plates are used in deep-cycle batteries, there is a commensurate lowering of amp capability. These power sources may not deliver as much amperage for starting an engine, but they are ideal for the deep repetitious cycling required by trailers, motorhomes, electric outboards, etc.

Lest you think that all this technical talk isn't important, be aware that most automotive supply salespeople don't understand what we have just discussed! Furthermore, most batteries which are offered to you for auxiliary (self-contained) use, even as original equipment by RV manufacturers, are starting types. If you know the difference, you're not going to get stuck with the wrong battery.

FULLY CHARGED BATTERY

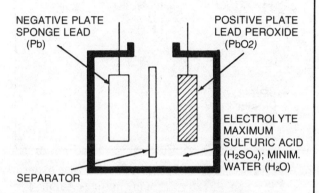

NEGATIVE PLATE
SPONGE LEAD
(Pb)

POSITIVE PLATE
LEAD PEROXIDE
(PbO2)

ELECTROLYTE
MAXIMUM
SULFURIC ACID
(H2SO4); MINIM.
WATER (H2O)

SEPARATOR

In a charged battery, active material of the negative plate is sponge lead (Pb); active material of the positive plate is lead peroxide (PbO2); the electrolyte contains sulfuric acid (H2SO4) and a minimum of water.

BATTERY DISCHARGING

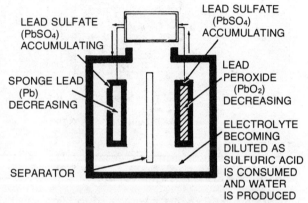

LEAD SULFATE
(PbSO4)
ACCUMULATING

LEAD SULFATE
(PbSO4)
ACCUMULATING

SPONGE LEAD
(Pb)
DECREASING

LEAD
PEROXIDE
(PbO2)
DECREASING

ELECTROLYTE
BECOMING
DILUTED AS
SULFURIC ACID
IS CONSUMED
AND WATER
IS PRODUCED

SEPARATOR

When the battery discharges, the electrolyte reacts with both the positive and negative plates . . . oxygen from the lead peroxide in the positive plates combines with hydrogen from the sulfuric acid to form water . . . lead from the lead peroxide combines with the sulfate from the sulfuric acid to form lead sulfate . . . hydrogen from the sulfuric acid combines with oxygen from the lead peroxide to form more water . . . lead from the sponge lead in the negative plates combines with the sulfate from the sulfuric acid of form lead sulfate . . . and electric current flows.

DISCHARGED BATTERY

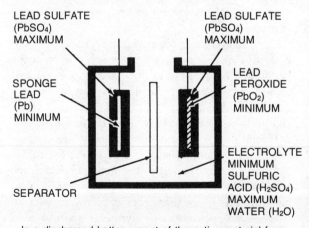

LEAD SULFATE
(PbSO4)
MAXIMUM

LEAD SULFATE
(PbSO4)
MAXIMUM

SPONGE
LEAD
(Pb)
MINIMUM

LEAD
PEROXIDE
(PbO2)
MINIMUM

ELECTROLYTE
MINIMUM
SULFURIC
ACID (H2SO4)
MAXIMUM
WATER (H2O)

SEPARATOR

In a discharged battery, most of the active material from negative and positive plates has been converted to lead sulfate (PbSO4), and the electrolyte is greatly diluted with water (H2O).

BATTERY RECHARGE

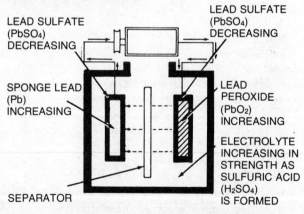

LEAD SULFATE
(PbSO4)
DECREASING

LEAD SULFATE
(PbSO4)
DECREASING

SPONGE LEAD
(Pb)
INCREASING

LEAD
PEROXIDE
(PbO2)
INCREASING

ELECTROLYTE
INCREASING IN
STRENGTH AS
SULFURIC ACID
(H2SO4)
IS FORMED

SEPARATOR

When the alternator recharges your battery, the chemical reaction between plates and electrolyte is reversed . . . lead sulfate from positive and negative plates reacts with the electrolyte to form sulfuric acid . . . removal of sulfate from the negative plates restores sponge lead as the active material . . . oxygen from the water recombines with the lead in the positive plates to form lead peroxide . . . and the strength of the battery is restored.

Figure 1.

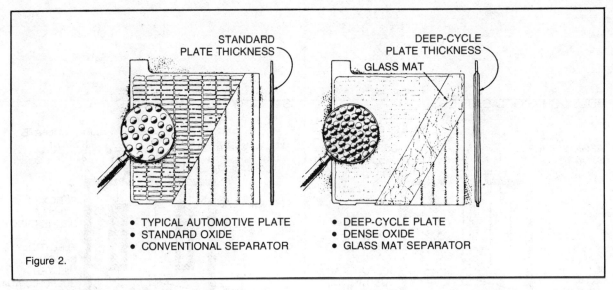

STANDARD
PLATE THICKNESS

DEEP-CYCLE
PLATE THICKNESS

GLASS MAT

- TYPICAL AUTOMOTIVE PLATE
- STANDARD OXIDE
- CONVENTIONAL SEPARATOR

- DEEP-CYCLE PLATE
- DENSE OXIDE
- GLASS MAT SEPARATOR

Figure 2.

08.03 BATTERY TERMINOLOGY.

While it's unlikely that you'll need to know most of the associated vocabulary, Figure 3 can be used as a reference source.

08.04 GETTING CHARGED.

Next to having the right battery, using correct charging methods will allow that battery to serve you both well and long. Unfortunately, though, far too many batteries come to an untimely end because their owners didn't have good charging habits.

The cardinal rule for all types of batteries is to recharge them as soon as possible after use. Batteries which have less than a full charge for any length of time can actually undergo enough internal chemical change that their capacity for recharge is reduced or eliminated.

Also, be sure that you restore more charge to your battery than you used. Whenever energy is converted from one form to another, some portion of it is lost to the environment. The manufacturer's instructions may tell you precisely how much to charge, or you can check for a full charge with a hydrometer (see Section 08.09). If the battery is less than completely recharged each time it's used, it will become progressively less effective.

Recharging on most RVs is accomplished by wiring both the automotive and auxiliary battery to an isolator (see Section 08.15) which distributes power from the vehicle's alternator. As you drive away from the campground, the batteries are automatically brought to full charge if your trip is long enough.

Most RVs with generators aboard, or which are wired to accept campground power, use a power convertor (see Chapter 9). The auxiliary battery can be tied directly to many of these units for charging while you're connected to outside power or while the generator is operating.

Small rechargers can be purchased from automotive supply houses. One of the little two-amp units, for instance, will take 60 hours (2½ days) to bring a 105-amp battery back to capacity. If you use it overnight only, you're going to start the day with only a partial charge.

Overcharging is just as destructive to a battery as undercharging. An overcharge destroys the plates by "boiling off" the water. A worthwhile option if you're going to use a plug-in type charger, then, is to buy one which has an automatic shut-off feature which trips when full charge is reached.

Commercial charging machines yield anywhere from five or less amperes per hour up to 50 amps per hour. While gas stations like to use the fast end of this scale because it gets you in and out quicker, your battery responds best to a slow charge — somewhere between three and 15 amps.

If charging is to be accomplished while the battery sits in place, be sure to disconnect the cables (ground side first) and be absolutely sure that each cell has the correct electrolyte level before proceeding. Also, see that there is plenty of ventilation and no open flame or source of ignition nearby. Battery gas is combustible!

It's a very good idea to periodically monitor the charging as it progresses. Be certain that electrolyte temperature doesn't exceed the maximum 125 degrees F., and use your voltage meter to see that the charger isn't delivering more than 15 volts to your 12-volt battery.

When the specific gravity remains constant for

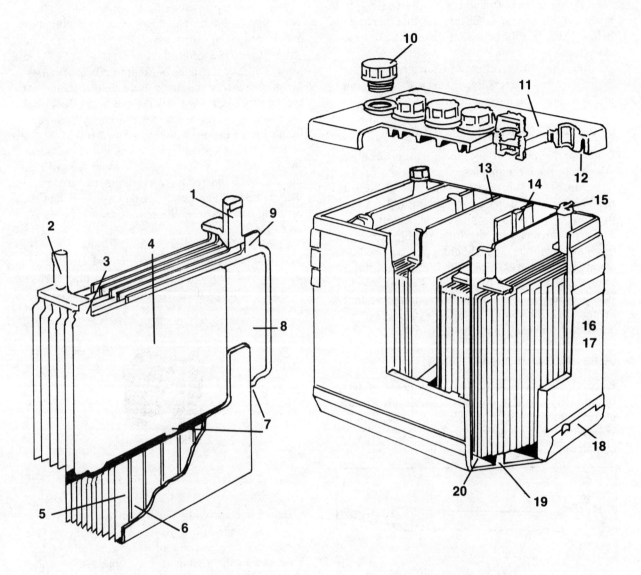

1. POSITIVE CELL TERMINAL AND STRAP
2. NEGATIVE CELL TERMINAL AND STRAP
3. NEGATIVE TERMINAL LUG
4. NEGATIVE PLATE (GRID AND SPONGE LEAD)
5. SEPARATOR
6. SEPARATOR RIB
7. PLATE FEET
8. POSITIVE PLATE (GRID & LEAD DIOXIDE)
9. POSITIVE TERMINAL LUG
10. VENT PLUG

11. ONE-PIECE COVER
12. EPOXY RESIN SEALING LIP
13. CELL PARTITION
14. OVER-PARTITION CONNECTOR
15. TERMINAL POST
16. CONTAINER
17. AMPERE-HOUR RATING
18. MOUNTING LEDGE
19. ELEMENT REST
20. SEDIMENT SPACE

Figure 3.

several hours, you'll know that the battery has taken on its maximum charge. If that reading is below 1.26, you'll know your battery is not in top condition.

After charging, recheck the electrolyte level, adding more if necessary; then clean the battery and reconnect the terminal cables.

08.05   BATTERY MAINTENANCE.

Other than simple old age, most battery problems arise from poor maintenance.

Before we tackle specific maintenance and troubleshooting, you'll need two special tools: a temperature-corrected hydrometer and a volt meter. The hydrometers with the little floating balls are not very accurate and should only be used for "rough" measurements. The voltmeter should read the usual scale for 12-volt systems — between about eight and 16 volts. Automotive tune-up meters read voltage as well as amperage and are useful for many purposes (Figure 4).

08.06   CLEANING BATTERIES.

Keeping a well-charged battery putting out at maximum efficiency also requires connections that are clean, tight and free from corrosion. Corrosion restricts the flow of power and may even block it completely.

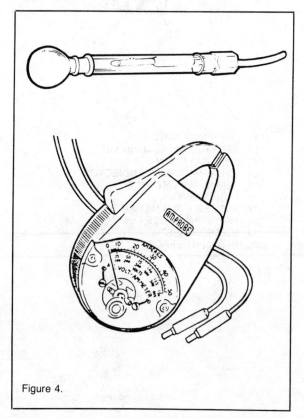

Figure 4.

The first step in cleaning batteries is to address yourself to the terminals, as they often accumulate a fair amount of corrosion. Start by removing the connectors (the ground connector — "+" on most domestic vehicles — should come off first). Most connectors require a little help to come off the terminal post, but always use a "puller" tool for this job. *Never* try to force a sticky connector by hitting or prying it with a screwdriver.

The connector should be thoroughly scraped clean inside and out. A wire brush or sandpaper will do the job, but a little connector cleaning tool will make the job easier. The beauty of these tools is that the opposite end fits over the terminal and abrades the corrosion off of it.

The battery itself can be washed in a water and baking soda solution, brushed off and towel-dried. Be sure that vent caps are securely in place before doing this, so no dirt or solution gets inside (Figure 5).

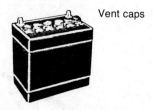
Vent caps

Figure 5.

Before reconnecting the terminals, inspect your battery as suggested in Section 08.07, then apply a light protective coating of petroleum jelly (e.g., Vaseline) to the terminals and replace the ground connector first.

08.07   BATTERY INSPECTION.

With everything clean, you have a good opportunity to inspect the battery. Go over the case carefully to find any cracks, dents, loose terminals or anything else that indicates the battery will soon be useless. Don't forget to look in the battery tray and around the tie-down mechanism for corrosion and clean there if necessary. Be sure that cables and connectors are in good condition; replace them if they aren't. And don't forget to inspect the electrolyte level.

08.08   TESTING THE BATTERY.

Here is where you use your temperature-corrected hydrometer. This instrument measures specific gravity (sp. gr.) of the electrolyte. Specific gravity is

1.265 sp. gr.	100% charged
1.225 sp. gr.	75% charged
1.190 sp. gr.	50% charged
1.155 sp. gr.	25% charged
1.120 sp. gr.	Discharged

Figure 6.

found by dividing the weight of a quantity of water into the weight of an equal quantity of whatever is being tested. Battery electrolyte, when fully charged, has a specific gravity of 1.260. As the battery is discharged, though, the electrolyte loses weight, thus the specific gravity measurement is a reliable indicator of the degree of charge.

The accompanying specific gravity scale offers an interpretation of what you'll see on the hydrometer scale (Figure 6).

The only true test of battery condition is made when the battery has as much charge as it will accept. When you think you've driven long enough, or when you have been connected to an outside power source for at least 24 hours — so the power convertor has had enough time to recharge the battery — check all six cells with the hydrometer. If the specific gravity reading is not at least 1.230, corrective measures are in order. If you see a substantial deviation in the reading on one cell in comparison to the others, you may have to suspect a dead cell.

08.09 HOW TO READ A HYDROMETER.

The simple admonishment is that an incorrectly used hydrometer will yield incorrect results. Here's the correct method:

The hydrometer bulb should be squeezed to fill the device in such a way that the float does not bottom or hit the top. The hydrometer should be lightly thumped, tapped or shaken to make sure that the float is not sticking to the side of the tube. The scale should be read looking straight across the level of fluid in the tube — not from above or below.

Temperature correction is important. For example, in 20-degree weather a hydrometer might read 1.250 specific gravity, but employing the temperature correction factor reduces that reading to 1.226 — and this is a substantial difference.

08.10 TROUBLESHOOTING THE BATTERY.

If the specific gravity reading is definitely below 1.230, recharge it on a charging machine to the 1.265 mark. Make sure this procedure isn't done at a charging rate which will raise the electrolyte temperature above 125 degrees F. A slow charge is always best if you have the time. (See Section 08.04 on charging.)

When sulfate has hardened on the battery plates (see Section 08.01), the battery often is permanently derated or ruined. But in the case of only partial formation of the hard sulfate, a sustained charge of about 10 amps over a period of several hours sometimes can break the sulfate and bring the battery back to somewhere near the original capacity.

If the cause of the discharge is not known, use your voltmeter to measure the voltage reaching the battery. Take your measurements at the battery, as readings taken at the alternator or power convertor don't reflect the "bottlenecks" which can develop in the transmission line.

With the voltmeter connected, run the engine at about 2,000 rpm and check voltage at your auxiliary battery (which should be holding a full 1.265 charge). The voltmeter should show around 14 volts. It could be as high as 14.5 volts when the engine is cold because the voltage regulation system compensates for temperatures. (This is necessary because a battery's ability to accept a charge and to provide power is reduced in cold weather.) This is why RVers have more battery problems in winter than at other times.

If the voltage level is below 14, check the voltage at the alternator. If it's 14 volts or higher there, the voltage drop is occurring between the alternator and the auxiliary battery.

Continuing to use the voltmeter, check the charge line at intervals — moving toward the alternator until you find the bottleneck. It could be a loose connection, a poorly operating mechanical battery isolator or simply a damaged wire or a length of wire of inadequate size.

One note of caution: When you read voltage between a diode-type (solid state) dual battery isolator and the alternator, voltage will be higher than normal because the isolator induces higher voltage. This will not be the case with a mechanical isolator (relay). If the wire between the alternator and isolator is at least a No. 10 in size, and if the distance is less than two feet or one foot, you can assume no voltage drop between the alternator and isolator. But check connections for corrosion and for tightness. Otherwise, temporarily bypass your isolator with a length of No. 10 or No. 8 wire so that you can pursue your investigation.

One possible place of trouble can be the connectors; they should be soldered on the wires but they can loosen.

08.11 HOW TO USE A VOLTMETER.

It's a good idea to make sure the voltmeter is measuring correctly. An easy test is to take it to a gas station and ask them to compare its readings to those of their larger (and more accurate) diagnostic equipment. If your meter is off, determine the error and make corrections in your readings.

In reading a voltmeter for proper charging, you're looking for levels between 11.8 and 14.5. But in reading the meter for battery condition, the load on the battery at the time will affect the reading. For comparative readings, check the voltmeter with the same load on the line. For instance, check it with two interior lights on — nothing else. Never check it with any load or the readings will be abnormally high.

Experience will tell you your tolerances — how far your battery is from depletion when you see a particular reading. The built-in battery condition monitors are handy for this, even though they have color-bands rather than numerical scales. But the portable voltmeter with a numerical scale is best for general use and troubleshooting.

You can use your voltmeter to check on how much recharge has occurred, too. After the charging source has been turned off, turn on a few interior lights and let them use up the battery's surface charge. It takes about five minutes to do this. Then check voltage with the same load on the line that you used to check battery depletion, and you should get readings which relate directly to those you noted while depleting the battery.

HINT: A very handy way to keep track of battery condition is to install a zero to 60 amp ammeter on the charge line from the alternator to the battery. Viewed from inside the rig, you'll always know what's happening (Figure 7).

08.12 JUMPING A DEAD BATTERY.

It happens to the best of us, but not many people know that there is a safe way and an unsafe way to get a jump start. Batteries have been known to explode during this procedure!

Incidentally, don't try to jump (or charge) a frozen battery as it will probably rupture. Thaw the battery before proceeding.

Safety experts recommend loosening the cell caps on the disabled battery before doing anything; this allows gas which may build rapidly during the jump to escape. And never let the vehicle you're getting the jump from touch your vehicle.

The correct technique for jumping a battery follows:

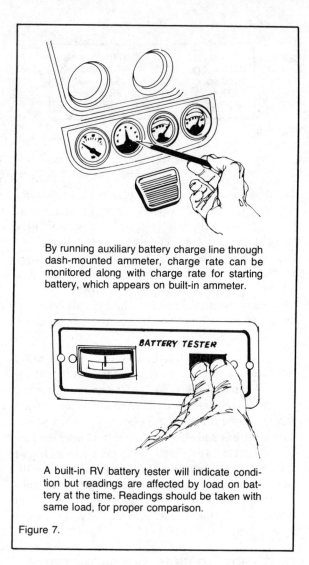

By running auxiliary battery charge line through dash-mounted ammeter, charge rate can be monitored along with charge rate for starting battery, which appears on built-in ammeter.

A built-in RV battery tester will indicate condition but readings are affected by load on battery at the time. Readings should be taken with same load, for proper comparison.

Figure 7.

How to Use Jumper Cables

Before you attempt to connect jumper cables, there are several precautions which should be taken:

• In very cold weather, check the battery to see if the electrolyte is frozen. Do not use jumper cables if the electrolyte is frozen — you may damage the battery beyond repair.

• Check to see that both the booster battery and the run-down battery have the same voltage — six-volt or 12-volt.

• Turn all accessory switches and the ignition key to the off position.

• Place the gearshift or gear selector in the neutral or park position.

• Remove vent caps from both the booster battery and your run-down battery. This will release any accumulated gases.

Follow the next procedure in exact sequence:

A. On run-down battery, find terminal connected to starter switch or solenoid. Note if positive or negative. Then clip one end of jumper cable to like marked terminal of booster battery.

B. Clip the other end of the same jumper cable to the terminal of the run-down battery having the same marking; that is, *positive* to *positive* or *negative* to *negative*.

C. Connect one end of the second jumper cable to the other terminal of the booster battery. The other end of this cable should be fastened securely to the bumper or engine block of the vehicle with the run-down battery.

D. Engage the starter of your vehicle. If it does not start immediately, it is well to start the engine of the other vehicle to avoid excessive drain on the booster battery.

E. Restore the cell caps to both batteries after your vehicle starts and is running normally.

F. Remove the ground connection from the bumper or engine block of your vehicle.

G. Remove the other end of the cable from the booster battery.

H. Remove the other cable first from your vehicle; then the other end from the booster battery.

Be sure that the positive terminal marked (POS), (P), or (+) of one battery is connected to the positive terminal of the other; and that the negative terminal marked (NEG), (N), or (−) is connected to the negative terminal of the other. Connection of a positive terminal to a negative terminal may result in alternator damage or a possible explosion.

CAUTION: Whenever working around batteries, be careful of two things: acid and electricity. The acid in the electrolyte can give painful skin burns and it's hard on clothing, but the greatest danger is from splashing it in your eyes. The electricity in a battery is enough to do you harm, so handle it with care and don't wear rings or jewelry when placing your hands near the terminals — that could attract an arcing.

Most "splash" accidents occur because a battery is dropped. It is heavy and difficult to carry, so always use a carrying strap if you have to move one.

08.13 MAINTENANCE-FREE BATTERY.

There's not much that a maintenance book can say about a maintenance-free battery. Because the cells are sealed, you can't add electrolyte and you can't test with a hydrometer. The battery has a built-in indicator which will give you a rough reading of charge status, but you can still make voltmeter tests as described in Section 08.11. Beyond that, just keep it clean and protected.

08.14 CHOOSING A NEW BATTERY.

Batteries are rated in four ways:

Cold Cranking Rating: This is the best measurement for a battery which will be used for starting; the number designates the amperage which the battery will deliver for a short spurt of about half a minute at zero degrees F.

Amp Hour Rating: This indicates what you can expect in the way of power withdrawal. To use the ratings, divide the amp-hour rating of the battery by the average load you expect to use and you'll get the number of hours the battery will support that load.

Reserve Capacity: This is the number of minutes which the battery will support a 25-amp load.

Watts Rating: This is similar to cranking power, except it's expressed in watts. The figure is mathematically determined by simply multiplying amps (at zero degrees F.) times voltage. (Watts = amps x volts is a handy formula to remember.)

A good philosophy to follow when replacing a battery is that you can't go wrong buying one with a larger capacity than you previously had. This is especially true with auxiliary (deep draw) batteries, where the size of the power reservoir directly relates to how long you can function self-contained.

08.15 BATTERY ISOLATION.

On most trailers and motorhomes, both the auxiliary and the starting battery receive charging through the vehicle alternator. Simply wiring them directly into the alternator, though, would create an interconnection which would allow one to drain the other. This happens in some rigs, and a typical repercussion occurs when the auxiliary battery has been heavily depleted. In these cases, the heavy alternator output called for by the auxiliary, combined with the fact that the starting battery will try to help the alternator charge the weak auxiliary, results in higher-than-normal shedding of material from the plates of the starting battery. This leads to shorter battery life, and it may even harm the alternator.

A diode-type isolator wired as in Figure 8 will electronically separate the two batteries so that the negative effects of interconnection won't happen. If you're experiencing problems similar to that described, your answer is probably to install a diode isolator (Figure 9).

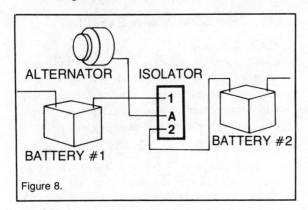

Figure 8.

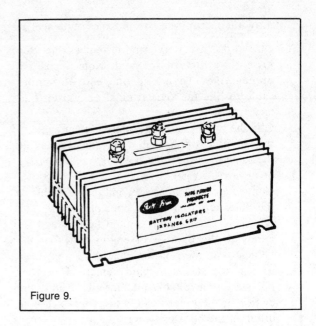

Figure 9.

Chapter Nine

Power
Convertors

Power convertors are another on the long list of devices which expand an RV's flexibility in differing environments. In this case, the benefit is the transformation of 115-volt alternating current (VAC) into 12-volt direct current (VDC). This conversion lets you save your batteries and use campground or generator power to operate many onboard electrical accessories. Many power convertors have the added dimension of being able to recharge the rig's batteries whenever outside power is available.

09.01 HOW POWER CONVERTORS WORK.

The power convertor is composed of three primary sections (see Figure 1): (1) the transformer which accomplishes the basic conversion from 115 VAC to 12-volt alternating current; (2) the rectifiers which then convert the 12-volt AC into 12-volt DC; and (3) the power switch, which lets you choose between using power from the battery or power which has been transformed by the convertor. Some power switches are automatic in that they sense the presence of campground or generator power and auto-matically switch to that source, or instantly switch back to batteries when the outside source disappears.

Figure 2 is a wiring diagram that shows how a convertor switch in the "transformer" position will route the outside power though itself and into the transformer and rectifier. With the switch in "battery" position (the lower position in the diagram indicated by the short dotted line), power to operate the RV accessories comes from the battery.

A relay rather than a switch is used on automatic power convertors, and this achieves an instant response when outside power is available.

09.02 THE ELECTRICAL CONTROL CENTER.

Power convertors may be physically combined with what is in effect a distribution panel for both 12 VAC and 115 VDC power (Figure 2). In these cases, there is a division between the three functions: (1) power convertor unit; (2) 12 VAC fuses, power switch (manual or automatic relay) and an optional battery charger feature; and (3) 115 VAC main input breaker and individual branch circuit

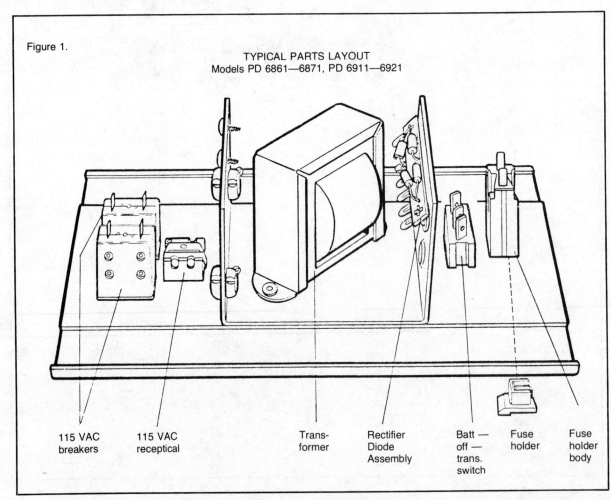

Figure 1.

TYPICAL PARTS LAYOUT
Models PD 6861—6871, PD 6911—6921

| 115 VAC breakers | 115 VAC receptical | Trans-former | Rectifier Diode Assembly | Batt — off — trans. switch | Fuse holder | Fuse holder body |

breakers for all the branch circuits. A typical diagram is shown in Figure 3.

09.03   BATTERY CHARGER IN CONJUNCTION WITH POWER CONVERTOR.

These are solid state devices which sense the condition of the charge in the battery. When 115 VAC power is available, and the battery needs additional charging, the convertor automatically channels some of its 12 VDC output to the battery. This optional function should not be tampered with by the consumer, although you can easily use your 12 VDC test light to be sure that the charger is putting out power for the battery. Often, you'll find that there is simply a loose or dirty connection or that the battery is incapable of accepting a charge.

This matter of battery charging is sometimes a point of contention between RVers and convertor manufacturers, but the conflict is often over a misunderstanding of what the convertor will do.

Without getting into complicated electronic theory, you should know that there are two types of battery charging power convertors: separate circuit convertors and battery floater or single circuit convertors. Both types perform most functions equivalently, but the second category does a better job of charging batteries. Here's why:

The battery floater type of convertor is designed to put out a high level of power (up to 60 amps in some designs) when the battery is in a seriously discharged condition. The power flowing to the battery begins tapering off as the battery gets closer to being fully charged — until finally there is just a trickle. With low output convertors, on the other hand, it's just a trickle from start to finish, and this means running the generator longer, or staying tied to shore power longer, before maximum charge is achieved.

Battery floaters are able to give the results described because they can channel all of their output to the battery when no appliances are in use. If power is required for appliances, it is subtracted from the battery charging capability.

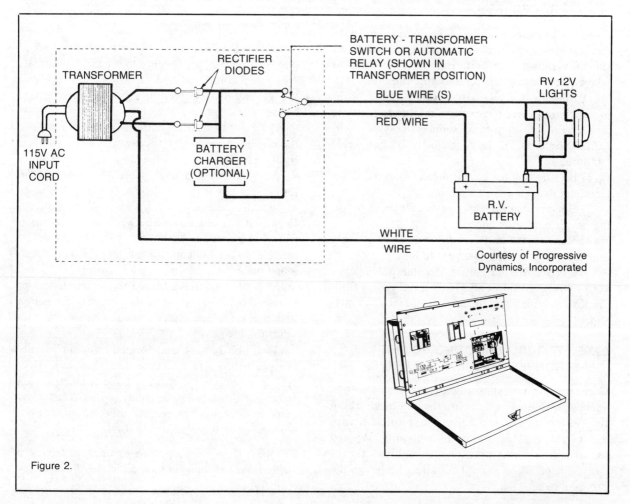

Figure 2.

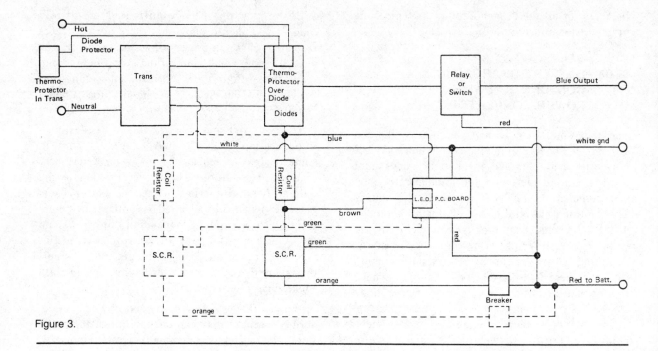

Figure 3.

09.04   PRE-TROUBLESHOOTING PROCEDURES.

Power convertors usually make more electricity than problems, so suspect a simple cure if the unit suddenly fails to perform. Here are the steps to take before actually troubleshooting the unit:

(1) Be sure that your connection to the outside or generator power is good and that there really is power available from these sources. This step will explain or cure the large majority of convertor "failures."

(2) Be sure that the circuit breakers on the RV's electrical distribution box are on.

(3) Be sure that the fuses or circuit breakers on the power convertor unit are on.

(4) Remove the unit's cover and check all wiring to be sure that no wires are loose.

CAUTION: Before getting into the power convertor box, disconnect all 115-volt AC power from the RV. Skipping this precaution can yield a lethal shock!

09.05   TROUBLESHOOTING POWER CONVERTORS.

Consumer troubleshooting of these devices is somewhat limited and consists mostly of checking for loose connections or, if you're proficient with a test light, checking electrical continuity. Beyond the simple investigations which follow, power convertor problems should definitely be left to the professionals.

PROBLEM: *12-volt appliances work when power comes from the convertor, but not when power comes from the battery.*

(1) Test the battery to be sure it is fully charged (see Section 08.08). Be sure that battery terminals are firmly connected and clean, and be sure that the ground is securely attached to the vehicle frame.

(2) Check to see that battery current is reaching the power convertor by testing with a 12-volt test light between the positive and negative supply wires. No current at this point indicates that the problem is either in the wiring, connections, fuses or circuit breakers between there and the battery. If current is present, test between the same negative wire and the positive load wire at the convertor. No power indication from this test may mean a bad battery/transformer switch or relay.

(3) If the unit has a manual battery/transformer switch, be sure it is set in the "battery" position and check for continuity through the switch with your test lamp.

(4) If the battery/transformer switching is accomplished by a relay, make sure it functions freely and the points are making good contact. Check for continuity through the relay points. These may sometimes be bent to achieve a better connection, but don't file them.

PROBLEM: *12-volt appliances operate from the battery but will not function from the convertor or transformer.*

(1) Be sure that the campground or generator power cord is firmly plugged in and that power is available through it. Be sure that no circuit breakers on the distribution panel are tripped.

(2) If you have a manual convertor switch, be sure it is in the correct position.

(3) With the 115-volt power disconnected, check for loose wiring connections and test all wiring to the transformer to be sure they are capable of carrying power.

(4) Check for continuity through the battery/transformer switch or relay.

PROBLEM: *The convertor will operate the RV appliances but won't charge the battery.*

(1) First, be sure that your convertor has the battery charging option.

(2) With the battery disconnected, test for voltage between the positive and negative wires at the convertor; it should be supplying approximately 11.5 VDC when the 115 VAC power supply is on.

(3) If there is no DC output, check for loose wires (be sure the AC input is disconnected first), then test the circuit breakers for continuity.

PROBLEM: *The convertor overcharges the battery.*

(1) Beyond checking for correct wiring according to the manufacturer's diagram, this is a problem for service technicians as it involves testing circuit boards.

PROBLEM: *The 115 VAC circuit breaker trips every time the power supply to the RV is plugged in.*

(1) This problem is normally caused by shorted diodes in the rectifier section of the convertor and should be serviced by an authorized technician.

Chapter Ten

Generators

Anyone with a little knowledge of automobile engines already understands half of their electric generator set. The other half is, in principle, similar to a turbine driven by a water wheel or windmill. We'll concentrate on the production of electricity in this chapter, and add a small amount of generator engine mechanics for good measure.

10.01 HOW TO MAKE ELECTRICITY.

Electromagnetic induction is classically demonstrated by taking an ordinary horseshoe magnet (as depicted in Figure 1) and moving a copper (or any other conductor) between the magnetic poles. If you attach a voltmeter to either end of the wire, it will prove that simply passing the wire through the magnetic field "induces" an electric current into the wire.

Trial and error demonstrates that the greatest voltage is induced when the conductor cuts the magnetic lines of force in a perpendicular path. Also, the current is seen to reverse when the conductor is moved in the opposite direction through the horseshoe magnet's field. Polarity at the ends of the conductor also changes with the reversal. This means that voltage, polarity and direction of current flow depends upon movement of the conductor (mechanical energy) and the conductor's relationship to the direction of magnetic force lines. Further, you can see that continuously moving the conductor back and forth through the magnetic field in our illustration yields what we can now call Alternating Current (AC); i.e., the direction of current flow changes with each cycle through the field. (Direct Current from the chemical action of a storage battery is a smooth, constant flow of current in the same direction.)

Now you understand generator theory, and that power plant in your rig uses exactly the same principle of electromagnetic induction just discussed. Instead of a horseshoe magnet, a simple generator uses two stationary field poles (see Figure 2), and instead of a single copper wire you have a revolving armature, which is wrapped with coils of electrically conductive material. No voltage is produced when the armature is motionless, but when the generator is started its engine turns the armature so it can cut through the magnetic lines of force. The highest voltage is produced when the armature moves at right angles (90 degrees) to the lines of force, and no voltage is produced when the armature is positioned parallel to these lines.

Again glancing at Figure 2, you'll see that each side of the armature moves through the magnetic influence of the north pole for 1/2 revolution and

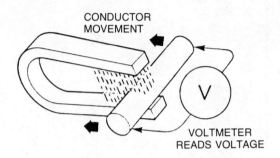

CONDUCTOR MOVEMENT

VOLTMETER READS VOLTAGE

V

Figure 1.

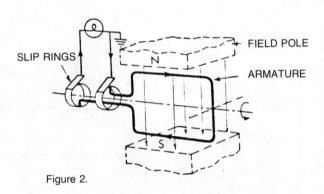

SLIP RINGS

FIELD POLE

ARMATURE

N

S

Figure 2.

through that of the south pole for 1/2 revolution. Voltage is thus reversed twice with each complete revolution. You'll also see that there are slip rings at the ends of the armature. As the slip rings rotate with the armature, the electrically conductive brushes make contact with them and allow the current to flow through to its eventual use, such as to operate your air-conditioner.

You can see that the number of complete revolutions made by the armature determines the frequency of the AC current (how many times it reverses directions during a specified time), and this is called hertz. Obviously, faster rotation creates higher frequencies and more current. But if instead of speeding up the armature we add another magnet (again consisting of two poles) to the system, the generator becomes four-poled and the frequency is automatically doubled. This is more efficient because the same input of mechanical energy produces twice as much electricity.

As you have probably noticed from reading labels, electrical appliances operating on AC need a specified frequency (usually 60 cycles). That's why generator engines run at constant speeds, and that's why it's important to keep this timing exactly correct.

Now you know enough to build a simple electrical generator which will produce an AC current. Modern technology lets us improve upon this basic system by using electromagnets, which can build much stronger lines of force and will thus yield more current.

Because an electromagnet's strength depends upon how much electricity it is fed, we can vary the generator's output voltage simply by controlling the strength of the magnet. The power required to activate these electromagnets can come from a storage battery or from the generator's own output, and this latter situation is called self-excitation. Electromagnets must run on DC power, so a simple switching device called a commutator is attached to convert AC to DC. When the entire output of the generator is converted in this manner it is a DC generator and is commonly used for battery-charging as well as other DC load requirements.

10.02 ALTERNATORS.

In many RV generator sets the electromagnets do not remain stationary but rather rotate within a fixed armature coil. These revolving field generators are technically called alternators, and different names are given to the parts; the revolving field is now the rotor and the armature is called the stator. Slip rings are not always required because the stator does not move. An exciter converts AC output to DC and regulates the amount of current reaching the rotor.

Proponents of the revolving field-style claim greater efficiency because slip rings aren't needed, there may be no brush wear and there is no arcing across a bad connection between the two. There is no arguing with these claims, but both types have advantages which make them uniquely efficient for RV use.

10.03 CHECKING YOUR INSTALLATION.

Generator experts agree on a simple relationship: Faulty Installation equals Poor Performance, plus Danger. Multiply this by the number of ''do-it-yourself'' installations which are deficient. Then add our conversation with one service executive who estimated that 10% of factory and 20% of dealer installations on some lines of RVs do not comply with regulations. Once again it's up to you, the consumer, to be your own quality control inspector. The operator's manual accompanying a new unit tells you precisely what to look for, but basically there are five major considerations (Figure 3): system restraint, fuel system integrity, exhaust requirements, correct electrical connections and proper ventilation. We'll deal with each briefly, but you should definitely cross-reference with

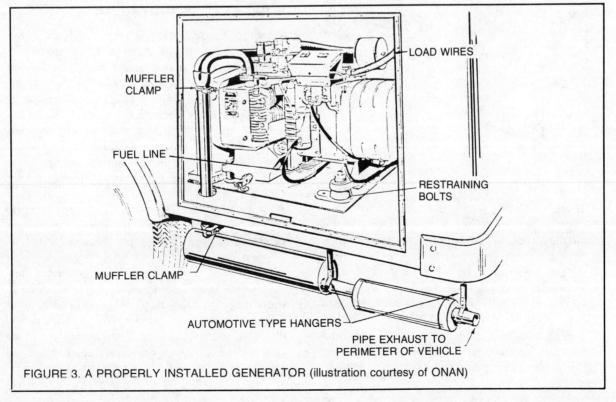

FIGURE 3. A PROPERLY INSTALLED GENERATOR (illustration courtesy of ONAN)

a copy of the generator manufacturer's literature which illustrates the specifics for your unit.

Checking for proper restraint means being sure that the generator is securely bolted to its frame and the frame to the motorhome. Spring snubber-type mounts or other vibration-absorbing devices should be in good condition and functioning.

The unit should be in a compartment large enough to allow overall free air circulation. Ventilation is important because high compartment temperatures can both reduce the generator's effective output and cause permanent damage. There should be louvers or screen material in the compartment door that allows outside air to be sucked in, circulated through and around the generator and finally expelled through another orifice. The size of these openings in relation to your particular generator unit is precisely designed by the manufacturer, so be warned that "any old compartment door" may not do the job (Figure 4):

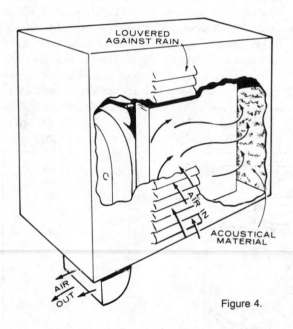

Figure 4.

Insulation lining within the compartment must be firmly attached to the walls and not flopping onto the generator. Make sure this insulation is non-combustible and is at least one inch away from the generator at all points. Definitely don't allow insulation material on the compartment door, because it will absorb flammable fuels. And be sure no flammable material is installed close to the generator compartment, because heat transferred through the metal walls can damage or even ignite materials such as fiberboard, seat cushions, etc.

Check the fuel system thoroughly for leaks; all fuel lines should be of specified materials and must be located away from hot exhaust channels to minimize chances of vapor lock. The fuel supply line must be located where it won't be severed or ruptured in the event of a crash. And when generator and vehicle engines share the same fuel tank, each engine should have its own dip tube; this prevents one engine from starving or draining the other.

Automotive-type exhaust hangers and connections should be used underneath the vehicle, and the termination of the exhaust outlet must extend beyond the perimeter of the vehicle. Also, be sure that your rig is airtight around the exhaust system — as a damaged line could introduce carbon monoxide gas into living quarters. Spark arrester-type mufflers are common on exhaust systems today, and because most national parks and many other areas now require them, you should be aware of the presence — or absence — of yours.

Installation of the AC electrical system must comply with at least three different electrical codes. Make sure that all wiring is securely tied to terminals and is properly insulated, supported and never pulled tight at any point. Ground should be established with the motorhome's body (there is often a grounding connection built into the generator compartment) and *never* to fuel lines.

10.04 RATINGS AND OUTPUT.

Knowing the total wattage you need is vital, because overdrawing the generator's capacity is damaging both to it and appliances. Before buying a new generator, or before adding more appliances, simply total the wattage requirements of everything that is electrically powered. While it's unlikely that all the AC appliances will be operating at the same time, do consider this as a possibility. Also, many tools consume double or triple their rated input when they are subjected to hard use, and this ought to be considered, as well. Additionally, electric motors (air-conditioners, heaters, etc.) require an extra-high wattage input surge power to get them going (Figure 5).

Some generators can momentarily meet this surge demand, even in excess of their rated output, but be careful not to ask a generator for more watts than it can produce. (A good practice is to start your appliances separately — don't throw them all at the generator simultaneously. To be safe and protect your generator, be sure that all appliances are turned off before starting the generator.)

Figure 5.

Motor HP Rating	Approx. Running Watts	Approximate Starting Watts Required			
		Universal Motors	Repulsion Induction Motors	Capacitor Motors	Split Phase Motors
⅙	275	400	600	850	1,200
¼	400	500	850	1,050	1,700
⅓	450	600	975	1,350	1,950
½	600	750	1,300	1,800	2,600
¾	850	1,000	1,900	2,600	*
1	1,000	1,250	2,300	3,000	*
1½	1,600	*	3,200	4,200	*
2	2,000	*	3,900	5,100	*
3	3,000	*	5,200	6,800	*
5	4,800	*	7,500	9,800	*

*Motors of higher horsepower shown in this classification are not generally used.

Here's something else to know about generators: The rated output is not always what you actually get. A number of factors influence performance, and while your maintenance leads the list, the environment also has an effect. For instance, the thinner air in high altitudes changes the carburetor's fuel-to-air mixture and lowers generator output. Expanded hot air has the same effect. A manual choke adjustment will let you partially compensate, but remember that mountains or deserts may mean fewer watts. A general rule is 3.5% output loss for every 1,000 feet of elevation and one percent loss for every degree (F.) over 60 degrees.

It's also interesting to know that generator output ratings may not have been measured in the same environmental conditions — which means they are not always directly comparable.

10.05 MAINTENANCE.

As consumers, we're accustomed to hurling barbs at manufacturers, but here's one coming in the opposite direction: According to industry sources, RV owners are notoriously sloppy about generator maintenance. One executive estimated that at least 50% of the units on RVs receive little or no maintenance until a problem develops. He commented that even people who religiously care for their vehicle's engine forget that the generator exists until it suddenly fails to keep the beer cold or the oil turns into bubble gum. One significant problem is that servicing is scheduled after *hours*, not miles, and many units don't have a cumulative running time meter (Figure 6). Without this monitor, people lose track of elapsed time and eventually forget altogether. Our advice to the "have nots" is to get one now; they're inexpensive, easy to install and can definitely save you many dollars and problems later.

Your generator owner's manual details a periodic maintenance schedule; so if you don't have this booklet, you should buy one now. Most routine maintenance operations are relatively simple, and you're already familiar with the tasks from encounters with your vehicle's engine. We'll go through some of the steps, but realize that our discussion is generalized and you must relate the information to your specific unit.

Before rolling up your sleeves, please consider some basic cautions: Remember that you're dealing with a power plant that can put out lethal quantities of electricity, so don't "poke around" in your set while it's running. Remember that the unit has many moving parts, so place your hands accordingly. Also be careful of hot surfaces after the unit has been operated. And don't store anything in the generator compartment. Good sense will prevent accidents, but it's wise to remind yourself of these realities every time you undertake generator maintenance.

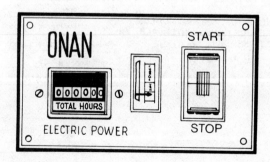

Figure 6.

10.06   THE DO'S AND DON'TS OF MAINTENANCE.

DO'S

Do keep your generator set clean; wipe dirt and grime off with a cloth, especially around and between cooling fins. Blow off the generator and engine with an air hose when you stop for gas.

Do turn off all lights, appliances, etc., before starting engine.

Do have the carburetor adjusted before using generator set in high altitudes.

Do have a running-time meter installed for convenience in determining servicing frequency.

Do check the air cleaner periodically and clean it by tapping on a flat surface. *Never* wash it in solvents or blow it out with an air hose!

DON'TS

Don't overload your generator set; total wattage of all lights and appliances used at any one time must not exceed the rated wattage of the generator set. Flickering lights indicate overloading.

Don't attempt to adjust the carburetor, governor, choke, etc., unless you are qualified to do so.

Don't obstruct the exhaust/air-intake with furniture, clothing, etc.

Don't connect the muffler to your vehicle's muffler.

Don't run the generator set for long periods of time with no lights or appliances turned on; this wastes gas, overheats the engine, and may cause it to misfire.

IN CASE OF TROUBLE . . .

- Is there gasoline in the tank?
- Check battery connections to be sure they're clean and tight.
- Check to see if oil level is near full mark (not over).
- Check for oil or gasoline leaks.
- Check for loose or broken electrical wires.
- Make sure your power consumption doesn't exceed wattage rating on generator set nameplate.

10.07   SERVICE TIMETABLES.

The following tables summarize the maintenance operations the owner of the generator set should perform and their frequencies.

ONAN

x1 — With set running, visually and audibly check exhaust system for leaks.

x2 — Perform more often in extremely dusty conditions.

x3 — Replace if necessary.

x4 — Replace annually or prior to storage.

NOTE: ON 3,600 RPM MODELS, REDUCE HOURLY INTERVALS BY ONE-HALF.

SERVICE THESE ITEMS	AFTER EACH CYCLE OF INDICATED HOURS				
	8	50	100	200	400
General Inspection	x1				
Check Oil Level	x				
Check Battery Electrolyte Level		x			
Change Crankcase Oil			x2		
Check Spark Plugs			x4		
Check Breaker Points			x3		
Clean Breather Valve			x		
Clean Governor Linkage			x		
Service Air Cleaner (Oil Bath)			x2		
Replace Air Cleaner Element (Dry)				x2	
Clean Cooling Fins				x2	
Change Oil Filter (If Used)				x2	
Replace Breaker Points				x4	
Clean Crankcase Breather				x	
Remove Carbon Deposits from Heads				x	
Adjust Tappets					x
Replace Fuel Filter (If Used)					x4
Clean Carburetor					x
Check Generator Brushes (Replace if Necessary)	As Required				

SERVICE TIMETABLES

KOHLER

SERVICE THESE ITEMS	AFTER EACH CYCLE OF INDICATED HOURS				
	EACH DAY	EVERY 25 HOURS	EVERY 50 HOURS	EVERY 100 HOURS	EVERY 500 HOURS
LUBRICATION SYSTEM					
OIL LEVEL—Check and add oil as needed.	x				
OIL CHANGE—Thoroughly drain, refill with oil of proper grade and weight.		x			
AIR INTAKE SYSTEM					
DRY TYPE AIR CLEANER—Clean element. (Replace element every 200 hours under normal operating conditions.)			x		
OIL BATH AIR CLEANER—Drain oil, clean bowl, wash element, add new oil to level mark.		x			
FUEL SYSTEM					
FUEL SEDIMENT BOWL—Remove and clean bowl. If filter element used, swish in clean fuel. Reinstall and check for and correct leakage.				x	
IGNITION SYSTEM					
SPARK PLUG—Remove plug, clean and regap. (Use new plug if needed.) Reinstall plug and tighten to 324 in. lbs. torque.				x	
BREAKER POINTS—Remove cover, check condition of point contacts, service (or replace) as necessary.				x	
IGNITION TIMING—Check and retime as necessary. Set breaker point gap to .020 degrees fully open or use timing light method.					x
ELECTRICAL (CHARGING-STARTING) SYSTEMS					
MOTOR-GENERATOR—Check and correct belt tension if needed. Check brushes and commutator—service as required.			x		
VOLTAGE REGULATOR—Remove cover, check condition and contact point gap. Service as required.					x
MAGNETO-ALTERNATOR—Regular service not required—check condition of leads, tighten loose terminals or connections.					x
STARTING MOTOR—Remove end cap, check condition of brushes and commutator, service or replace if needed.					x
ENGINE-GENERAL					
EXTERNAL SURFACES—Clean air intake screen, cooling fins and block especially in oil fill area.	x				
VALVE CLEARANCE—Remove cover, check clearance between valve stems and tappets, adjust as needed.					x
CRANKCASE BREATHER—Remove components, check reed valve and gaskets, clean filter. Reinstall in proper sequence.					x
CYLINDER HEAD—Remove head, scrape out carbon deposits with piece of wood. Install new gasket, reinstall head and tighten bolts in proper sequence and to specified torque value.					x

GENERAC

SERVICE THESE ITEMS	AFTER EACH CYCLE OF OPERATING HOURS					
	10	50	100	300	500	As Required
Check Oil Level	x					
Change Oil		x				
Service Air Cleaner		x				
Replace Spark Plug			x			
Replace Fuel Filter				x		
Decarbonize Engine					x	
Adjust Valves					x	

DOMETIC

Service These Items	Hours of Operation			
	10	25	50	100
Check oil level	X			
Change oil		X		
Service air filter			X	
Clean and gap spark plug				X
Clean spark arrester			X	
General tightening—nuts & bolts			X	
Clean engine and compartment			X	

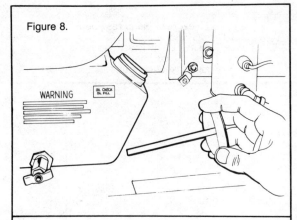
Figure 8.

WARNING

OIL CHECK
OIL FILL

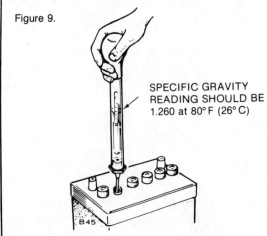
Figure 9.

SPECIFIC GRAVITY
READING SHOULD BE
1.260 at 80°F (26°C)

B45

- **12–VOLT NEGATIVE GROUND**
- **BATTERY MUST BE CONNECTED AT ALL TIMES UNIT IS RUNNING**
- **CHECK SPECIFIC GRAVITY**
- **KEEP WATER TO PROPER LEVEL**
- **BATTERY CABLES TIGHT – TERMINALS CLEAN**

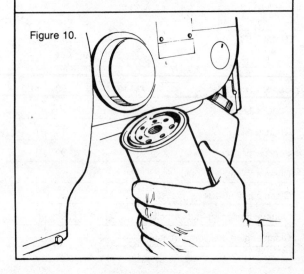
Figure 10.

10.08   HOW TO PERFORM ROUTINE MAINTENANCE PROCEDURES.

● The foundation of good maintenance is based on a daily inspection of your generator. It takes less than a minute to check the oil level (see Figure 8) and scan the unit for visible signs of problems. If you can train yourself to spot leaks, damaged wires, loose connections and clogged ventilation during this quick ''once over,'' you'll save a lot of time and trouble later.

After specified hours of running time, the following procedures are recommended with most units:

● Check battery electrolyte level (Figure 9) and cable connections. Maintenance-free or sealed batteries aren't recommended for generators. (Also see Chapter 8 for specific battery care details.)

● Change crankcase oil. Use the specified oil for your unit, and note the manufacturer's recommendation regarding different weight in lower temperatures. Don't mix different brands or weights of oil.

● Replace oil filter (Figure 10). You'll probably need an inexpensive oil filter wrench to unscrew the old cartridge.

● Remove spark plugs, clean or replace them and check for proper gap (Figure 11). If you're using a two-cylinder engine, remember to check both spark plugs — many people forget this when the second plug isn't readily available. (A visual inspection of the plugs yields valuable information about your engine: Black deposits indicate a rich mixture; wet plugs indicate misfiring; badly or frequently-fouled plugs show the need for a major tune up; and yellow plugs indicate bad gasoline. Badly-leaded plugs cause misfiring, poor operation or stopping when a load is applied.)

● Tighten all electrical connections.

● Check tightness of mounting bolts and condition of vibration absorbers (Figure 3).

● Check breaker points for condition of contacts (Figure 12) and service or replace. Points in bad condition will reduce the current which can pass and the engine won't operate or will miss. If the points are oxidized, dirty or oily, clean with a coarse cloth (not an abrasive). Check the resistance of your points with an ohmmeter or multimeter. If the resistance is over two ohms, replace the assembly.

● Also check the points for correct gap (Figure 13). The gap affects the time the contacts are open and closed, and a specified time is required for the magnetic field within the ignition coil to build up

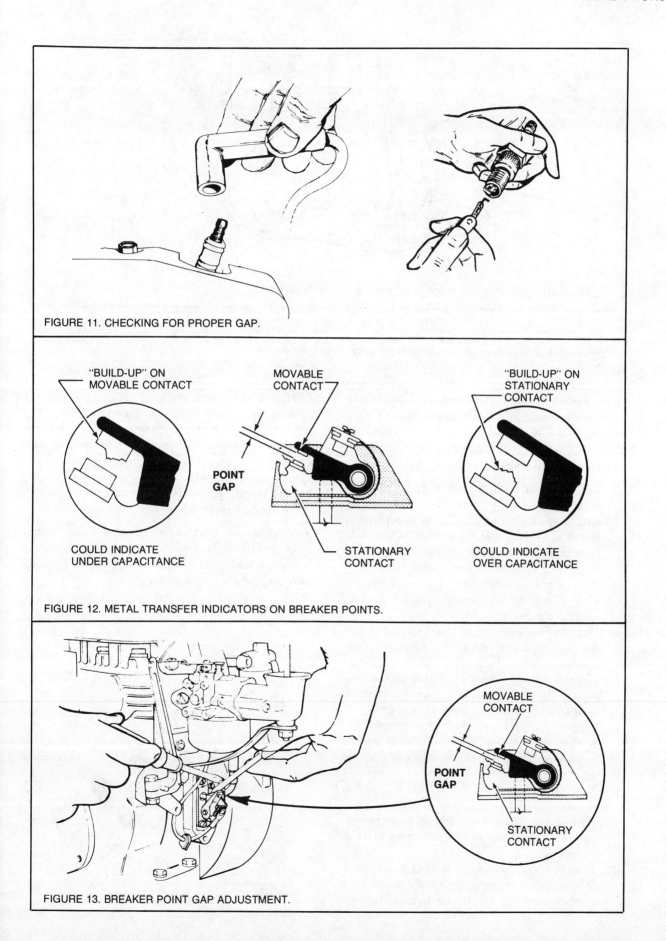

FIGURE 11. CHECKING FOR PROPER GAP.

"BUILD-UP" ON
MOVABLE CONTACT

MOVABLE
CONTACT

"BUILD-UP" ON
STATIONARY
CONTACT

POINT
GAP

STATIONARY
CONTACT

COULD INDICATE
UNDER CAPACITANCE

COULD INDICATE
OVER CAPACITANCE

FIGURE 12. METAL TRANSFER INDICATORS ON BREAKER POINTS.

MOVABLE
CONTACT

POINT
GAP

STATIONARY
CONTACT

FIGURE 13. BREAKER POINT GAP ADJUSTMENT.

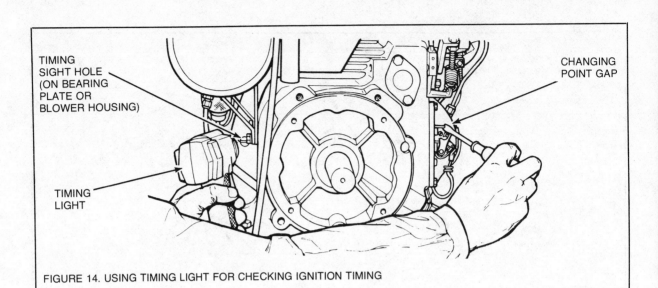

FIGURE 14. USING TIMING LIGHT FOR CHECKING IGNITION TIMING

to sufficient value. The correct gap for your specific engine must be checked in your service manual.

Adjusting the timing on most engines is best done with a timing light (Figure 14). Because there are a variety of timing lights available, you should follow the instructions that come with your light. The following procedure is generalized and can be used with most lights:

A. Remove high tension lead at spark plug — wrap one end of a short piece of fine wire around spark plug terminal. Reconnect lead to terminal — free end of wire must protrude from under boot. (Note: Step A for timing lights with alligator clips — some lights have sharp prongs on spark lead — on these simply push prong through boot until it contacts metal connector.)

B. Connect one timing light lead to the wire that has just been wrapped around spark plug terminal.

C. Connect second timing light lead to hot (ungrounded) side of battery — see timing light instructions for battery size, wiring, etc.

D. Connect third timing light lead to ground.

E. Remove snap button, rotate (by hand) engine until S mark* is visible — chalk S line for easy reading.

F. Start engine, run at 1200 - 1800 RPM, aim timing light into sight hole — light should flash just as S mark* is centered in sight hole or even with center mark on bearing plate or blower housing.

G. If timing is off — remove breaker point cover, loosen gap adjusting screw, shift breaker plate until S mark* is exactly centered. Retighten

adjusting screw before replacing breaker point cover.

*S or SP = Spark or Spark Run point.

NOTE: A few generators have breakerless ignition systems which function in the same general way as the conventional magneto ignition system — except they don't have breaker points or a conventional condenser. A trigger module containing solid state electronic devices serves the same function as the breaker points. Timing is permanently set on breakerless ignition systems.

● Servicing the electric fuel pump is usually confined to cleaning the filter. On newer Onan units, this is accomplished by draining the fuel pump and checking the filter element (Figure 15).

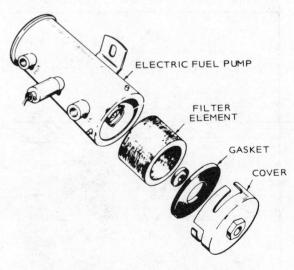

Figure 15.

Turn the hex nut on the base of the pump to gain access to the filter element. If the element appears dirty, replace it. Be sure to replace the gaskets when reassembling.

Earlier Onan models may have an external fuel shutoff solenoid.

Fuel pumps are often unrepairable and must be replaced when faulty.

Kohler generators may have a sediment bowl filter to trap solid impurities in the fuel. Before servicing, turn off fuel at the valve located on top of filter assembly, then loosen retaining bail at bottom of the fuel bowl, and remove and clean the bowl. After reinstalling and opening the fuel valve, use primer (if so equipped) on fuel pump to pump fuel back into bowl. Not all pumps have priming levers. On those without levers, rotate engine by hand to pump fuel back into the sediment bowl.

Generac advises replacement of the fuel filter (Figure 16) every 300 hours, or if it is dirty or clogged:

• A major cause of carburetor maladjustment is dirt which has reached the carburetor because regular preventive maintenance has not been performed. There are many different carburetor designs in use on RV generators, and your owner's manual should offer detailed adjustment instructions for yours. It's usually a good idea to have a carburetor adjusting wrench that is specifically intended for your model, as this will prevent your getting burned from a hot manifold or exhaust pipe. Two such wrench designs are illustrated in Figure 17:

FIGURE 16. FUEL FILTER

Here are more specific instructions, taken from several service manuals:

KOHLER

Carburetors are adjusted in the factory and should not have to be reset. If, however, one of the following conditions is noted, readjust carburetor immediately as continued operation with incorrect setting can lead to fouled spark plugs, overheating, excessive valve wear or other problems. If black exhaust smoke is noted, check the air cleaner first — an "overrich" mixture is usually caused by a poorly serviced, clogged air cleaner element, not an improperly adjusted carburetor.

If readjustment becomes necessary, stop the engine, then turn the MAIN and IDLE fuel adjusting screws (Figures 18 and 19) until they bottom lightly — don't force them closed as this will damage the needle valves. For preliminary setting, turn MAIN fuel screw out (counterclockwise) two full turns and the IDLE 1¼ turns. For final adjustments, start engine and allow it to warm up then operate at full throttle and under load, if possible.

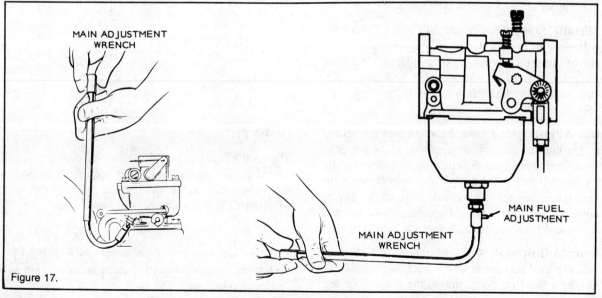

Figure 17.

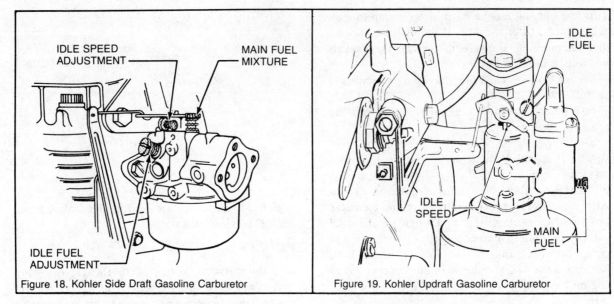

Figure 18. Kohler Side Draft Gasoline Carburetor

Figure 19. Kohler Updraft Gasoline Carburetor

Turn MAIN fuel in until engine slows down (lean side) then out until it slows down again from over-rich setting — note positions of screw at both settings, then set it about halfway between the two. The IDLE fuel setting can then be adjusted in the same manner for smoothest idle. Rough idle is often due to the idle speed being set too low — check this also.

IDLE SPEED: Idle no-load speed on most engines is set at 1,200 rpm; however, with parasitic loads such as presented by hydrastatic drives, the idle speed may have to be increased as much as 1,700 rpm for best no-load idle.

ONAN

Carburetor Adjustments
Though design may vary, carburetor adjustments are similar on all RV generating sets (Figure 20).

Throttle Stop: Remove all AC load. Connect a voltmeter to the AC leads or plug the meter into one of the set's receptacles (if available). Hold the governor arm to minimum speed and adjust the stop screw so the voltmeter indicates 75 to 80 volts.

Idle Adjustment: Leave the voltmeter connected as for the throttle stop adjustment. Hold the governor arm against the throttle stop and turn the idle jet in until voltage drops. Then, turn it out until the highest voltage is obtained. Release the governor arm. The engine should accelerate to governed speed and become stable.

Main Adjustment: Connect the AC leads to a suitable load test panel or connect appliances obtaining a full load condition on the generating set.

With a rated load applied, adjust the main jet to achieve the highest voltage. Remove the connected load and hold the governor arm to minimum speed. Release the governor arm and observe acceleration. If surging occurs at governed speed, open the main jet slightly. However, do not exceed 1/2 turn beyond the full load point. If surging continues, adjust the governor sensitivity.

Preliminary Carburetor Adjustment
Use this table when making preliminary carburetor adjustments on any of the RV model generating sets. Refer to appropriate Operator's Manual for each model for detailed carburetor adjustment procedures.

	TURNS OPEN	
UNIT	MAIN	IDLE
AJ	1¼	1¼
LK	1½	1½
CCK	1½	1½
NH (Prior to Spec J)	1½	1½
BF	1½	1½
BFA	1½	¾
BGA	1½	¾
NH (Begin Spec J)	1½	¾

DOMETIC

The carburetor main and idle fuel circuit are connected by a fuel passage. This requires that both the main needle valve and the idle needle valve be adjusted so that both circuits are balanced.

Adjust the carburetor needle valves as follows:

1. Close the high speed or main needle valve by turning clockwise until it stops and then turn it counterclockwise 1½ turns.

Figure 20. **RV CARBURETORS**

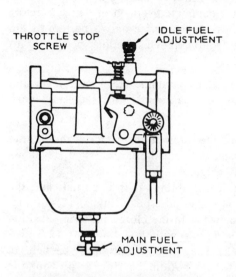

THROTTLE STOP SCREW

IDLE FUEL ADJUSTMENT

MAIN FUEL ADJUSTMENT

6.5 NH (Older Models)

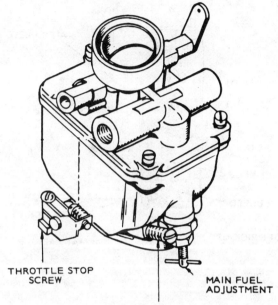

THROTTLE STOP SCREW

MAIN FUEL ADJUSTMENT

IDLE FUEL ADJUSTMENT

CCK/BF

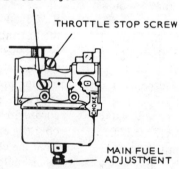

IDLE FUEL ADJUSTMENT

THROTTLE STOP SCREW

MAIN FUEL ADJUSTMENT

AJ/LK

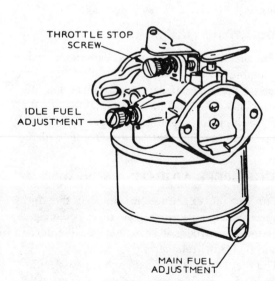

THROTTLE STOP SCREW

IDLE FUEL ADJUSTMENT

MAIN FUEL ADJUSTMENT

**BF/NH
POWER DRAWER**

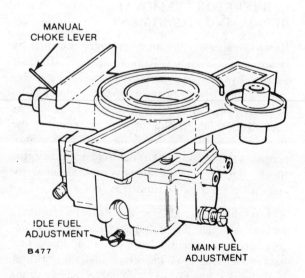

MANUAL CHOKE LEVER

IDLE FUEL ADJUSTMENT

MAIN FUEL ADJUSTMENT

B477

BFA, BGA AND NH   (Begin Spec J)

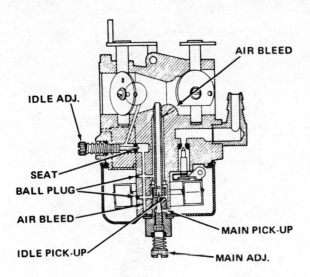

IDLE ADJ.

AIR BLEED

SEAT

BALL PLUG

AIR BLEED

MAIN PICK-UP

IDLE PICK-UP

MAIN ADJ.

Figure 21.

2. Close the idle speed needle valve by turning it clockwise until it stops and then turn it counterclockwise ¾ of a turn.
3. Start and run the engine. Turn the high speed needle valve in and out until the engine smooths out.
4. Let the engine run with a light load connected to it until it is warm.
5. Gradually close the high speed needle valve until the engine begins to stumble and die. Then gradually open the valve until the engine smooths out. Then open the valve another ⅛ turn.

CARBURETOR - REMOVAL, REPAIR AND ADJUSTMENT

Removal: Remove the air filter cover and filter by removing the wing nut. Remove the base of the air cleaner by removing the two clamp screws. Remove choke operating lever from the choke solenoid. Be sure to make a note of which hole is used. Remove the choke solenoid by removing the two clamping bolts. Remove the two Phillips-head screws holding the intake manifold to the engine block. For further disassembly of the carburetor see the detailed instructions that follow.

Reassembly: Assemble in the opposite sequence making sure that the mating surfaces of the manifold and the engine block are clean and that a new gasket is used. It is important that the Phillips-head screws are properly tightened and that the linkage wires are replaced in the same holes.

DETAILED CARBURETOR REPAIR

The following instructions are in a sequence easily followed for complete overhaul of the carburetor. If it is necessary to service only a portion of the carburetor, follow the instructions pertaining to that service.

A. THROTTLE. Examine the throttle lever and plate prior to disassembly. Replace any worn parts.

(1) Remove the screw in the center of the throttle plate and pull out the throttle shaft lever assembly (Figure 22).
(2) When reassembling, it is important that the lines on the throttle plate (Figure 22) are facing out when in the closed position. Position throttle plates with two lines, at 12 and 3 o'clock. The throttle shaft must be held in tight to the bottom bearing to prevent the throttle plate from riding on the throttle bore of the body, causing excessive throttle plate wear and governor hunting.

B. CHOKE. Examine the choke lever and shaft at the bearing points and holes into which the linkage is fastened (Figure 24) and replace if worn. The choke plate is inserted into the air horn of the carburetor in such a position that the flat surface of the choke (Figure 23) is toward the fuel bowl. Record the choke plate movement. Choke plates will operate either clockwise or counterclockwise. Hold the choke shaft securely into the bearing bore when replacing the choke plate. This will prevent binding and excessive choke plate wear.

C. IDLE ADJUSTING SCREW.

Remove the idle screw from the carburetor body and examine the point for damage to the seating surface on the taper. If damaged, replace the idle adjusting needle. Tension is maintained on the screw with a coil spring and sealed with an O-ring. Examine and replace the O-ring if damaged.

D. HIGH SPEED ADJUSTING SCREW.

(1) For service examine the taper of the high speed adjusting screw. If the taper is damaged at the area where it seats, replace the screw and fuel bowl retainer nut as an assembly.
(2) The fuel bowl retainer nut contains the seat for the screw. Examine the sealing O-ring on the high speed adjusting screw. Replace if it indicates wear or cuts.
(3) During high speed adjusting screw reassem-

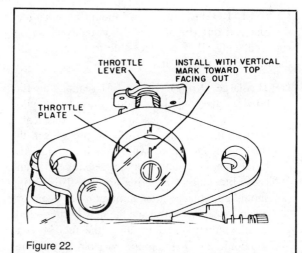

Figure 22.

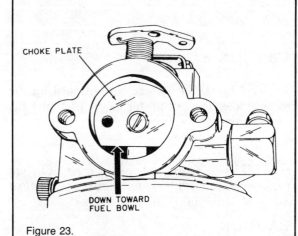

Figure 23.

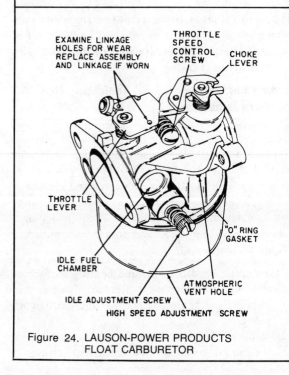

Figure 24. LAUSON-POWER PRODUCTS
FLOAT CARBURETOR

bly, position the coil spring on the adjusting screw, followed by the small brass washer and the O-ring seal.

NOTE: Check all adjusting screws for wear. Figure 25 shows a worn screw and a good screw. Replace screws that are worn.

Figure 25.

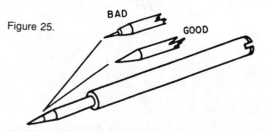

E. FUEL BOWL RETAINING NUT. Remove the fuel bowl retaining nut and fiber washer (Figure 26). Replace the washer, if cracked or worn.

(1) The retaining nut contains the transfer passage through which fuel is delivered to the high speed and idle fuel system of the carburetor. It is the larger hole closest to the hex nut end of the fitting. If a problem occurs with the idle system of the carburetor, examine the small fuel passage in the annular groove in the retaining nut. This passage must be clean for the proper transfer of fuel into the idle metering system.

(2) When replacing, torque the fuel bowl nut to 50 to 60 inch-pounds.

(3) The hold-on nut with two inlet ports is used on an internally vented adjustable carburetor. The increased port area compensates for the lower internal vent source pressure in comparison to the higher atmospheric pressure available to the externally vented carburetor (Figure 27).

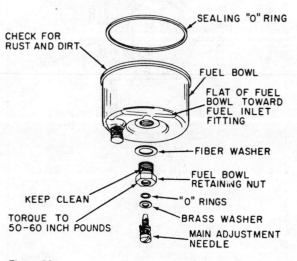

Figure 26.

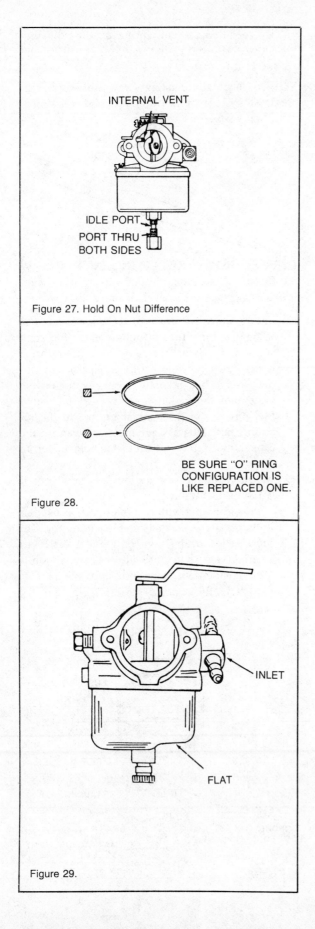

INTERNAL VENT

IDLE PORT
PORT THRU
BOTH SIDES

Figure 27. Hold On Nut Difference

BE SURE "O" RING
CONFIGURATION IS
LIKE REPLACED ONE.

Figure 28.

INLET

FLAT

Figure 29.

F. FUEL BOWL. Fuel bowl should be examined for rust and dirt (Figure 26). Thoroughly clean before replacing. If it is impossible to properly clean the fuel bowl, replace it.

(1) The large O-rings (Figure 28) sealing the fuel bowl to the carburetor body must be in good condition to prevent leakage. If the O-ring leaks, interfering with the atmospheric pressure in the float bowl, the engine will run rich. Foreign material can enter through the leaking area and cause blocking of metering orifices. This O-ring should be replaced after carburetor has been torn down for repair. Lubricate the new O-ring with a small amount of oil to allow the fuel bowl to slide onto the O-ring properly. Hold the carburetor body in an inverted position, place the O-ring on the carburetor body and then position the fuel bowl.

CAUTION

The fuel bowl flat surface is positioned on the same side of the carburetor as the fuel inlet fitting (Figure 29).

G. FLOAT. Remove the float (Figure 30) from the carburetor main body by pulling out the float axle with a pair of needle nose pliers.

CAUTION

When the float is being removed from the carburetor body the inlet needle will be lifted off of the seat, because it is attached to the float with an anchoring clip.

A lean engine may knock, indicating float adjustment is necessary.

Examine the float for crushing or holes. Examine the float hinge (Figure 30) bearing surfaces through which the float axle passes and replace if worn. Excessive wear on the tab of the float hinge that contacts the inlet needle will require replacement of the float to assure proper fuel metering within the carburetor.

(1) Examine the float axle and bearing surface of the float hinge for wear. Replace if worn. Accurate float setting is not possible with worn parts.

(2) Remove the float to make adjustments. Bend the tab on the float hinge to correct setting.

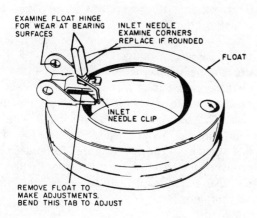

Figure 30.

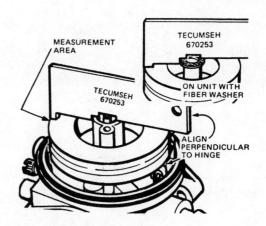

Figure 31. Measuring Float Height

CAUTION

Do not use compressed air to flush carburetor unless fuel bowl and float have been removed.

Then — always direct low pressure air through system opposite normal fuel flow to dislodge foreign matter toward reverse taper of any restricting passages.

SETTING THE FLOAT

With the float setting tool part No. 670253 check position of float as shown in Figure 31 for all Tecumseh carburetors. The tab edge of the measurement tool must rest without force or a gap on the float. If the float is too high or too low adjust the height by removing the float and bend the tab accordingly. (See Figure 30.)

If the required adjustment is minor the tab adjustment may be made without removing float and carefully inserting a small bladed screwdriver to bend the tab. Be careful not to affect other parts.

NOTE: On carburetors equipped with a fiber washer between the bowl and casting, use the fiber washer with the float setting tool as pictured in Figure 31.

H. INLET NEEDLE AND SEAT (Figure 32). The inlet needle and seat in this carburetor are of a different design than is normally found in a float carburetor. There is no inlet seat fitting to remove during disassembly. The inlet needle is anchored to the float tab by a clip (Figure 30) to assure proper movement of the inlet needle off of the seat when the float drops. The inlet needle clip must be positioned as shown in Figures 30 and 34 during reassembly.

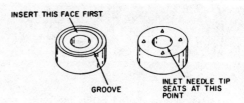

Figure 32.

Figure 33. Replacing Fuel Inlet Fitting

PRESS IN
PARTIALLY,
THEN APPLY
LOCTITE

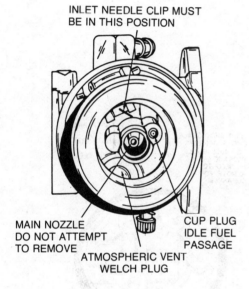

INLET NEEDLE CLIP MUST
BE IN THIS POSITION

MAIN NOZZLE
DO NOT ATTEMPT
TO REMOVE

ATMOSPHERIC VENT
WELCH PLUG

CUP PLUG
IDLE FUEL
PASSAGE

Figure 34.

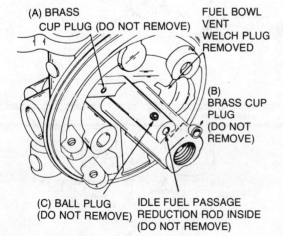

(A) BRASS
CUP PLUG (DO NOT REMOVE)

FUEL BOWL
VENT
WELCH PLUG
REMOVED

(B)
BRASS CUP
PLUG
(DO NOT
REMOVE)

(C) BALL PLUG
(DO NOT REMOVE)

IDLE FUEL PASSAGE
REDUCTION ROD INSIDE
(DO NOT REMOVE)

Figure 35.

(1) Examine the inlet needle. If any wear is evident, or any of the corners show signs of rounding, the needle should be replaced.

(2) The inlet needle seals on a Viton rubber seat in the carburetor body. To remove, put a few drops of heavy engine oil on the seat. Place an air hose to the inlet fitting and allow a short blast of air to pass through blowing out the seat. The seat may also be pried out with a short piece of hooked wire. Examine for cuts and scratches. The seat (Figure 32) is inserted grooved side first. Moisten the cavity with oil and use a flat-faced punch to press the inlet seat into position.

I. FUEL INLET FITTING.

(1) The fitting may be removed from the carburetor by twisting and pulling. Make a note of the position in which the fitting was originally installed for proper fuel flow when the carburetor is reinstalled on the engine.

(2) When inserting the fitting into the carburetor body, seal it with Loctite grade A. Insert the tip of the fitting (Figure 33) into the carburetor body, then coat the remainder of the shank with Loctite grade A. Press the fitting in until the shoulder contacts the carburetor. Use inlet fittings without screens for replacement only.

J. CARBURETOR BODY. Examine the carburetor body for wear and damage.

(1) It may be necessary to remove the large welch plug (Figures 34 and 35) if excessive dirt has accumulated in the atmospheric vent cavity, or it may be possible to clean this cavity with carburetor cleaner or compressed air without removing the welch plug.

(2) The carburetor body contains a main nozzle tube (Figure 34) pressed into the carburetor body to a predetermined positioning within the venturi of the carburetor. *Do not* attempt to remove this main nozzle. Any movement of this nozzle will seriously affect the metering characteristics of the carburetor and will require replacement of the entire carburetor.

(3) Clean the accelerating well surrounding the main nozzle with compressed air and carburetor cleaning solvents. With the choke plate and shaft removed, compressed air may be blown in through the high speed air bleed (located just behind the lower choke shaft bearing and immediately in front of the venturi), to remove any dirt that may have accumulated.

(4) The carburetor body contains two cup plugs (Figure 35), neither of which should be removed.

    (a) A cup plug, located near the inlet seat cavity, high up on the carburetor body, seals off the idle air bleed. This is a straight passage drilled into the carburetor throat. Do not remove this cup plug.

    (b) Another cup plug is located in the base (Figures 34 and 35) where the fuel bowl nut seals the idle fuel passage. Do not remove this cup plug or the metering rod.

    (c) A small ball plug (Figure 35) located on the side of the idle fuel passage seals this passage. Do not remove this ball plug.

(5) A welch plug on the side of the carburetor body, just above the Idle Adjusting Screw seals the Idle Fuel Chamber (Figure 35). This welch plug may be removed for thorough cleaning of the idle fuel mixture passage and the Primary and Secondary Idle Fuel discharge ports. Clean with solvent and compressed air. *Do not* use any tools that may change the size of the discharge ports.

● All chokes perform the same function — they control the amount of air intake to the carburetor venturi. When the engine is first started, the choke is closed but gradually opens as the engine warms up. Rough operation of a cold engine indicates the need of choke adjustment.

    Onan equips their generating sets with one of three kinds of chokes: electric bimetal, Sisson and thermo-magnetic. You'll find similar chokes on many other brands, also.

● Loosen the two screws on the electric choke and turn to obtain smooth operation of a cold engine.

● Adjust the Sisson choke by loosening the screw holding the choke wire and repositioning it to obtain smooth cold engine operation.

● Adjust the thermo-magnetic choke by loosening the screw and rotating the entire assembly to obtain smooth cold engine operation.

If the engine starts and runs roughly after a minute or two of operation, the choke is set too rich. If the engine starts, and assuming that fuel, ignition and compression are adequate, but the engine sputters or stops before it warms up, the choke is set too lean.

    When an electric choke valve is used (e.g., in Dometic models), it is closed by an electric solenoid mounted on the engine shroud above the carburetor. It only operates when the start button is pushed. If the choke does not operate, check for voltage at the

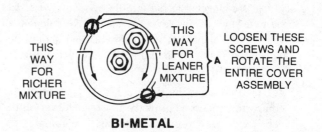

BI-METAL

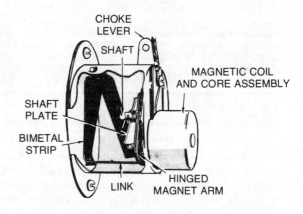

SISSON

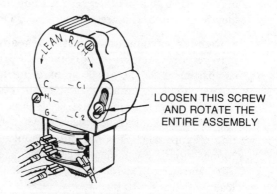

THERMO-MAGNETIC

Figure 36.

terminal on the choke with either a DC voltmeter or with a test light when the start switch is activated, or connect a jumper wire from the positive starting battery terminal to the terminal on the operating lever which is connected to the throttle by a stiff wire. At the outer end of this lever are two choke solenoids. The choke solenoid is not repairable and should be replaced if faulty. It should not operate when hot.

• **Clean cooling fins** (Figure 37). If your generator compartment door is properly constructed, very little debris will get into the cooling fins. Use compressed air to blow away accumulated dust.

• **Clean governor linkage.** Your manual will tell you if lubrication of the joints is also necessary. The governor's purpose is to keep your engine running at a constant speed, which keeps the AC output at the required 60 cycles.

• **Service air cleaner.** Air cleaner design will vary, but the importance of a clean filter is constant, as dirt introduced through infrequently serviced elements wears out more engines than does long hours of operation. And while you have the cover off, don't neglect to check other air intake components such as adapters, hoses, clamps, etc., to see that they are secure and in good condition. (Replace or service the air cleaner more often than specified in dirty environments — and do the same favor for your RV or tow vehicle engine.)

• **Clean crankcase and breather valve.** This is a one-way valve which maintains a slight vacuum within the crankcase by allowing pressure to be expelled while preventing air from getting sucked back in. Some breather valves can't be serviced, only replaced, but in either case it's important that they be dirt-free. (Figure 40 courtesy of Onan.)

• **Remove carbon deposits from heads.** This may require removing the generator from the compartment. Scrape away carbon deposits which have accumulated around the valves and cylinders. To avoid scratching the metal, use sharp wood or similar material. Use new gaskets when reinstalling (Figure 41). This operation should be performed any time you inadvertently use leaded gasoline and want to switch back to unleaded or low-lead (see Section 10.09).

• **Valves and tappets.** When the cylinder head is decarbonized, have the valve tappet clearance checked and adjusted if necessary. If valves require lapping or grinding, this can also be accomplished at this time. Tappet clearance is adjusted by grinding the end of the valve stems.

• **Check generator brushes.** Remove the brush cover and check the commutator and AC slip rings for wear. These parts should all have a long life, and if they don't you should suspect dirt. Brushes should have at least 50% contact with the slip rings.

• **Servicing exhaust spark arrester/mufflers.** The spin-out type (internally bypassed) removes carbon particles by centrifugal force, catching them in a holding chamber. To clean the chamber, just remove the plug in the bottom of the muffler and run the set for five minutes; then replace the plug.

The screen-type of spark arrester (not bypassed) traps carbon particles in its screen. The screens must be periodically removed and either scraped or blown-clean, or else replaced.

• Finally, the fact that you "keep it clean" should be visible throughout your generator compartment. Wipe off any grease accumulations, because they make the engine run hotter. Pools of oil or grease are flammable, and if everything is kept spotless you'll immediately see the first signs of fuel or oil leaks.

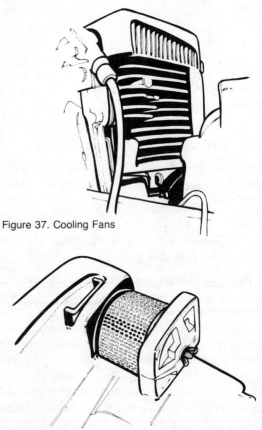

Figure 37. Cooling Fans

Figure 38. Air Cleaner

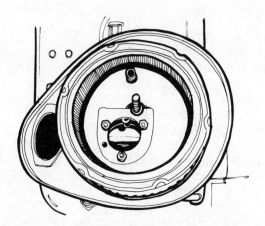

Figure 39. Another Type of Air Cleaner

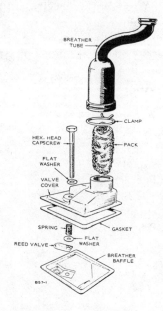

Figure 40.

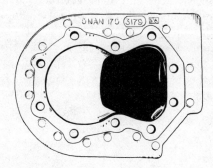

Figure 41.

10.09 GENERATOR FUEL.

Some makers are finding that low-lead or unleaded gasoline produces fewer maintenance problems. Tests performed by Onan show that non-lead gasoline helps reduce problems such as these: cylinder head deposits (low power), sticking valves or burned valves, spark plug fouling, piston wear, ring wear and sticking, cylinder wall wear and poor oil control after ring fouling. They also found that if lead deposits are not removed from the engine before switching from leaded to non-leaded gasoline, preignition could occur and cause severe damage to the engine. This means that even if you accidentally use one tank-full of leaded fuel, you must service the engine before switching back to non-leaded.

10.10 TROUBLESHOOTING.

ENGINE WILL NOT CRANK:

- Battery Connections
- Generator Ground Cable
- Battery Condition
- Start Solenoid Bad
- Correct Generator DC Brushes
- Engine Seized
- Cranking Motor Bad
- Generator Output AC Wires Connected Wrong
- Faulty Control Board Contacts

ENGINE CRANKS BUT WILL NOT START:

- No Fuel in Tank
- Air Leak in Fuel System
- Electric Fuel Pump Failed
- No Ignition Power
- Spark Plugs Fouled
- Choke Stuck (Closed or Open)
- Faulty Start Solenoid
- Fuse Out of PC Board
- Faulty Disconnect Circuit
- Faulty Control Board Contacts
- Faulty Relay

ENGINE MISFIRES:

- Incorrect Ignition Timing
- Wrong Spark Plug Gap or Fouled Plugs
- Worn Points or Improper Gap Setting
- Bad Ignition Coil or Condenser
- Lean Fuel Mixture
- Rich Fuel Mixture or Choke Stuck
- Dirty Carburetor
- Dirty Air Cleaner
- Faulty Plug Wires

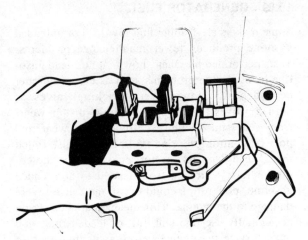

Figure 42. Generator Brushes

Figure 43. Armature and Slip Ring

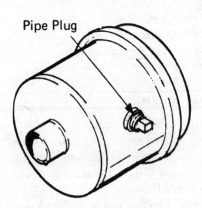

Pipe Plug

Figure 44. Exhaust Spark Arrester/Muffler

ENGINE OVERHEATS:

- Ignition Timing Wrong
- Lean Fuel Mixture
- Poor Air Circulation
- Dirty or Oily Cooling Fins
- Oil Too Light or Diluted
- Low Oil Level
- Generator Overloaded
- Faulty Exhaust System

LOW OR NO OUTPUT VOLTAGE:

- Brushes Stuck
- Open Field Circuit
- Open AC Coil
- Circuit Breaker Tripped
- Diode in Bridge Shorted
- Reactor Open
- AC Output Wires Not Connected at Brushes
- Brushes Too Short
- Field Blocking Diode Open
- Bad Battery, Poor Connections or Battery Cables Too Small

ENGINE STOPS:

- Burned Points
- No Fuel in Tank
- Engine Flooded
- Dirty Carburetor
- Defective Fuel Pump
- Generator DC Brushes Defective
- Faulty Alternator
- Faulty LOP Switch
- Low Oil
- Fuse Out
- Fouled Spark Plugs
- Overheating

(Courtesy of Onan)

A NOTE OF INTEREST: In developing this section on generators, we spoke with executives of all the major RV generator manufacturers and, frankly, we're impressed. These people were unusually knowledgeable, helpful and candid; the material they supplied was well-organized and pertinent. Special thanks, then, go to the representatives of (in alphabetical order) Dometic, Generac, Kohler and Onan.

Chapter Eleven

Water Systems

Fresh water on board is certainly one of the nicer luxuries of modern RVing and, fortunately, it doesn't take much effort to keep the flow flowing. Aside from the basic tools which you should already have, the most important ingredient in handling on-the-road problems is a willing mind. Unquestionably, it's easy to procrastinate about mucking around in plumbing lines, and the reasons most RVers use to explain their negligence usually boil down to a lack of understanding. But your plumbing system operates with a logic that is easily grasped, and it's seldom necessary to even get wet when working with it.

11.01   HOW WATER SYSTEMS WORK.

Basically, there are two types of RV water systems: demand and air pressure. In the first type, a pump is activated either manually or automatically to pull water from the tank and push it along the lines each time an outlet is opened. It works on demand. In the second type, a compressor keeps a minimum air pressure in the water storage tank, and it is this pressure which drives the water through the lines when a faucet is opened. Just listening will tell you which type you have; the demand pump only runs when an outlet is opened, while an air compressor will sound like it's thinking for itself.

Figure 1 is an overview of both types of water systems. Both consist of a supply side (tank and city water entry), a delivery side which routes through the accumulator (not present in newer layouts), clarifier and heater before it reaches the outlets and a pump to move the water from one end to the other. Even though it's an overused comparison, seeing the similarity between this and your body's blood circulation system is a valid analogue.

Starting with the supply side, we'll take a detailed look at each component. The physical location of these pieces will vary between individual rigs, but you can avoid guess and search procedures by obtaining a diagram from the maker of your RV.

11.02   WATER TANKS.

Your freshwater storage tank can be made of metal, fiberglass or one of the newer light synthetic materials. Short of an impactful accident, it's unlikely that synthetic water tanks will ever develop leaks. But if they do, you should suspect the soundness of the entire tank and replace it with a new one.

Metal tanks are used primarily for air pressure systems. They may eventually develop weak points from rusting and should be replaced at that time.

Internal baffles are important in larger tanks simply because they impart strength (Figure 2). Think of water weighing eight pounds per gallon, then consider 50 or more gallons sloshing back and forth as you round corners or brake quickly. That's over 400 pounds which could both strain the tank walls and even affect your rig's maneuverability if the baffles didn't help absorb much of the energy. Smaller tanks on lighter rigs may not need this safeguard, but you should at least know about the availability of baffles.

Demand system tanks must have a vent, as failure to vent will produce an internal air pressure situation which seriously inhibits both filling and drawing water from the tank. (On the other hand, an air pressure system requires an air-tight tank and will therefore omit the vent.)

The tank's fill hole is located along the top surface and is connected by a hose to the filling port on the rig's external skin. The filling port should be clearly labeled "Potable Water Only" as it's not unusual for strange things, including gasoline, to be injected into the freshwater tank through unlabeled filling ports.

11.03   CITY WATER ENTRY.

To avoid continuous water tank refills when city water is available, most RVs provide a port which will accept the male end of a conventional hose fitting. When connected, water from any potable tap can flow directly into your water system without the necessity of operating your pump. Internally, the connection to your plumbing system is generally made at almost any point on the output side of the pump (see Figure 3).

Some city water entry valves also incorporate mesh-type filters designed to keep out bits of solid debris sometimes found in municipal supplies. Just like the strainers on faucets, these should be periodically cleaned.

11.04   REGULATORS.

CAUTION: Most RVs have plumbing which will tolerate 35 to 45 psi (pounds per square inch) of pressure, but city water sources frequently provide much higher pressure. Exposing your pipes, water heater and other components to these sometimes extreme pressures will certainly cause damage, but a regulator will instantly reduce the pressure to the desired quantity. Many entry valves already contain a regulator, but separate regulating devices

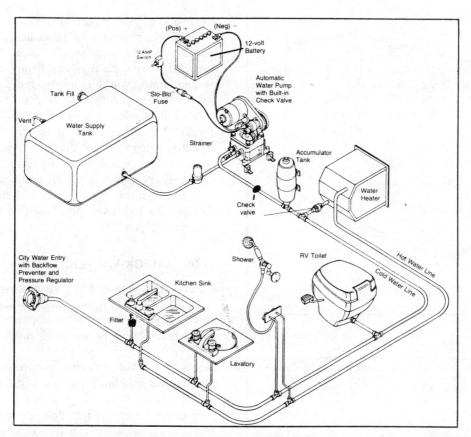

Figure 1. The demand (at top) and air pressure (below) RV water systems use different methods to accomplish the same purpose. A demand pump draws water from a vented tank and propels it through the pipes whenever an outlet is opened. Pressure systems compress air into the closed water tank and this stored pressure drives the water flow. Note that the strainer and accumulator tank are not necessary in the AP design. (Diagram courtesy ITT Jabsco Products.)

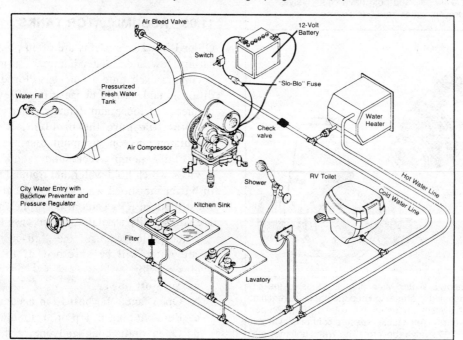

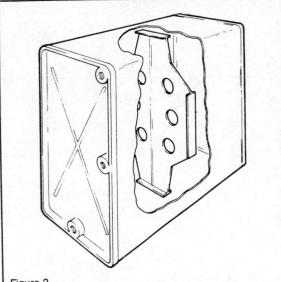

Figure 2.

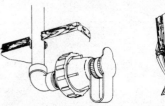 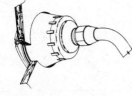

(IN-LINE HOSE MODEL)   (FLUSH MOUNT MODEL)

Figure 3. Two types of city water entry valves. Both have built-in regulators which reduce incoming water pressure from as high as 200 psi to a safe 35 psi, and both have check valves which prevent water from backflowing.

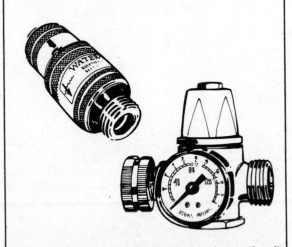

Figure 4. Benbow's Water Mate (top) attaches to the city water input hose and is preset to keep the pressure reaching the RV water system under 45 psi with a 16-gallon-per-minute flow capacity. Adjustable pressure control is available with the Watts T56G valve (bottom). The Watts unit may also be used on some trailers to provide a continuous flow of water directly to the water tank, eliminating the need for a city water inlet. Used in this manner it automatically shuts off when water tank pressure reaches 40 psi.

are also available (Figure 4).

HINT: To protect your input hose, a regulator may be attached to the supply faucet. If you use a wrench to screw the regulator firmly onto the end of your hose, you'll eliminate the possibility of leaving it behind (Figure 5).

A word of caution about using adjustable regulators: When people get into a very low pressure area they often find that the flow of water to their system is less than desired. To remedy this situation, they try adjusting the regulator to a new setting, find that this doesn't help and then forget to change it back to a safe position. This is obviously a dangerous practice.

11.05 CHECK VALVES.

Check valves (Figure 6) are required by many federal and local laws to prevent the water already in your system from backflowing into the supply lines should there be a sudden drop in pressure. This can actually happen when nearby fire hydrants are opened, reducing city pressure to almost nothing and creating a vacuum in the water pipes. What's more, if your neighbor's rig contains contaminated water, and it doesn't have a check valve, that bad water can run backwards and get into your pipes. Additionally, the valve keeps water pumped out of your storage tank from escaping through an open city water intake valve.

11.06 ACCUMULATOR TANKS.

Older RV water systems are often plagued by pulsating flow and "water hammer" (violent shocks occurring each time a faucet is closed). This condition is undesirable because it will eventually jar connections loose and damage other appliances in the line. To cure the problem, install an accumulator tank on the main line near the output side of the pump. Accumulator tanks are simple devices which hold water and trapped air to absorb or buffer the shock waves and prevent their travel. Most modern RVs seldom need one, but the tanks are still readily available just in case (Figure 7).

After prolonged use, the "air-cushion" in an accumulator will be absorbed. If the pump then cycles rapidly:

a. Turn off power.
b. Open faucet farthest from accumulator tank.
c. Remove plug in top of accumulator tank.
d. Open drain cock and empty the system of water.
e. Replace plug, close the drain cock and reactivate the system.

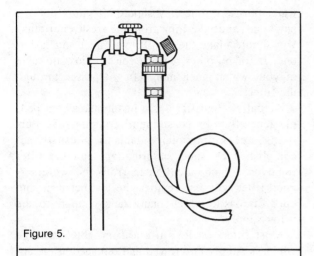
Figure 5.

Figure 6.

Figure 7. Jabsco's accumulator tank decreases the water pulsation and rapid on/off pump cycling found in some systems. The air and water in the accumulator cushion sudden surges of water. Some manufacturers build an accumulator into their pumps.

11.07 TRANSMISSION LINES.

The entire system is interconnected by pipes and hosing which have been approved by the Food and Drug Administration (FDA) for potable water (some materials are not safe). Plastic pipe, copper tubing or high-pressure flexible poly hose are the generally accepted materials. Experts caution that these arteries should never be smaller than 1/2- or 3/8-inch internal diameter, as lesser dimensions will create a back-pressure and limit flow. Also, remember to use an approved high-pressure hose between city water faucet and intake valve. Some people who use regular garden hoses have lived to regret the taste!

Sections of plumbing should always be joined with correctly sized fittings, and proper clamps must be used on hose connections (Figure 8). Adhering to this advice will eliminate junction leaks which also create a hardship on the pump. And don't use pipe dope on the input side of the pump, as it can get into the pump head and create problems.

Copper tubing, often used as risers from the main transmission lines, must be periodically inspected, especially at places where they bend and at junctures. If flared fittings are used on your system, they can be replaced as shown in Section 14.14.

Exercise care whenever tightening junctures on any type of line, as overtightening can eventually yield as much leakage as undertightening. Periodically unfasten all connections, clean them thoroughly and replace washers. Reconnect by tightening with your fingers, then use a wrench to add another 1/4 turn. But do this carefully, as some connections, especially plastic, will not tolerate even this amount of wrenching. Copper flared connections should be tightened with *two* wrenches, each manipulating the opposing sides of the juncture (Figure 9).

11.08 WATER STRAINERS.

Finally, every RV water system should contain an in-line strainer close to the pump on the output side to catch dirt, sand or debris which may have entered the water tank. Figure 10 shows PAR's Pumpgard strainer, which features a transparent housing for quick inspection. To clean, simply unscrew the housing, remove the screen and rinse with cold water until all dirt is flushed out.

11.09 WATER PURIFIERS/FILTERS.

Many RVs don't come equipped with so-called

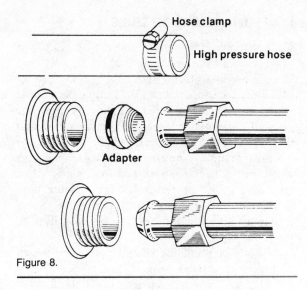

Figure 8.

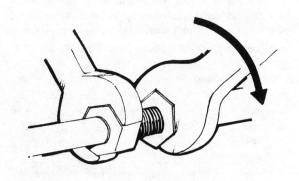

Figure 9.

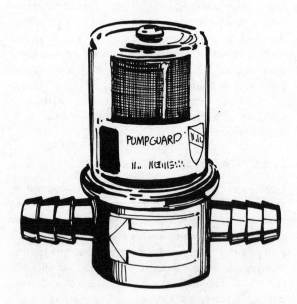

Figure 10. RV water systems should contain an in-line close to the pump on the output side to catch any dirt, sand or debris which may have entered the water tank. Pictured is PAR's Pumpgard strainer which features a transparent housing for quick inspection.

water purifiers, but they should. If yours doesn't have one, and you drink from the freshwater tank, you should make the small investment and install one. If for no other reason, you'll enjoy the taste of your water much more after it passes through the filter.

Actually, "purifier" is a misnomer which people generally use to describe filtering devices. Purifying, i.e., killing microorganisms, is usually accomplished by super chlorination, and the filter removes the chemical taste from the water. A good filter will also remove the distinct taste and odor of plastic which many tanks impart to the water supply.

Most filters on RVs use a disposable cartridge which is simply unscrewed and replaced at the appropriate time. There is no further maintenance than seeing that this is done on time (Figure 11).

11.10   WATER FAUCETS.

Water faucets probably last as long as the whole RV, but washers do deteriorate from age and use. When this happens, it's important to change washers immediately. The sign of a worn washer is a faucet that needs a hard twist to completely shut off — or one that persists in dripping. The best procedure is to routinely change all your washers whenever a single one needs changing.

Fixtures made by different manufacturers will differ, but many washers can be replaced as shown for the Price Pfister faucet (Figure 12).

11.11   HAND PUMPS.

In essence, pumps are the hearts of water systems, and they range in complexity from simple, manually-controlled types to highly complex electrical instruments.

The simplest pump operates on the old principle, "The more you give, the more you get." Manually pumping a handle moves an internal piston and alternately creates a suction which pulls water from the tank, and a pressure which shoots it out the faucet. These pumps have very few parts and are relatively trouble-free (Figure 13).

Hand pumps are obvious when they malfunction — they don't "feel" right. Many brands must simply be discarded when they fail, but the more expensive models have replacement kits for the major wearing parts. The only way to tell which one you have is to query the manufacturer — and this is something you should do long before it is time to discard and/or repair it.

Units such as the model in Figure 13 can be eas-

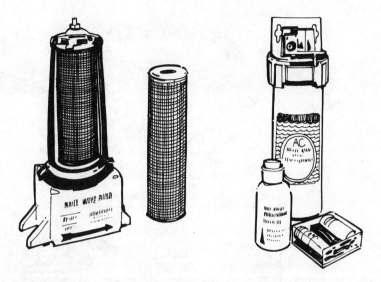

Figure 11. The Miller clarifier (left) is installed in the main water line and removes chlorine taste and smell from the entire water supply, even hot and bathing water. The cartridge slips easily into place and should, according to the maker, last for an entire season under normal usage. Everpure's filter (right) also uses a replaceable cartridge and, mounted directly under a sink, efficiently dechlorinates the water dispensed by a single faucet. It is pictured along with a water tank chlorination test kit.

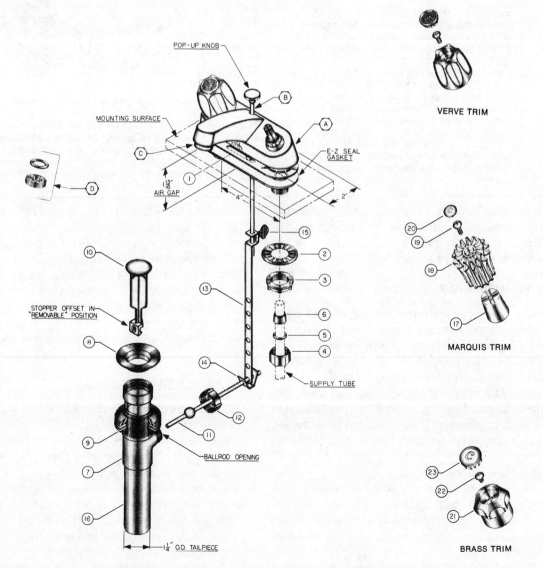

Figure 12.

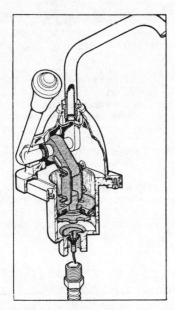

Figure 13. This cutaway view of the Rocket hand pump and faucet combination made by VSI shows how a manual pump operates. Each "push-pull" cycle on the handle moves the piston up and down, drawing water into the domed housing. When the unit is full the pump is fully primed and additional piston cycles will drive the water out of the faucet as more is pulled from the tank. The gray shaded area contains the major wearing parts for which a replacement kit is available. (Some manufacturers don't offer replacement parts and the whole pump must be discarded when pieces wear out.)

Figure 14. Even small RVs can have an electric water system with this mini pump and single cold water faucet made by PAR. The pump is designed to attach directly onto the out port of most water tanks, and the faucet assembly contains the operational switch.

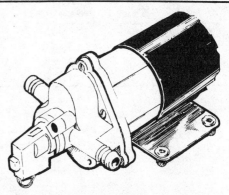

Figure 15. RV demand water systems require a pump to pull water from the reservoir tank and push it along the pipes and hosing. This Shurflo Model 200 develops enough power to operate a multi-fixture system and features an easily removable head assembly for replacement of worn moving parts.

ily disassembled for replacing parts. No specific instructions are necessary, as the job isn't complicated. Many other models, though, must be returned to the factory for repairs.

11.12   DEMAND PUMPS.

While hand pumps are fine for single cold water outlets, electrics are more convenient (Figures 14 and 15). Demand electric pumps operate on basically the same principle of suction and pressure, except that they usually employ spinning vanes or rotors. The rotational speed is so high that considerable centrifugal force can be translated into water line pressure almost instantly. Actually, though, the pump shouldn't have to start from zero each time — a tight system will retain some residual pressure in the pipes.

There are two convenient ways to activate a demand pump, and a third which isn't so convenient. The first method uses a switch built into the faucet so that turning water on or off also controls the pump.

The second method uses a pressure-sensitive

switch in the water line. The device registers pressure changes caused by opened or closed faucets and operates the pump almost simultaneously.

One essential on your water system is a master switch for deactivating the pump. Lacking this, a leak or malfunction could have your pump running continuously. Some RVers have tried to simplify by using this switch as their only pump control, and this is the less attractive alternative mentioned above.

11.13   COMPRESSORS.

Compressors operate on the familiar piston principle (Figure 16). The piston forces air — rather than water — through its chamber with sufficient power to "compress" it into the water tank up to around 35 psi (or higher in large installations). A pressure-sensitive switch automatically starts the machine when sufficient water has been withdrawn to bring tank pressure down between 15 to 20 psi. The electrical wiring is identical to a demand pump's, including the master switch requirement.

Many trailers with air pressure systems also

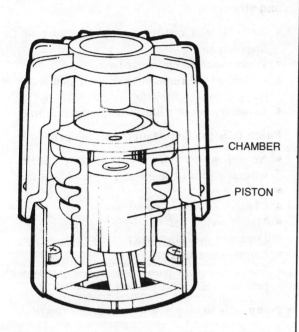

Figure 16.

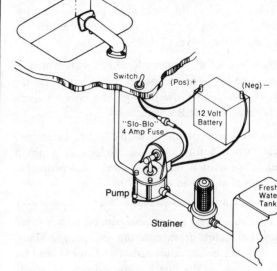

Figure 17.

have a second inlet valve through which the tank can be charged from an external source. This is handy if you lose power and have a hand pump available. Don't, however, be tempted to save electricity by using gas station air; it often contains both objectionable taste and dangerous liquid contaminants.

11.14 PUMP WIRING.

Correct pump wiring is simple and direct, as it must be connected to the battery on a circuit of its own. Be sure you follow the manufacturer's instructions pertaining to the correct gauge of wire, as this can vary according to the length of installation. A fuse which meets the manufacturer's specifications (commonly an automotive-type, or "slo-blo") must be wired in-line as close to the battery as is practical (Figure 17).

11.15 WATER SYSTEM MAINTENANCE.

In routine operation, pumps are activated either manually or automatically. Very little can go wrong with a manual switch, and when it does you simply replace it (always using the correct replacement). Automatic switches vary with the type of system: Air compressors are controlled by

pressure-sensitive switches within the water tank, while demand pumps are turned on and off by an in-line switch which senses the change in water pressure when a faucet is opened or closed. The complexity of replacement sometimes necessitates professional assistance (see the specific diagrams in Section 11.17).

Any condition (such as an empty water tank) which lets an electric pump run continually is asking for trouble. The motors are usually substantial enough for normal duties, but they can't withstand continuous operation. Always switch off the master control whenever you notice the pump working too long, or before letting the rig stand unoccupied.

Low voltage, the most prevalent electrical problem, will make a pump run too slowly and is evidenced by low water pressure. More than just an inconvenience, low voltage can easily cause serious damage because pumps can't build sufficient pressure to activate their cutoff switches, and thus run continuously. Beyond actual battery condition, look for corrosion on the battery terminals which can inhibit power flow.

Vibration is the nemesis of water systems because it loosens connections and the resultant leaks cause the pump to work overtime. Additionally, if air penetrates the system and fills a demand pump chamber, you'll have a condition known as air lock. Some pumps can overcome air lock and reprime themselves, but many can't push the air past the check valves (check valves prevent backflow, so there will be water pressure on their far side). Usually, the blockage can be cleared by opening a faucet to relieve the water pressure on that side of the valve.

Also, use of an unsuitable check valve on the output line just after the pump might have that effect. If you can't blow through the check valve, it's not suitable for RV use.

Another form of air lock (or failure to prime) occurs when a foreign object lodges in a pump head valve so that the valve can't seal properly. The cure is simply to remove the object.

To prevent such occurrences, it's important that the inlet line to the pump be equipped with a filter to prevent debris from entering the pump. Many new RVs are not so equipped. The filter should be self-cleaning; as the coach moves down the road, water sloshing against the fine-meshed screen washes off any debris. The particles remain in the tank and may be flushed out when the tank is drained.

Disassembly should only be attempted if the pump is designed for consumer repair *and* if you feel confident to do the job. Most units are self-lubricating, so disassembly will not be necessary for that purpose. But should another problem justify taking the pump apart, the following illustrations may help. (You should also have at hand the service manual for your specific unit.)

11.16 TROUBLESHOOTING DEMAND PUMP SYSTEMS

Pump operates but no water flows through faucet.

- Low water level in tank
- Hoses clogged or kinked
- Air leak in suction line
- Loose hose clamps or fittings in suction line
- Filters plugged

Pump cycles on and off when faucets are closed.*

- Water leak in plumbing
- Defective toilet flush valve
- Internal leak in pump
- Outlet valves not sealing

Pump operates roughly and has excessive noise and vibration.

- Intake line is restricted in suction hose or fittings too small
- Pump mounted on flimsy base
- Deformed or ruptured pulsation dampener in pump
- Loose screws at pulleys and connecting rod

Pump fails to start when faucet is opened.

- No voltage to pump (check battery condition, wiring, corroded terminals)
- Blown fuse
- Clogged or kinked outlet line
- Master switch off
- Defective pressure switch
- Empty water tank
- Water frozen in pump head (thaw slowly with heat from electric light bulb)

Pump fails to stop when faucets are closed.

- Empty water tank
- Outlet valve not sealing
- Very low voltage to pump
- Defective pressure switch

Pump operates but water sputters.

- Air leaks in the input side of the pump
- Air not bled from lines and water heater

Pump cycles rapidly and water comes intermittently.

- Accumulator tank needs adjustment (see Section 11.06)

11.17 TROUBLESHOOTING AIR PRESSURE SYSTEMS

Compressor continues to run but fails to build up pressure.

- Air leak in piping
- Dirty air filter
- Low voltage to compressor motor (check wiring and battery charge)
- Worn piston seal
- Leaking discharge valve

Compressor fails to restart.

- Defective or stuck pressure switch
- Clogged air line between compressor and tank
- Pressure switch not making electrical contact
- Blown fuse
- Low voltage
- Loose or corroded electrical connections

Repeated fuse blowing.

- Low voltage to compressor motor (check wiring and battery charge)
- Piston out of adjustment (check free running of piston)
- Wires shorting

Pressure builds up but compressor fails to shut off automatically.

- Pressure switch failure

Compressor comes on periodically although no water is used.

- Leaks in water or air lines
- Leak in discharge (check valve compressor)

Compressor operates but no water is delivered.

- Low water in tank
- Hose kinked
- Clogged strainer
- Stuck backflow valve

*When you can't decide whether you have leaks within the water system or in the pump, here's a good way to check:

Shut pump off. Remove the output hose where it joins the system (not at the pump), insert a plug in the hose and clamp it. (You can make a perfect plug from a barb fitting, 1/2-inch size, with a cap tightly screwed on the threads.) Turn the pump switch on. The pump should come on, run a few seconds and then shut off. If it remains off, the problem is not with the pump. The problem is in the system. If, however, the pump goes on and off, there may be a problem in the pump.

There may be an internal leak in the pump which allows water to escape from the high pressure area back into the low pressure area. Look for a pump valve held open or a crack in the plastic parts.

11.18 SELECTED PUMP DIAGRAMS.

While the variety of water pumps on the market today is much too large for a complete technical encyclopedia, the following models have been selected as being both typical and representative. CAUTION: Most pump disassemblies should not be attempted by anyone but an authorized technician so be sure you understand the complixity of the job before you undertake it.

The Shurflo combination hand and electric pump should be installed in a manner which is similar to the diagram.

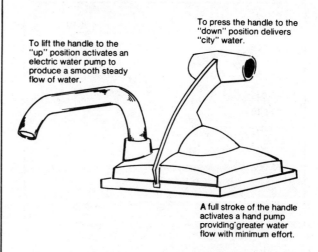

To lift the handle to the "up" position activates an electric water pump to produce a smooth steady flow of water.

To press the handle to the "down" position delivers "city" water.

A full stroke of the handle activates a hand pump providing greater water flow with minimum effort.

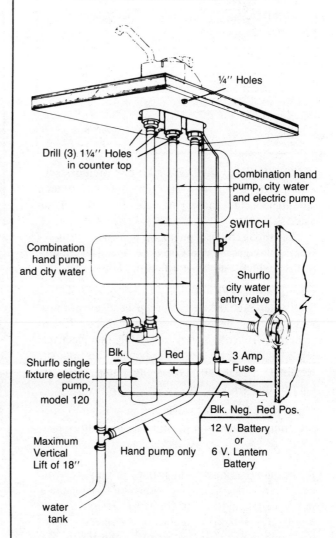

¼" Holes

Drill (3) 1¼" Holes in counter top

Combination hand pump, city water and electric pump

SWITCH

Combination hand pump and city water

Shurflo city water entry valve

Blk.   Red +

3 Amp Fuse

Shurflo single fixture electric pump, model 120

Blk. Neg. Red Pos.

Maximum Vertical Lift of 18"

Hand pump only

12 V. Battery or 6 V. Lantern Battery

water tank

The fixture disassembles as follows. The numbers apply only to Shurflo units and are used for reordering the specific parts.

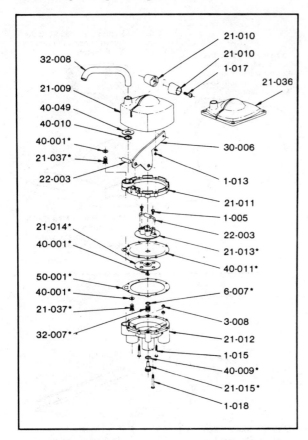

*This company also sells a kit that includes several parts which they recommend be replaced simultaneously. These parts are marked with an asterisk.

The single fixture pump is relatively trouble-free, although there are several specific circumstances which can cause a failure. These are:

Pump motor will not run

The water retained in the pump head evaporates, leaving a lime deposit. This often causes a locked impeller. To correct, try reversing the electrical leads and flick the hot lead against the opposite terminal. This usually frees the pump head. Be careful to rewire correctly.

If the impeller is still stuck you may have to open the pump and turn the impeller by hand to free it.

Inability to prime

If the pump is unable to prime, it may be from excessive wear. Open the pump head and check the impeller and rollers for wear. If excessively worn, they should be replaced. Another cause of no prime may be air getting in on the input side.

Check the clamps and hose condition. A cracked hose should be replaced.

Foreign objects in hose or pump head

Check the input hose to be certain that it is not kinked. Also check to see that the hose is free of chips or foreign objects. These can plug the hose if a filter has not been used. These chips can also lodge in the impeller area. To correct, remove the foreign objects and install a tank filter to prevent future problems.

The electric pump runs backwards

If the motor has been wired incorrectly (polarity reversed) the pump will run backwards. To correct, switch the wires to the opposite terminals.

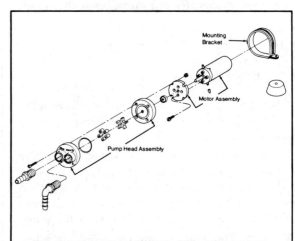

The pump head assembly is available only as a complete unit. The pump head, including the impeller, roller, base and cap is a matched set. If a single part is replaced by itself, it might be difficult to achieve the fit and balance required for satisfactory priming. (Shurflo part #90-501.)

SERVICING

VALVE ASSEMBLY REPLACEMENT

1. Remove four tie-down screws.

2. Lift off motor and diaphragm assembly from the pump base.

3. Lift valve assemblies from pockets and clean all foreign materials from valve and seat.

4. Reinstall valve assemblies into same pockets, being sure rubber valve with small hole is "up" on intake and rubber valve without the small hole is "down" on discharge.
CAUTION: Do not use valve with small hole in rubber on discharge side of pump.

DIAPHRAGM AND CONNECTING ROD REPLACEMENT

1. Remove four tie-down screws.
2. Lift off motor and diaphragm assembly from the pump base.
3. Remove two diaphragm retainer screws and detach diaphragm retainer.
4. Remove two motor nuts. Pull motor and eccentric from connecting rod.
5. Remove diaphragm screw to separate diaphragm from connecting rod assembly.
6. Inspect diaphragm for cuts and cracks.
7. Check connecting rod assembly for breaks, cracks or excessive wear on eccentric rod and bearing if connecting rod is to be reused, open cover and relubricate by packing built-in reservoir with a water pump grease. Original lubricant normally lasts the lifetime of the pump.
8. When reassembling connecting rod to diaphragm, be sure to align. Proper alignment is achieved when the rod slips straight onto motor shaft and the diaphragm rests squarely on the motor mount pad. Misalignment will create a strain on diaphragm and significantly shorten its life.

PULSATION DAMPENER REPLACEMENT

1. Remove pump from installation.
2. Remove nine screws from bottom of base and the bottom plate.
3. Pull out rubber pulsation dampener from base.
4. Inspect dampener for excessive deformation, ruptures and leaks.
5. When installing new pulsation dampener, make sure flange is correctly seated to effect a proper water and air seal.

PRESSURE SWITCH REPLACEMENT

1. Disconnect wires from pressure switch.
2. Unscrew switch from base.
3. Thread switch with sealing washer into pump base, metallic side of washer facing switch. Tighten securely.
4. Rewire according to wiring diagram.

BASE REPLACEMENT

1. Follow service instructions above to remove pressure switch and pulsation dampener.
2. To separate base from motor mount and diaphragm assembly remove four tie-down screws.
3. When reassembling, do not overtighten screws.

EXPLODED VIEW

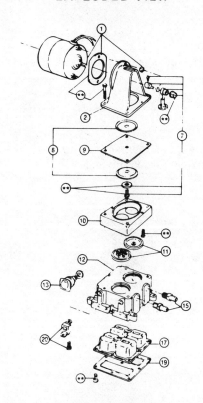

PARTS LIST

36970-Series

Key	Part Description	Part No.	Qty
1	Motor Kit 12-Volt DC	30201-0000	1
1	Motor Kit 24-Volt DC	30201-0010	
1	Motor Kit 32-Volt DC	30202-0020	
2	Motor Mount	35452-0000	1
7	Connecting Rod Assembly	30033-0000*	1
8	Diaphragm Plate	35479-0000	2
9	Diaphragm	30015-0000*	1
10	Retainer	35454-0000	1
11	Valve Set (Inlet & Outlet)	30004-0000*†	1 Set
12	Base Assembly†	35620-1100†	1
13	Pressure Switch	37121-0000— See Note 2	1
		35620-1100† See Note 3	
15	Ports (Inlet & Outlet) Barb	37176-0000 † — See Note 4	1 Set
17	Pulsation Dampener	37178-0000*†	1
19	Bottom Plate	35686-0000†	1
20	Vibration Pad Kit	37180-000†	1 Set
21	Hardware Kit	37167-0000	1 Set
	Service Kit*	30123-0000	

*Indicates Parts Contained in Service Kit.
†Indicates Parts Supplied with Base Assembly
NOTE 2—Includes Switch and Conversion Kit to Mount New Style Switch Onto Older Style -J and -0000 Pumps.
NOTE 3—Direct Replacement Switch Only for -1000 Series Pumps.
NOTE 4—Threaded Outlet Port 43006-2000
Threaded Inlet Port 42986-2000

MOTOR REPLACEMENT

1. Disconnect one motor wire from pressure switch terminal, the other from splice connector.
2. Loosen eccentric set-screw on motor shaft.
3. Remove two motor nuts and pull motor away from motor mount, while holding back eccentric/connecting rod assembly.
4. When installing new motor, adjust eccentric on motor shaft so little or no contact is made between teflon washer and connecting rod bearing.
5. Rewire motor leads to terminal on pressure switch, and splice connector.

Another popular demand pump, the Shurflo Tri-A-Fram model:

MODEL SERIES 200

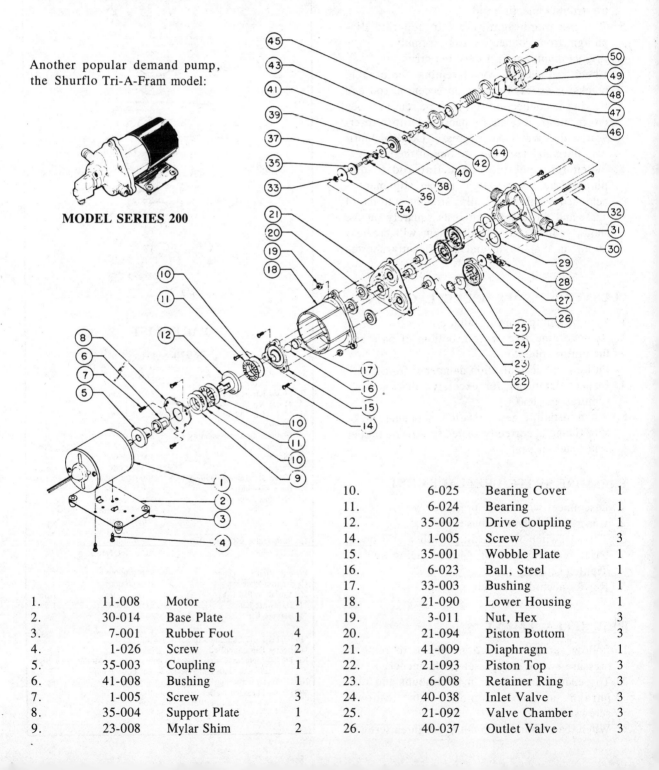

1.	11-008	Motor	1
2.	30-014	Base Plate	1
3.	7-001	Rubber Foot	4
4.	1-026	Screw	2
5.	35-003	Coupling	1
6.	41-008	Bushing	1
7.	1-005	Screw	3
8.	35-004	Support Plate	1
9.	23-008	Mylar Shim	2
10.	6-025	Bearing Cover	1
11.	6-024	Bearing	1
12.	35-002	Drive Coupling	1
14.	1-005	Screw	3
15.	35-001	Wobble Plate	1
16.	6-023	Ball, Steel	1
17.	33-003	Bushing	1
18.	21-090	Lower Housing	1
19.	3-011	Nut, Hex	3
20.	21-094	Piston Bottom	3
21.	41-009	Diaphragm	1
22.	21-093	Piston Top	3
23.	6-008	Retainer Ring	3
24.	40-038	Inlet Valve	3
25.	21-092	Valve Chamber	3
26.	40-037	Outlet Valve	3

27.	6-005	Retainer Ring	3	39.	21-071	Valve Plate	1
28.	30-047	Filter Screen	3	40.	22-002	Seal Washer	1
29.	40-036	Gasket	1	41.	21-068	Poppet	1
30.	21-091	Upper Housing	1	42.	32-013	Spring	1
31.	1-052	Screw	3	43.	22-002	Seal Washer	1
32.	1-053	Screw	3	44.	41-002	Diaphragm	1
33.	6-007	Retainer Ring	1	45.	21-070	Plunger	1
34.	40-020	Check Valve	1	46.	32-015	Spring	1
35.	21-069	Valve Stem	1	47.	21-067	Bridge Ring	1
36.	32-010	Spring	1	48.	10-113	Switch	1
37.	6-013	Retainer Ring	1	49.	21-076	Switch Cap	1
38.	40-014	Seal Washer	1	50.	1-006	Screw	2

ELECTRICAL WIRING REQUIREMENTS

| Pump Series | Wire Gauge | | | Fuse Requirement |
Model	14 Gauge	12 Gauge	10 Gauge	10 to 15 Amp
200	0 - 20 ft.	20 - 50 ft.	Over 50 ft.	in-line fuse

The pump should be on a circuit of its own. Do not use a skin ground. Run the ground back to the source or to a 10-gauge wire common ground.

The Model 200 is not affected by polarity. But, it is preferable to attach the positive line to the pump switch.

In an accessible location install a 10-amp or greater wall-mounted switch. This switch is used to shut off the pump when traveling, when the coach is unattended, or in an emergency such as running out of water.

PLUMBING TUBING — HOSE — AND PIPE

A special hose is available for installing the pump. It is a high-pressure potable water hose. The length used depends on the installation situation. However, the output hose should not exceed 24 inches in code approval installations. Any length may be used on the input side or non-pressure side.

Avoid Kinks in the Hose. Kinks will prevent proper operation. Use clamps at both ends of each hose. Clamps prevent air leaks into the water line. Air leaks prevent proper priming. Remember the output hose may see high water pressure when the coach is hooked up to city water sources.

The internal diameter (ID) of the plumbing lines is of the utmost importance. Lines that are too small increase the back pressure and reduce the flow. Excessive pump cycling results. The main lines should be at least 1/2-inch ID and risers or short lines to one fixture at least 3/8 inch also. Filter screens should be removed from faucets. They clog up and create problems.

Check Valves used in the system must be a free-flow design. If you can blow through in the direction of flow, the check valve is suitable. If you cannot it may present excessive restriction.

Fittings used to join sections of plumbing should have the same flow diameter as the lines. Do not use pipe dope of any kind between the tank and the end of the output hose. Pipe dope may get into the pump mechanism and create problems.

Water Purifiers must be on a separate line. They create a high back pressure.

CHECK FOR LEAKS

This can be done visually but many connections are hidden. We recommend a positive pressure check with a pressure gauge. This will indicate any leaks by a drop in the gauge. Even a tiny leak will cause the pump to cycle on and off. And, in transit, even a small leak can become a big leak.

TROUBLESHOOTING

If Motor Does Not Operate. Make the following checks. Is the battery charge too low? Are the wires disconnected or terminals corroded? Is the switch in the ''on'' position? Is the fuse good? Is the pump head frozen? If so, thaw with a lamp bulb placed near the pump.

If Pump Runs But Water Does Not Appear. Is there water is the tank? Are there kinks in the inlet hose? Is air leaking in at the inlet fittings? Tighten or add clamps. Is there a plugged-up inlet line? Remove the output hose and try again. If water appears the problem is farther into the system.

If Motor Runs But Water Sputters. Air is getting into the lines. Check or add clamps on the input side of the pump. Restart and try again. Allow time to clear air from the hot water tank and lines.

PUMP CYCLING a rapid on and off condition.

Normal — and not harmful to the pump. The Model 200 has been set to flow water just like home. However, many times water conservation is important and faucets are opened only a little bit. Under these conditions — high pump output and low faucet flow — the pump will cycle on and off in a rhythmic interval. This is normal and will not harm the pump.

Abnormal cycling — If the pump cycles on and off when all faucets are closed something is wrong. Most likely there is a leak somewhere. Check faucets for dripping and especially the toilet valve. Correct any leak no matter how small.

If no leak can be detected shut the pump off. Remove the output hose where it joins the system (not at the pump). Insert a plug in the hose and clamp it. (You can make a perfect plug from a barb fitting, 1/2-inch size with a cap tightly screwed on the threads. It must not leak.) Turn the pump switch on. The pump should come on, run a few seconds, and then shut off. If it remains off — the problem is not the pump. The problem is in the system. If, however, the pump goes on and off there may be a problem in the pump. There may be an internal pump leak which allows water to escape from the high pressure area back into the low-pressure inlet area. Look for a valve held open or a crack in the casting. Although this can happen it is not common.

If Pump Does Not Shut Off. The wall switch may be used for temporary control of the pump. A low battery charge may be the cause. Or the switch mechanism may be stuck. Try tapping the switch cap on the end of the pump with the handle of a screwdriver. If you decide to open the switch mechanism be sure to note the assembly sequence of the parts. The cap retains a spring. Hold the cap when removing the screws.

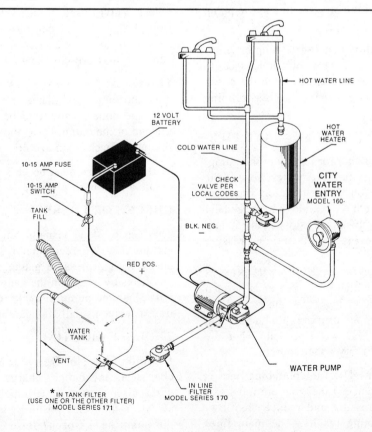

Another kind of demand pump made by Atwood Mobile Products requires no periodic lubrication. If troubleshooting requires that the pump be disassembled, here's how:

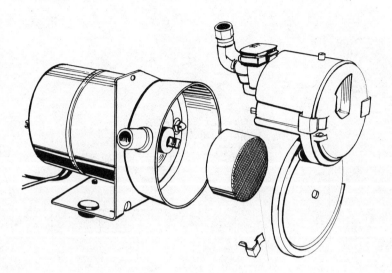

REASSEMBLY

Hold motor side down as illustrated. Center filter screen in housing. Square up flat surfaces on motor shaft hub with matching hole in impeller. Lugs on Flow Control Assembly fit into holes on motor frame. Refasten clips on housing cover.

Fasten clips on in X pattern. ➡

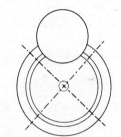

IMPORTANT:

Should it become necessary to disassemble pump:
1 — Shut off electricity and disconnect lead wires.
2 — Shut off city water supply.
3 — Drain water tank.
4 — Remove hoses from pump.

CAUTION: These steps must be followed to prevent electrical shock or water damage.

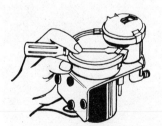

After removing the pump from the water system, hold on end, motor side down. See illustration.

Remove clips with screwdriver.

Lift off impeller housing.

NOTE: Filter screen can now be cleaned.

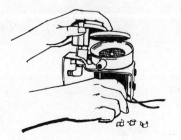

RP 815 DEMAND PUMP made by VSI

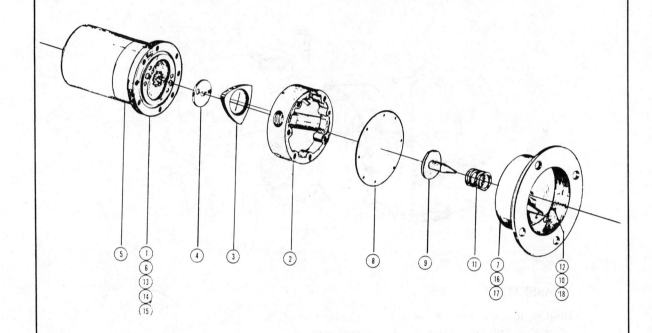

PARTS LIST

Key	Part No.	Description	Qty
1	P852	BODY	1
2	P853	MANIFOLD	1
3	P854	ROTOR	1
4	P855	CAM	1
5	P856	MOTOR ELEC	1
6	P857	BUSHING	1
7	P858	BASE	1
8	P859	DIAPHRAM	1
9	P860	TAPER PIN	1
10	P861	MTA ADJ SCREW	1
11	P863	SPRING	1
12	P864	MICRO SWITCH	1
13	A414	ASSY SCREWS	8
14	P866	SEAL	1
15	P867	O-RING	1
16	P868	GROMMET	1
17	P871	PUMP MOUNTS	4
18	P872	LEAF SPRING	1

ITT Jabsco Products makes this air compressor for RV demand water systems:

MODEL 37000-1000

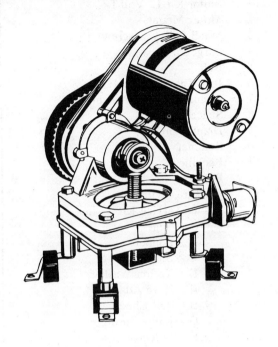

PLUMBING

Connect compressor discharge port to water tank using air hose provided. Water tank air connection should be located on top, above normal water level, to prevent siphoning of water to compressor. Make all connections airtight.

WIRING

Compressor should be wired independently to the battery. Use stranded copper wire No. 14 AWG for a two-wire length up to 15 feet and No. 12 AWG up to 25 feet.

In positive lead, install an on-off switch to keep the water system turned off when vehicle is unattended, stored, or in transit. On the same wire, close to the pump, connect a 10-amp ''Slo-Blo'' type fuse or 15-amp automotive-type fuse to protect motor against overcurrent conditions. Larger fuse could cause motor burn-out.

After installation, it is advisable to check the electrical system to make sure that adequate voltage, 10 VDC minimum, is supplied to compressor motor at all times. Check voltage using voltmeter when compressor is in operation and all inside electrical appliances and fixtures are turned on.

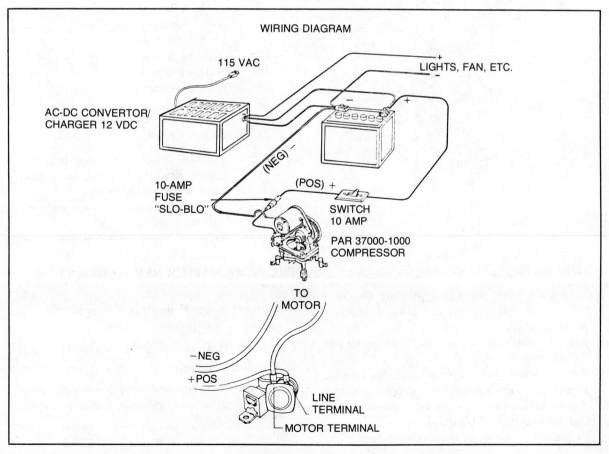

WIRING DIAGRAM

EXPLODED VIEW

PARTS LIST	
Key	**Description**
1	Motor Kit 12 Volt DC
2	Motor Mount
3	Small Pulley w/screw
4	Large Pulley w/screw
5	Belt
6	Jack Shaft Assembly
7	Connecting Rod Assembly
8	Spacer Ring
9	Diaphragm
10	Retainer
11	Backing
12	Base
13	Pressure Switch
14	Valves Service Kit — Includes:
	A - Seat
	B - Poppet
	C - Small Spring
	D - Teflon Washer
	E - Hose Adapter
	F - Ball Check
	G - Large Spring
	H - O-Ring
	I - Filter
	J - Inlet valve kit (eyelet & flapper)
	K - Inlet valve cage
15	Retaining Screw
16	Tie-Down Screw
17	Diaphragm Screw
18	Screw
20	Vibration Pad Kit
21	Hardware Kit

NOTE 2 — Includes switch and conversion kit to mount new style switch onto older Style K and -0000 Pumps.

NOTE 3 — Direct replacement switch only for -1000 Series Pumps.

MOTOR REPLACEMENT

1. Disconnect motor wires from pressure switch.
2. Remove two motor nuts and slide motor off mounting plate.
3. Remove small pulley from shaft and install on replacement motor.
4. Replace motor onto mounting plate. Be sure to adjust belt tension before tightening nuts. Proper adjustment: belt can be depressed 1/4-inch halfway between pulleys.
5. Reconnect motor wires to pressure switch.

PRESSURE SWITCH REPLACEMENT

1. Turn off power to pump and open air bleed to relieve system pressure.
2. Disconnect wires from pressure switch.
3. Unscrew switch from base.
4. Thread new switch and washer into pump base, with metallic side of washer facing switch. Tighten securely.
5. Rewire according to wiring diagram.

DISCHARGE VALVE(S) REPLACEMENT

There are two discharge check valves in the compressor. To service, use Kit No. 44490-0000.

- Remove and replace Keys 14A through 14E in order shown.
- Remove and replace Keys 14F through 14H in order shown. (Refer to Exploded View and Parts List.)

INTAKE VALVE FLAPPER REPLACEMENT

1. Do not replace unless wear or damage is noted.
2. Remove four tie-down screws (16) and two base-to-spacer screws (18) to separate base.
3. Disassemble intake valve from center of base by prying out eyelet and removing flapper. *Do not* remove valve cage (14K).
4. Replace flapper and eyelet using new valve kit Parts (14J). Locate tiny hole in flapper so it lines up with one of the holes in inlet valve cage (14K). Lock flapper in place by lightly tapping eyelet into center hole till seated.

CONNECTING ROD/DIAPHRAGM REPLACEMENT

1. Remove connecting rod screw and four tie-down screws (16) to separate jack shaft assembly (6) from spacer ring (8).
2. Separate diaphragm and connecting rod from base (12) by removing two screws (18).
3. Remove diaphragm screw (17) to separate diaphragm and connecting rod.
4. Replace diaphragm and connecting rod. During reassembly, check that connecting rod is properly oriented: screw-sleeve extension is against jack shaft and no twisting stress is placed on diaphragm.

DISMANTLE UNIT:

- Remove motor leads from pressure switch.
- Unscrew pressure switch assembly from cylinder head.
- Install new water check valve in pressure switch "T" using pipe compound to ensure an airtight seal, but be careful not to contaminate the check valve itself.
- Remove cylinder head (four screws), discard old valve reed, gaskets and check valve filter, but save stainless steel valve plate.
- Clean inside of cylinder head thoroughly to ensure that the new check valve is not contaminated by metal chips or corrosion present in the air chamber of the cylinder head.
- Install new air filter inside of cylinder head at the air outlet to the check valve assembly.
- Remove old cylinder (four screws) and piston/connecting rod assembly. It might be necessary to break old connecting rod by twisting head if it is rusted solid into the cylinder.
- Remove base plate (four screws)

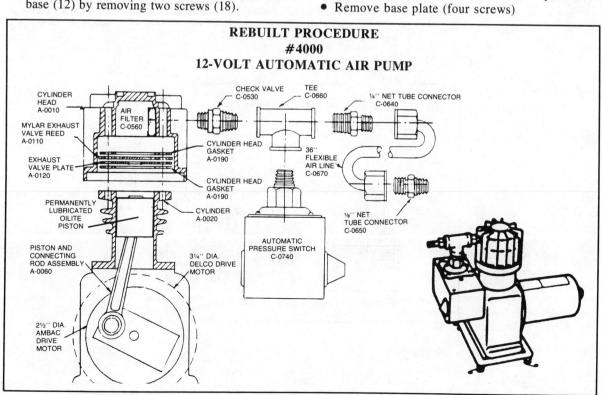

REBUILT PROCEDURE
#4000
12-VOLT AUTOMATIC AIR PUMP

TROUBLESHOOTING

Problem	What to Check
Compressor fails to build up pressure.	— Air leak in tank or excessive water leak in plumbing. Check connections in water distribution system. — Low voltage to compressor. See instructions for electrical test. — Defective compressor check valves. Check to see that valves are clean, free to operate and no cuts in rubber seals (small hole in intake valve flapper is normal). — Check for cuts or ruptures in diaphragm.
Compressor fails to shut-off after pressure build up.	— Check voltage to compressor motor. Low voltage may prevent full build up of pressure. — Defective pressure switch.
Compressor fails to start automatically.	— No power to compressor. If fuse is blown, check cause for over-current before restarting compressor. See wiring instructions for proper fuse valve. — Defective pressure switch.
Excessive operating noise.	— Check to see that compressor is not touching anything other than installation connections, and is mounted to solid surface. — Loose screws. Tighten large and small pulley screws and connecting rod screw.
Compressor restarts although no water has been used.	— Check for air and water leaks in the plumbing system. — Check compressor discharge valves to make sure they are sealing properly. To do this, remove compressor air hose and seal off the air discharge port. Run compressor until it shuts off. Discharge valves are defective if compressor restarts within a few minutes.

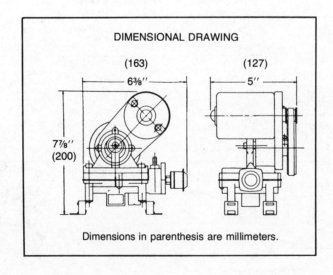

DIMENSIONAL DRAWING

(163)   (127)

6⅜''   5''

7⅞''
(200)

Dimensions in parenthesis are millimeters.

OTHER LESS COMMON CAUSES OF 12-VOLT MOTOR FAILURES ARE:

Low Battery. Do not attempt to operate your air compressor or other 12-volt motor-driven appliances on a very low battery. Poor performance will indicate the situation; you can save your motor-driven equipment from burning out by shutting it down properly.

Switch. The on/off switch that is wired into the compressor circuit should be a *DC type* switch rated for 10 to 15 amps. Do not use an AC type switch; it may not make a proper contact and cause resistance that will reduce the voltage at the motor to a destructive level.

Inadequate Convertor. Even the best power convertors generate a pulsating form of DC current that can be very hard on 12-volt motors. We recommend that the automatic air pump be wired directly to the battery. The air pump only runs two or three times a day (for two or three minutes at a time), and the power convertor can very readily maintain the battery charge. This arrangement will prolong the life of both the 12-volt motor and the power convertor.

Air Leak. The automatic air compressor will try to do its job regardless of the circumstances. If the system is leaking air, the compressor will try to make up the difference, but it can be a losing battle and may result in an overheated and burned out motor.

CAUTION: DO NOT INSTALL A REPLACEMENT UNIT OR MOTOR UNTIL THE CAUSE OF THE ORIGINAL PROBLEM IS ESTABLISHED AND CORRECTED.

CHECK LIST:
- Adequate wire size
- All connections clean and tight
- Proper system on/off switch
- Battery (convertor) condition
- Air leak

REASONS FOR 12-VOLT MOTOR PROBLEMS:
MILLER #4000
12-VOLT AUTOMATIC AIR PUMP

The 12-volt drive motor on your Miller Automatic Air Pump is a rugged, almost indestructible device, similar to the hundreds of thousands of motors that are used in automobiles and trucks to drive windshield wipers, heater blowers, power windows, power seats, etc.

It is designed to operate efficiently at 12 volts with a reasonable margin for error, but it cannot tolerate excessively low voltage for long periods of time. If the compressor is forced to operate at reduced voltage, it will try to do its job, but it will perform poorly, run slowly, perhaps never reach full pressure, the motor will overheat, the insulation will break down and cause a short circuit, which in turn will blow the fuse. The motor is then burned out and will continue to blow fuses; the only cure is to replace the burned out motor.

However, the replacement motor is also likely to burn out unless the cause of the low voltage is determined and corrected.

The most common reason for the low voltage at the motor is excessive loss through the feed wires. The 12 volts (plus) that is available at the battery can be significantly reduced if the wires between the battery and the air pump are too small or too long. Both wires must be full size; these wires should not generally be expected to serve other 12-volt equipment simultaneously.

The following wire sizes are recommended based on the *total* length of wire (*to* and *from*) the 12-volt source (including the on-off switch, etc.)

- # 14 gauge wire (total wire length up to 15 feet).
- # 12 gauge wire (total wire length up to 15 feet).
- # 10 gauge wire (total wire length up to 60 feet).

Truck Campers and some travel trailers which rely on the battery under the hood as a power source should be served by # 10-gauge wire minimum from the battery to the camper or trailer. All equipment in the unit (including the air pump) should be able to operate simultaneously without noticeable loss of efficiency.

MILLER #4000
12-VOLT AUTOMATIC AIR PUMP

REASSEMBLE UNIT:

- Make sure that drive motor mounting nuts are tight.
- Assemble new connecting rod/piston and cylinder, (lubricate very lightly).
- Assemble exhaust valve plate, reed, gaskets and cylinder head. Note that the burr side of the exhaust valve plate faces down toward the piston, and the valve reed is on the top side. One gasket goes under the valve plate and one on top of the

valve reed. Use two nails or similar pins to align these components before mounting the cylinder head and don't forget the aluminum collar that goes between the cylinder head and the crankcase.

- Replace the base plate.
- Screw the switch assembly into the head using a little light grease on the threads but no pipe compound that might contaminate the very important water check valve.
- Rewire the motor to the pressure switch.
- The pressure settings should be - on (15-20 psi), and - off (30-35 psi). Higher settings simply work the pump harder for no good reason.

Please follow instructions inside the pressure switch cover.

NOTE:

- If the drive motor has been overheated and burned out there is no alternative but to replace it.

  #C-0610 — 12-volt motor assembly (includes crank 2½-inch diameter).

- It is important that the reason for the low voltage that led to the motor failure is determined and corrected or the replacement motor will simply overheat and fail in the same fashion.

Chapter Twelve

Sanitation Systems

The sanitation system is the second half of the water system — it completes the cycle as waste water flows down to a holding tank for later removal, or directly into a campground disposal connection.

The largest problem with this rather simple system is that it is out of sight, thus it is also out of mind — at least until an obvious problem develops. Often these problems would not have occurred if the system had been properly maintained, so the best way to avoid them is to place your rig's plumbing on a regular search and service schedule.

12.01 PLUMBING.

Drain pipes drop from each sink or shower pan into a P-joint, a U-shaped section which entraps a small amount of water (Figure 1). Many people think that this curve is designed to keep diamond rings and other solids from washing into the sewer, and certainly that end is well-served by the design. Equally important, however, is that the captured liquid creates a very effective oneway valve which prevents sewer (or holding) tank gases from rising beyond that point.

As in home plumbing systems, most problems will occur either at the sink or shower drain, or in the P-joint, and will be simple clogs from hair, grease and accumulated dirt. If the obstruction isn't total, i.e., if the sink merely drains too slowly, pouring a tea kettle full of boiling water may be enough to melt grease and move it along. This failing, try the old standby "plumber's friend" before resorting to the ultimate solution, which is to disassemble and clean.

Drains should be cleaned periodically as part of your maintenance program, but be careful not to use highly acidic compounds. Most RV drain pipes are plastic (although you'll occasionally encounter copper), and conventional household drain cleaners are strong enough to attack the plastic.

The P-joint is also easily disassembled and, once removed from the rig, can be flushed out with a garden hose or a blunt flexible probe. (CAUTION: Reaming with a sharp instrment will obviously damage plastic pipes.)

From the P-joint, drain pipes are sloped downward to their terminus at the holding tank. Stoppages seldom occur in these sections unless there are abrupt bends which encourage solids to accumulate, although such "corners" are contrary to industry construction standards and indicate an amateur installation.

It's always good to know the route these pipes take, because if trouble develops it can be quickly traced. And good preventative maintenance dictates that pipes should be checked occasionally for condition and stability, as travel vibration is quite hard on plumbing.

You'll notice that pipes are supported by either straps or blocks at four-foot intervals. If you'll periodically check these supports for firmness you're unlikely to ever experience falling pipes.

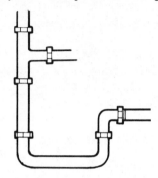

Figure 1.

12.02 REPAIRING PIPES.

Plastic pipe sections are usually solvent-welded together. This means that a substance, usually methyl-ethyl-ketone (MEK), temporarily dissolves a thin layer of the plastic at the juncture, which literally fuses the two parts together. It's just as pointless to attempt disengaging these sections as it would be to try to undo welding. If a new section of pipe must be inserted, simply cut out the damaged area and install a new piece which conforms to the space.

Making a new solvent-welded joint is simple, but the chemicals react quickly and you must work accordingly. Apply the solvent in a moderate quantity to the fitting first, then to the end pipe, using a brush which is wide enough to apply the material rapidly. Now insert the pipe into its fitting and make sure it's snug by giving it about a 1/4 turn while applying pressure towards the juncture. Depending upon the temperature, it will take plus-or-minus three minutes for the joint to set. If you discover a mistake before that time, don't try to correct it. Instead, pull the pieces apart, let them completely dry, and do the job over again.

12.03 WASTE DISPOSAL.

Waste disposal is handled in various ways, but the most frequent system especially on smaller rigs which don't have toilets, is a single screw-capped 1½-inch pipe to the outside world.

The next step up in both complexity and convenience is a holding tank mounted beneath the rig. The same tank can be used to receive both black (toilet) and gray water, although larger rigs often separate this storage into two tanks. The holding tank drain is connected to a disposal pipe which terminates at a 3-inch port; a removable hose connects the drain port to either a campground sewer system or a dumping station. Holding tanks must also be vented from their highest point to the outside (Figure 2).

Dual holding tanks generally share the same drain port, although they should have separate gate (also called "slide") valves controlling the flow into this common terminus (Figure 3). These separate gate valves are essential because you must be able to drain one tank at a time.

Broken slide valves are not always repairable, but they are easily replaceable. As the size is standardized, you can buy the valve along with various configurations of plastic pipe at most RV supply stores. The sections are held together by friction, primarily from a screw-tightening tension band (Figure 4). To remove the old pipe section and defective valve, simply turn the screw counterclockwise to loosen the band, then manipulate the old pipe until it comes loose and slides out. If force is necessary, try twisting the old section with a wrench — but be careful about banging the plumbing with hammers as you may tear loose more than you expect.

If, as sometimes happens, you are absolutely unable to free the slide valve, it could be that someone has solvent-welded it in place. You must then cut the section of pipe free and replace it.

12.04 HOLDING TANK REPAIR.

RV holding tanks are almost universally made of plastic these days, although some galvanized iron tanks are still riding the road.

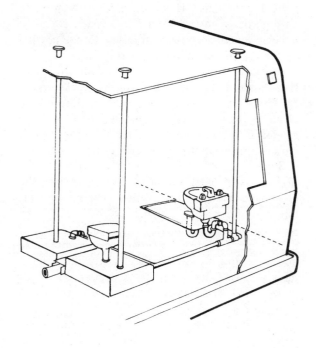

Figure 2.

Metal tanks which are allowed to stand empty will eventually begin rusting from the inside. (See Chapter 24 on storing RVs for more on this point.) Small "pinholes" are usually the first sign that rust is well-established and then it's just a matter of time until the tank becomes useless. Patching the holes is only temporary relief; the problem is bound to recur.

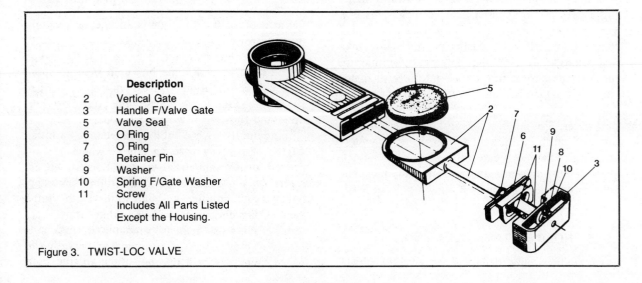

Description

2	Vertical Gate
3	Handle F/Valve Gate
5	Valve Seal
6	O Ring
7	O Ring
8	Retainer Pin
9	Washer
10	Spring F/Gate Washer
11	Screw
	Includes All Parts Listed
	Except the Housing.

Figure 3. TWIST-LOC VALVE

ABS, or plastic tanks, are more effectively repaired — and the process is quite simple if you don't have to go through the lengthy process of removing the tanks. However, don't be tempted to only partially unstrap a tank for repairs as it can develop a permanent warp from the torque applied by the remaining uneven support.

Cracks in an ABS tank are repaired by first drilling a small hole at both ends of the crack (Figure 5). This prevents the crack from spreading. Next, clean the area scrupulously and abrade it with fine sandpaper or steel wool to make a rough surface. Now you're ready to apply ABS cement.

Some types of ABS cement require a few shavings from an old pipe; these are mixed into the compound and quickly dissolve. The recipe usually calls for enough shavings to make a viscous solution — thick enough to pour slowly. Next, using a piece of clean cardboard or something else you're willing to throw away, apply the cement thickly in sufficient quantity to overlap the edges of the crack. The material can require up to two days for a set to occur.

Small holes in an ABS tank can be similarly repaired, but a large gouge calls for cutting the wound to even-sided dimensions, inserting a precisely measured piece of new plastic, and sealing as above. Making a good repair under these circumstances, meaning one that will hold, is so difficult that it's almost always better to just replace the tank.

Polyethylene tank cracks can be repaired in much the same manner as ABS (see above), but not always with the same compounds. Check the labels before you buy. Larger gouges require professional welding.

As polyethylene dissolves under sufficient heat, it is often commercially repaired by simply melting a strip of the material over a crack. This is a very precise operation as too much heat will also melt the tank. If you're using polyethylene tanks and want to develop the judgment for making these repairs, try it first on an old piece of material. Rather than buying a professional heater you can try using a powerful (1,000-watt) blower-type hair dryer. Try holding the nozzle at various distances from the work until you arrive at an understanding of the tool's capabilities. Also, in a pinch you can cut a strip of material from many inexpensive polyethylene products normally sold in hardware stores.

12.05   HOLDING TANK CLEANING.

Both holding tanks benefit from periodic clean-

Figure 4. Screw tightening tension band

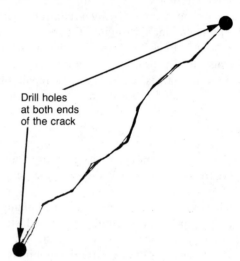

Drill holes
at both ends
of the crack

Figure 5. Crack in ABS tank

ings, but the black water tank also requires constant chemicalizing. Solids introduced into this tank must be dissolved, or substantially reduced, if blocks at the drain outlet are to be avoided. Most holding tank chemicals sold at RV supply stores will hasten this dissolution process if used in both the quantities and frequencies suggested on the package. They also help control odors and, as holding tanks are vented to the outside world, it's soon apparent to those camped downwind if you haven't used them.

Basic cleansing of both tanks means flushing them with fresh water, i.e., after emptying, refill with water and drain again. For a more thorough periodic flush, add some houseold bleach (about one cup per 10 gallons of fresh water), allow it to slosh in the tank a few hours while you're driving, drain and flush again with fresh water.

Incidentally, why not be an ecology-minded citizen and always use chemicals which are approved for RV sanitation systems? Bacteria are essential to the eventual decomposition of wastes, both in your holding tank and in the earth. Some very strong chemicals will annihilate useful bacteria, causing problems in campground septic systems and preventing the all-important recycling of waste chemicals back into the stream of life.

12.06 EMPTYING HOLDING TANKS.

Most holding tank stoppages occur at the slide valve or at the tank drain opening. The reason for this, generally, is that solids have accumulated there, and that's usually because the tank hasn't been maintained properly. Failing to cleanse is the main culprit, but it can also be that you've disregarded the "3/4 full" rule.

Whenever you're using a black water holding tank, don't try to empty it unless it is at least 3/4 full, even if this means adding fresh water to reach that mark. The reason is simple: A partially-full tank empties with less force, so solids have a chance to either avoid evacuation or to accumulate at the opening. If the solids remain in the tank and dry, they pose a serious threat to further smooth tank emptyings.

NOTE: Section Chapter 24 on Winterizing and Storage contains important information about protecting holding tanks.

12.07 MACERATORS.

One device which will help you eliminate stoppages is a macerator (Figure 6). This unit is tied into the waste system ahead of the holding tank and it grinds or pulverizes solids into smaller particles. Macerators are electrically powered, so they can't be used on every rig in every situation. But when they are feasible they make a valuable addition.

Alternate macerator applications are behind the holding tank and outside of the RV altogether (Figure 7). In these latter situations, you'll need a macerator which can both empty the tank and lift the liquid to the required height for disposal. In addition, a garden-sized hose is generally used rather than the customary larger-dimensioned disposal hose.

A popular model for RVs is the Jabsco Model 17260-0013, 12-volt unit. An exploded view and service instructions are in Figure 8.

12.08 THERMASAN II.

For the RVer on the go. Thetford's Thermasan® II waste system permits on-the-road destruction and disposal of some of the holding tank contents. The immediate advantage to this system is that you can go much longer between actual disposal station emptyings of the tank. Here, briefly, is how the manufacturer describes Thermasan's functioning:

"With the vehicle traveling at least 35 mph under load (not coasting or idling), and the Thermasan II system 'On,' waste is slowly liquified by the action inside the holding tank and then pumped into the vehicle exhaust system ahead of the muffler. The waste mixes with the extremely hot exhaust gases and is destroyed at the rate of approximately one gallon (3.785 liters) for every 15 miles of driving."

When Thermasan units were first offered to RVers, they quickly earned a reputation for being finicky and prone to malfunction. The manufacturer readily admits to some early difficulties, but most of them now appear to be history. While basically reliable, Thermasan units do require careful use and maintenance regimens, and here are the manufacturer's recommendations (see Figure 9).

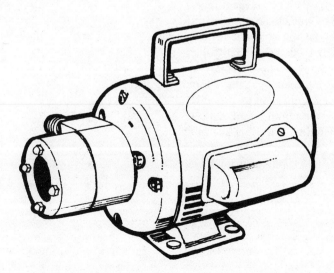

Figure 6.

1. *Dump and flush holding tank once every three months.* At an approved dumping station, open the termination valve to empty the contents of the holding tank. Before closing the termination valve, pour several gallons of fresh water through the toilet into the holding tank. This will help eliminate the buildup of waste particles in the termination valve seal.

Next, close the termination valve and put approximately 10 gallons (37.85 liters) of fresh water into the holding tank. This can be easily done by activating the flushing mechanism and pouring water down through the toilet. Then empty the tank by opening the termination valve.

A more thorough cleaning can be accomplished by following the above instructions and using 1/2 cup (4 ounces/120 cubic centimeters) of Aqua Bowl® cleaner in the waste holding tank.

Pour in Aqua Kem Concentrate holding tank deodorant, together with enough fresh water to cover the bottom of the holding tank. It is best to use liberal amounts of water to dilute the concentrated waste in the holding tank.

The importance of dumping and flushing properly is to remove the buildup of insolubles which collect beneath the filter level. These insolubles could eventually plug the filter screen, making evacuation of liquified waste from the holding tank impossible. Under continuous use, you should dump your holding tank once every three months.

2. *Inspect the metering injection assembly once every 12 months.* The metering injection assembly is located between your holding tank and the point where the waste is injected into the exhaust pipe (See item four, Figure 9). Visually inspect the assembly for leaks. (When Aqua Kem Concentrate holding tank deodorant is being used, the leak would be blue in color.) Leakage probably indicates that the pump hose inside the assembly has ruptured and should be replaced by your Thermasan-approved service center as soon as possible.

Dumping and flushing the holding tank and visually inspecting the metering injection assembly (items 1 and 2 on the Thermasan II Maintenance Schedule in Figure 9) should take you no longer than 30 to 45 minutes.

Maintenance generally performed by a Thermasan approved service center: Changing the pump hoses and replacing the sanijector screen (items 3 and 4 in Figure 9) are more difficult to perform. Therefore, this maintenance should be handled by a Thermasan-approved service center.

Thermasan II installation manuals and service

FIGURE 7. TYPICAL RECREATIONAL VEHICLE USES

HOLDING TANK PUMP OUT PERMANENT INSTALLATION

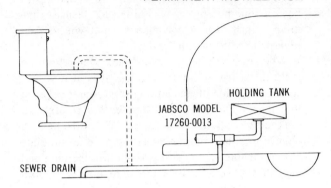

HOLDING TANK PUMP OUT EXTERNAL CONNECTION

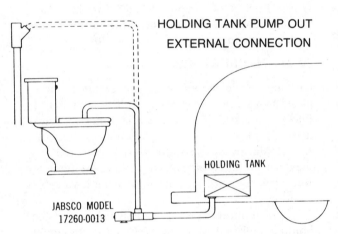

FROM RETENTION TANK TO MAIN HOLDING TANK

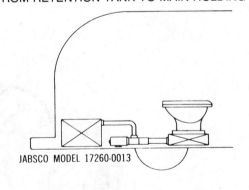

bulletins that contain complete maintenance procedures are available from Thermasan Customer Relations, Thetford Corporation, PO Box 1285, Ann Arbor, Michigan 48106.

Figure 8.

EXPLODED VIEW
JABSCO MODEL 17260-0013 MACERATOR

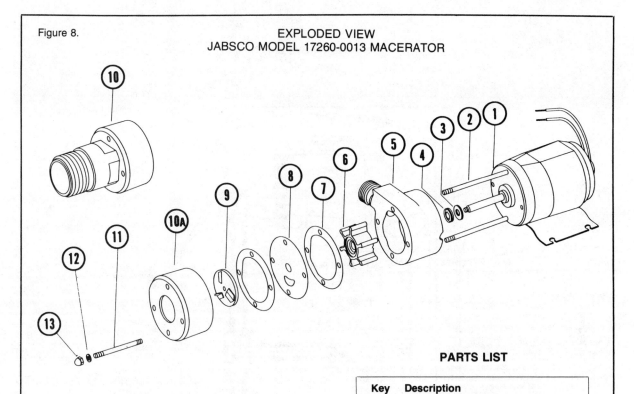

PARTS LIST

Key	Description
1	Motor Sub-Assembly - 12 Volt
	Motor Sub-Assembly - 24 Volt
	Motor Sub-Assembly - 32 Volt
2	Stud
3	Slinger
4	Seal
5	Body
6	Impeller
7	Gasket
8	Wearplate
9	Cutter Plate
10	Macerator Housing
10A	Macerator Housing
11	Stud
12	Fiber Washer
13	Acorn Nut

SERVICE INSTRUCTIONS

1. Remove acorn nuts (13) and inlet housing (10).

2. Unscrew cutter plate (9) from shaft by turning counterclockwise facing cutter blades. (Hold motor shaft behind plate to prevent turning.)

3. Remove gaskets, wearplate and slide pump assembly off mounting studs.

4. Replace seal, impeller gaskets or other parts as necessary. To remove seal, put out evenly with screwdriver from impeller bore side of body. To reassemble seal, coat outside of metal case with Permatex or similar sealant and press into body with lip facing impeller. A light coating of grease should be applied to impeller bore and wearplate to aid initial dry startup.

5. Reassemble body, impeller, gaskets, wearplate, suction housing and acorn nuts.

RECOMMENDED WIRE AND FUSE SIZE

Voltage	Wire Size Connection Length Between Battery and Motor		Fuse
	1' to 10'	10' to 20'	
12	No. 12	No. 10	25 amp.
24	No. 14	No. 12	20 amp.
32	No. 14	No. 12	10 amp.

HEAD CAPACITY TABLE*

Head Ft	GPM	Amps		
		12 Volt	24 Volt	32 Volt
Free flow	9.0	18.8	10.0	7.0
5	8.5	19.0	10.2	7.2
10	7.8	19.1	10.3	7.4
15	7.0	19.3	10.4	7.6
20	6.0	19.5	10.5	7.8

* Flow rates and amperage will vary slightly depending on pump loading.

The Thermasan II System

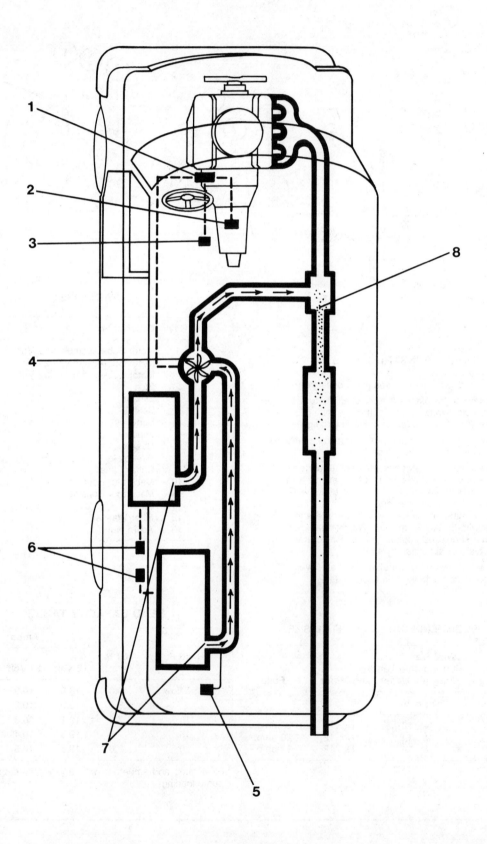

Figure 9.

The Thermasan II System

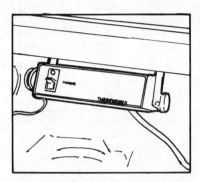

1. Indicator Panel: The indicator panel houses the "on and off" switch which activates the system. The panel also indicates when the system is operating and/or needs to be serviced as follows:
1. "pumping"
2. "pumping completed"
3. "service filter"
4. "service injector

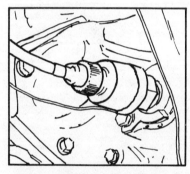

2. Speed Switch: When the vehicle reaches a minimum speed of 35 mph and the engine is under "load," pumping begins. At speeds less than 35 mph the pump will not operate.

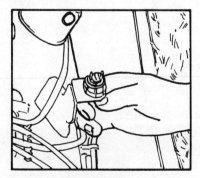

3. Vacuum Switch: The vacuum switch monitors the "load" on the vehicle engine. Before the Thermasan system will begin pumping, the engine must be working under a load (i.e. not coasting or idling).

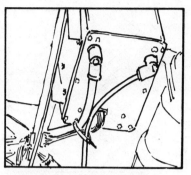

4. Metering Injection Assembly: The metering injection assembly receives signals from the vacuum switch and the speed switch. The pump (or pumps in the dual pump assembly) draw the waste liquids from the holding tank(s). It then pumps the waste into the exhaust system for destruction. When this occurs, "pumping" appears on the indicator panel.

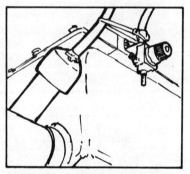

5. Back-Flush Assembly (Optional): Should the toilet system holding tank filter every become plugged so that liquid cannot pass through it, the back-flush accessory is a convenient method of cleaning the filter. Simply attach a gas station air hose to the air fitting. This will blow the solids, which caused the plugging, away from the filter.

6. Level Switch: The level switch(es) indicates to the pump when the content of the holding tank(s) is above or at the same level as the filter. When above the filter, the system will pump. When at the same level, the pump shuts off and "pumping completed" will appear on the indicator panel.

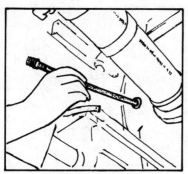

7. Filter: The filter(s) fits into the holding tank(s). It is a stainless steel screen which allows only liquids to pass into the pump. If the filter becomes plugged, ''service filter'' will appear on the indicator panel.

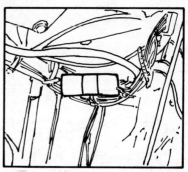

8. Sanijector: The sanijector fits into the engine exhaust pipe ahead of the muffler. The liquid waste coming from the pump is injected into the exhaust at this point. If the sanijector becomes plugged, ''service injector'' will appear on the indicator panel.

THERMASAN II MAINTENANCE SCHEDULE	Owner Performs		Thermasan Approved Service Center (TASC) performs
	3 months	12 months	12 months or 20,000 miles
1. Dump and flush holding tank	X		
2. Visually inspect metering injection assembly		X	
3. Change pump hoses			X
4. a. Change sanijector screen			X
b. Inspect sanijector for any obstruction inside the stainless steel tube			X

Chapter Thirteen

Toilets

RVers who opt for toilets aboard may have any of numerous brands and models, but they all fall within one of three general categories. Because of basic similarities, troubleshooting and maintenance information will be combined with the description that follows. (Also see Troubleshooting Chart, Section 13.06.)

13.01   PORTABLES.

The most popular, because they are small and inexpensive, are portables with familiar names like Porta Potti, SaniPottie, Tota and Weekender. These are very simple devices, and if they are given fair treatment they will stay in service for a long time.

Outside of the simplest, which is basically just a bucket, portables consist of a seat, bowl, sliding gate valve between bowl and holding tank, a freshwater reservoir with a manual water pump and a top cover. Two-piece units have a detachable holding tank (Figures 1, 2 and 3).

The convenience of portable toilets is experienced when it's time to empty the holding tank. In two-piece models the lower portion is simply detached for easy carrying and the contents are dumped into a conventional toilet (Figure 4). One-piece units are also easily evacuated through a special port.

As there are few moving parts, the biggest problem a portable owner may encounter is a slide obstructed by bits of toilet paper or a worn out pump (see Troubleshooting Chart).

One difficulty that takes some people by surprise may occur after the unit has been stored in a warm place. The decomposing wastes, as well as the chemicals which are used to subdue odors, produce a gas in the airtight holding tank. The longer the unit is stored the greater the gas pressure, and heat only makes the condition worse. If the unit becomes sufficiently pressurized, it may "erupt" when the slide is next opened. Prevention simply calls for frequent cleanings and habitually emptying the holding tank between trips. And as a precaution in extremely hot environments, open the slide valve *slowly* to dissipate any accumulated pressure.

Aside from "accident prevention," frequent cleansings of portables is well-advised because dirty units eventually absorb a permanent odor. This may even occur after prolonged service, but the problem is usually solved by disassembling the unit and soaking the parts in a manufacturer-approved cleaning compound.

Figure 1.

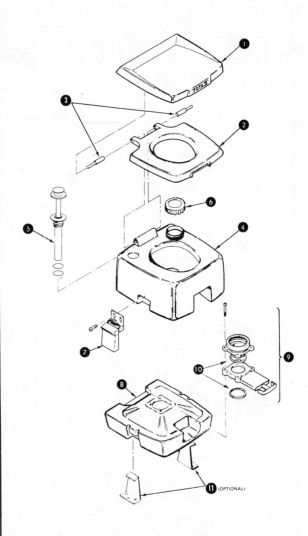

Key	Description
1	Lid Assembly
2	Seat
3	Hinge Pin Set
4	Upper Tank
5	Pump Assy.
6	Cap
7	Latch Assembly
8	Lower Tank (color)
9	Valve Assy.
10	Seal Set
11	Brackets, Mounting (opt.) Tank & Drain Valve (complete) — color

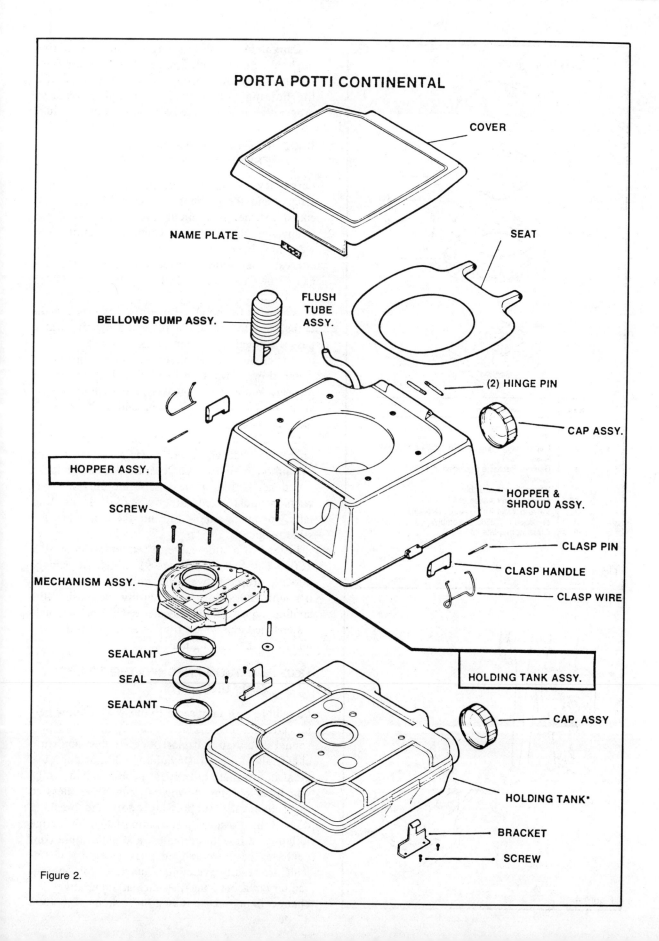

PORTA POTTI CONTINENTAL

COVER

NAME PLATE

SEAT

BELLOWS PUMP ASSY.

FLUSH TUBE ASSY.

(2) HINGE PIN

CAP ASSY.

HOPPER ASSY.

SCREW

HOPPER & SHROUD ASSY.

CLASP PIN

CLASP HANDLE

MECHANISM ASSY.

CLASP WIRE

SEALANT

SEAL

SEALANT

HOLDING TANK ASSY.

CAP. ASSY

HOLDING TANK*

BRACKET

SCREW

Figure 2.

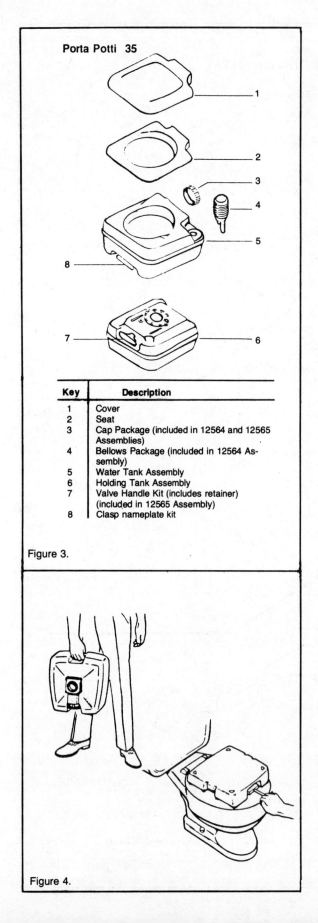

Porta Potti 35

Key	Description
1	Cover
2	Seat
3	Cap Package (included in 12564 and 12565 Assemblies)
4	Bellows Package (included in 12564 Assembly)
5	Water Tank Assembly
6	Holding Tank Assembly
7	Valve Handle Kit (includes retainer) (included in 12565 Assembly)
8	Clasp nameplate kit

Figure 3.

Figure 4.

Careful usage also means visually monitoring the holding tank level. Some units have more fresh water than waste capacity, so it's easy to overfill the holding tank and make dumping a messy proposition if you fail to perform such monitoring.

13.02 PERMANENTLY MOUNTED FRESHWATER TOILETS.

Larger RVs generally have permanently mounted toilets, and these can be either freshwater (also called marine) or recirculating. Of the two, the freshwater category is mechanically simpler, so we'll look at it first.

Freshwater toilets are easy to understand because they are conceptually similar to portables (see Figures 5 through 7).

Water for flushing is drawn from the rig's main tanks, but to prevent a reverse flow the water passes through a vacuum breaker device. (A vacuum is created in the toilet water supply line when water flows toward an open faucet elsewhere in the rig. Without the breaker, the vacuum would suck water from the toilet tank and let it mix with the fresh supply.)

On most models, one foot pedal simultaneously opens the slide valve and water gate (see Figure 8), although some have separate pedals for these functions. Unlike home toilets, the unit must always be positioned directly above the holding tank, so wastes simply fall into the tank when the slide is opened.

Instead of a slide valve, a few toilets employ a Teflon half-ball (see Figure 9), which fits snugly into the orifice between the toilet bowl and holding tank and swings aside during the flush. Still another type, called a "water seal," has a small water-filled cup which flips over to dump its contents into the holding tank.

13.03 COMMON FRESHWATER TOILET MALFUNCTIONS.

Incredible as it may seem to those who know better, a recent manufacturer's survey of service personnel disclosed that most RVers either don't use chemicals in their waste holding tank, or don't use them in adequate quantities. (These are the folks you love to camp downwind from!) Needless to say, chemically suppressing odors and breaking down solid wastes is just as important with marine toilets as it is with portables, and both liquid concentrates or pre-measured packets of dry chemicals are readily available. Outside of the obvious sanitary reasons, the mechanical imperatives for chemicalizing are discussed in Sections 12.05 and 12.06.

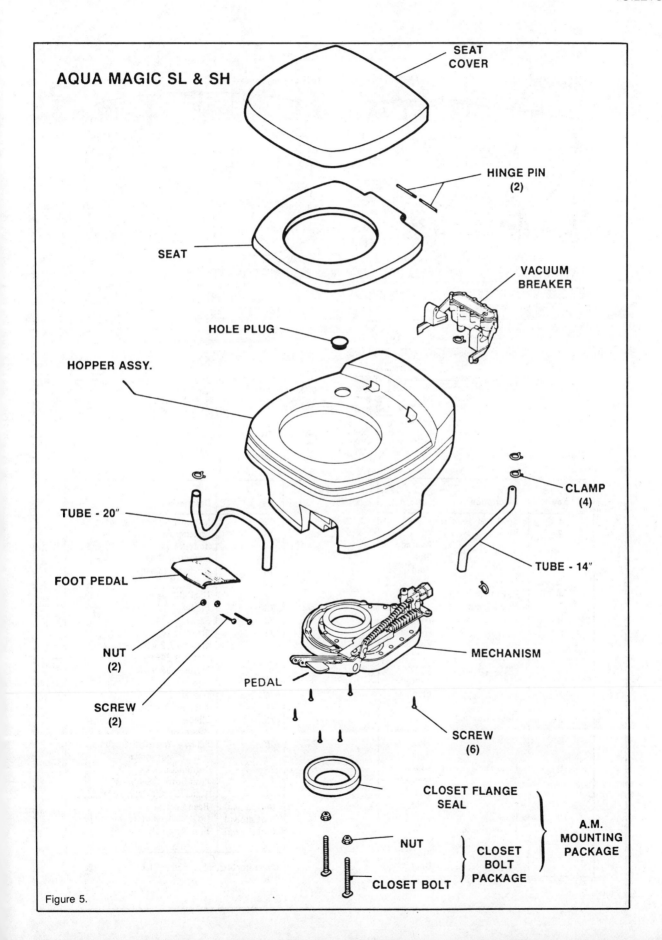

AQUA MAGIC SL & SH

SEAT COVER

HINGE PIN (2)

SEAT

VACUUM BREAKER

HOLE PLUG

HOPPER ASSY.

TUBE - 20"

CLAMP (4)

TUBE - 14"

FOOT PEDAL

NUT (2)

MECHANISM

PEDAL

SCREW (2)

SCREW (6)

CLOSET FLANGE SEAL

NUT

CLOSET BOLT PACKAGE

A.M. MOUNTING PACKAGE

CLOSET BOLT

Figure 5.

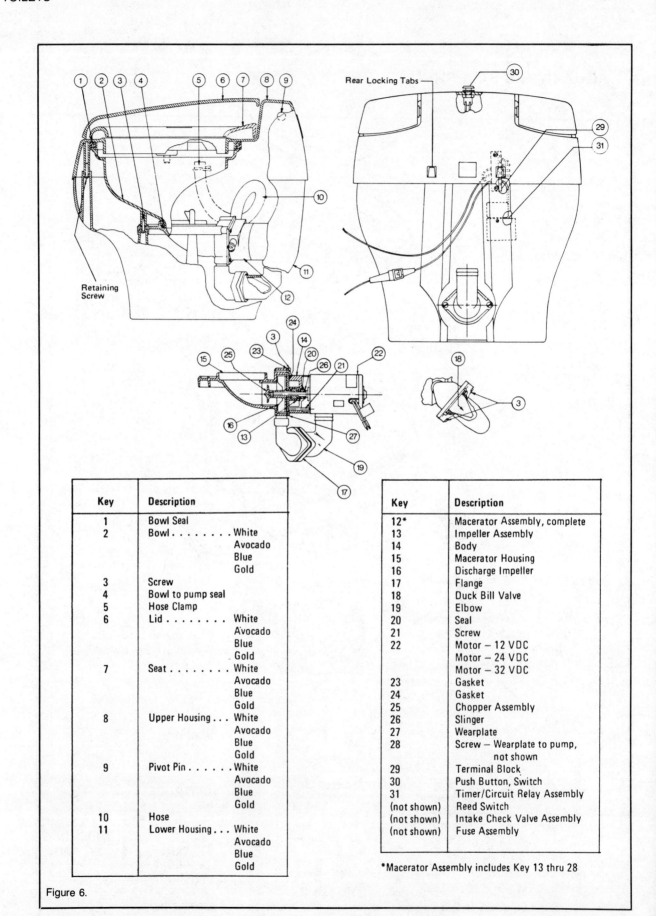

Retaining Screw

Rear Locking Tabs

Key	Description	
1	Bowl Seal	
2	Bowl	White
		Avocado
		Blue
		Gold
3	Screw	
4	Bowl to pump seal	
5	Hose Clamp	
6	Lid	White
		Avocado
		Blue
		Gold
7	Seat	White
		Avocado
		Blue
		Gold
8	Upper Housing	White
		Avocado
		Blue
		Gold
9	Pivot Pin	White
		Avocado
		Blue
		Gold
10	Hose	
11	Lower Housing	White
		Avocado
		Blue
		Gold

Key	Description
12*	Macerator Assembly, complete
13	Impeller Assembly
14	Body
15	Macerator Housing
16	Discharge Impeller
17	Flange
18	Duck Bill Valve
19	Elbow
20	Seal
21	Screw
22	Motor – 12 VDC
	Motor – 24 VDC
	Motor – 32 VDC
23	Gasket
24	Gasket
25	Chopper Assembly
26	Slinger
27	Wearplate
28	Screw – Wearplate to pump, not shown
29	Terminal Block
30	Push Button, Switch
31	Timer/Circuit Relay Assembly
(not shown)	Reed Switch
(not shown)	Intake Check Valve Assembly
(not shown)	Fuse Assembly

*Macerator Assembly includes Key 13 thru 28

Figure 6.

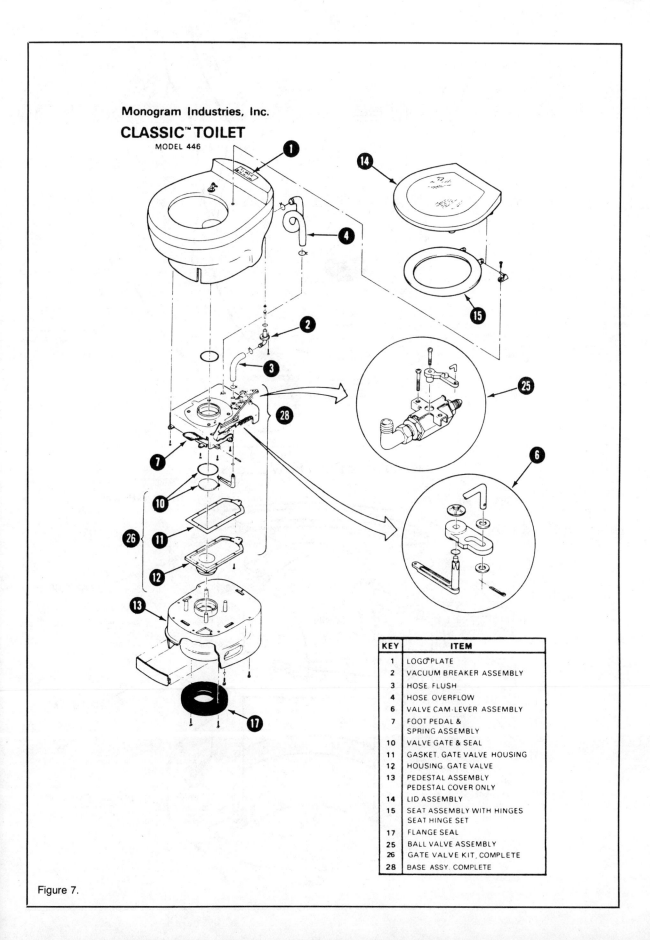

Monogram Industries, Inc.

CLASSIC™ TOILET
MODEL 446

KEY	ITEM
1	LOGO PLATE
2	VACUUM BREAKER ASSEMBLY
3	HOSE FLUSH
4	HOSE OVERFLOW
6	VALVE CAM-LEVER ASSEMBLY
7	FOOT PEDAL & SPRING ASSEMBLY
10	VALVE GATE & SEAL
11	GASKET, GATE VALVE HOUSING
12	HOUSING, GATE VALVE
13	PEDESTAL ASSEMBLY PEDESTAL COVER ONLY
14	LID ASSEMBLY
15	SEAT ASSEMBLY WITH HINGES SEAT HINGE SET
17	FLANGE SEAL
25	BALL VALVE ASSEMBLY
26	GATE VALVE KIT, COMPLETE
28	BASE ASSY. COMPLETE

Figure 7.

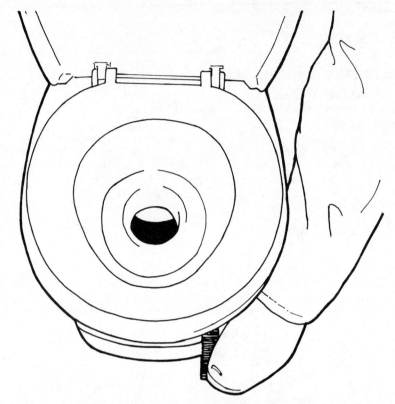

Figure 8.

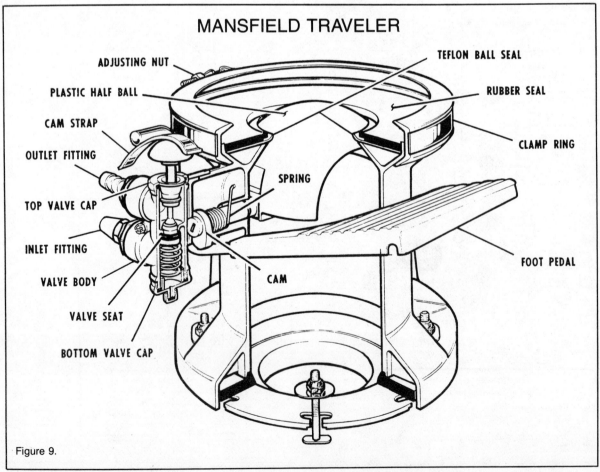

MANSFIELD TRAVELER

ADJUSTING NUT

PLASTIC HALF BALL

CAM STRAP

OUTLET FITTING

TOP VALVE CAP

INLET FITTING

VALVE BODY

VALVE SEAT

BOTTOM VALVE CAP

TEFLON BALL SEAL

RUBBER SEAL

CLAMP RING

SPRING

FOOT PEDAL

CAM

Figure 9.

The most common malfunction in marine toilets is a sticking or obstructed slide valve, usually signaled by a continuous freshwater bleed. If the problem is too small to be observed, you'll become aware of it when your rig's water pump cycles at odd times to replenish water lost from the lines. Often, you can catch this problem before it amounts to anything by periodically filling the bowl with water to an easily observed mark. If the water doesn't seep out, the slide is sealing correctly and the seals are in good condition.

Debris, like little bits of toilet paper, usually cause a sticking valve — and the cure is cleaning. Use a coat hanger or bent screwdriver to gently ream out the slide groove. Cleanse the plastic ball or slide, wipe carefully around the seals and lubricate the slide if it is dry. If the problem persists, the seals probably need replacing (Figures 10 and 11).

A sheared pin on the link between the foot pedal and the gate or slide valve mechanism (Figure 12) is a common problem when the unit has been abused (foot pedal has been operated too abruptly or with too much pressure). The pin is easily replaced.

Believe it or not, the second most common marine toilet problem occurs when the unit fails to flush because the RV's water tank ran dry. Enough said!

As freshwater conservation is sometimes important, marine toilet users employ tricks like pre-

moistening or lining the bowl with toilet paper to reduce the amount of water needed for each flush. Carrying such measures to an extreme can eventually work against you, however, as an adequate quantity of liquid is essential to solid waste breakdown. If water scarcity is a problem associated with your style of RVing, then the recirculating-type of toilets are probably your best bet (see Section 13.04).

Running water in a marine toilet can result from a sticking foot pedal; see that it is free from grit, the spring is in good condition and the parts are lubricated. Units having a water-control knob may have air in the ball valve (Figure 13) beneath the knob. If cleaning doesn't cure the leak, the ball valve assembly can be replaced.

If water is found leaking onto the floor, check the base hold-down nuts. (Be careful not to tighten them too tightly, though, as the base can break.) If this doesn't cure the problem, remove the toilet and check the flange height against the unit's installation instructions. Note the condition of the flange seal before reinstalling. Too little water with each flush can signal either a low reservoir or an obstruction in the freshwater supply line. First check the water tank, then remove the supply line for inspection.

When the water valve assembly (Figure 14) gets dirty after prolonged use, it allows water to run continuously into the bowl, but it's easily cleaned or replaced.

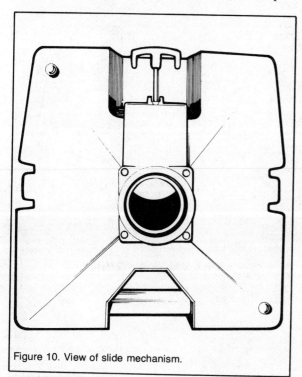

Figure 10. View of slide mechanism.

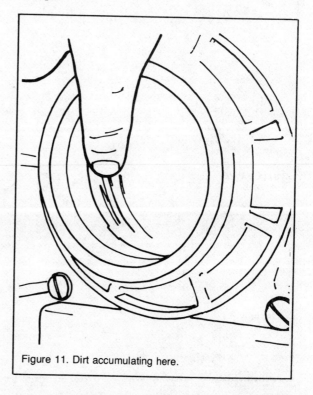

Figure 11. Dirt accumulating here.

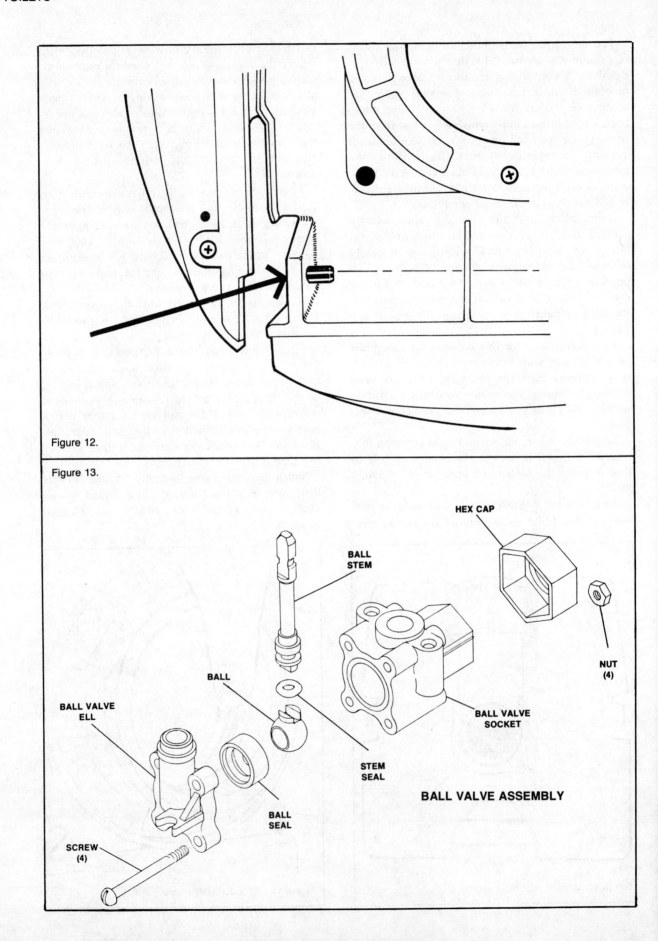

Figure 12.

Figure 13.

HEX CAP

BALL
STEM

NUT
(4)

BALL

BALL VALVE
ELL

BALL VALVE
SOCKET

STEM
SEAL

BALL VALVE ASSEMBLY

BALL
SEAL

SCREW
(4)

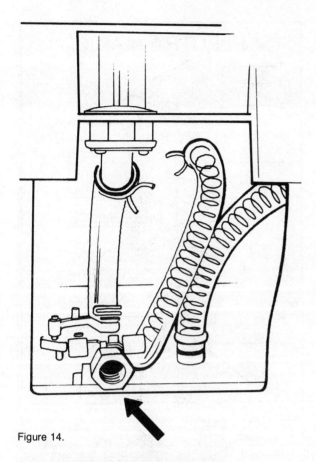

Figure 14.

13.04 RECIRCULATING TOILETS.

Recirculating toilets (Figures 15 and 16) are the most complicated of the three types, because in addition to the parts you're familiar with, they also contain a pump (usually electric). The reservoir and the holding tank are the same in this design; and as liquid is required for each flush, the pump draws it from that source. A screen is positioned in-line to prevent solids from being sucked into the recirculating process. Some units have a built-in timer which automatically switches the pump off after a few seconds; other types must be turned on and off manually. A few recirculating models (e.g., the Monomatic Twin) have the capacity to be operated as either a marine or recirculating toilet.

Recirculating toilets can be drained into exterior disposal stations or, alternatively, directly into the rig's own holding tanks (Figure 17). Some RVers prefer the recirculating toilet because it lets them get by without a holding tank.

13.05 COMMON RECIRCULATING TOILET PROBLEMS.

Recirculating toilets can have some of the same problems as freshwater designs, but now you have the added dimension of the recirculating pump. Before checking into any flushing problems, be sure there is adequate water in the reservoir. With electric models, failure to flush or an inadequate flush can often be traced to the RV's battery condition. Also check the in-line fuse. Further troubleshooting is suggested in Section 13.06.

If you must remove or replace a circulating pump, be sure you rewire correctly. Reversed polarity will make the pump run backwards which, incidently, is a useful technique for reaming a clogged pump.

Regular and sufficient chemicalization of recirculating toilets is an obvious and important maintenance step that controls odor and hastens waste decomposition. Most instructions specify that initial chemicals be added to fresh water before using the unit, while some recommend a waiting period for the water to become sufficiently charged. Then a definite time period is set after which the charge must be renewed. Be sure to use chemical types which are approved by your toilet's manufacturer (e.g., Electra Magic owners are cautioned to use only liquid concentrates, as powders may eventually leave a residue which clouds the Prismatic Level Indicator. The indicator can be removed and cleaned, but why incur the problem?). Additionally, each unit must be drained cleansed and refilled with fresh water and chemicals after a specified number of flushes. Failure to do this on schedule may lead to both malfunctions and persistent odor problems.

If odors aren't treated promptly, it is possible for the odor to permeate toilet parts. The remedy is to disassemble the unit and soak the parts in a manufacturer-approved cleanser. Even with carefully chemicalized units, this kind of periodic cleansing is well-advised.

13.06 TROUBLESHOOTING THE TOILET.

The following are symptoms and probable causes and remedies:

A. Slide Sticks
1. Hard water deposits or debris in slide channel. Cautiously insert a dull instrument and ream the channel clean.
2. Slide is dry or dirty. Cleanse with mild compound and apply manufacturer-approved lubricant (usually Vaseline or silicone spray).
3. Worn-out slide seals. Replace.
4. Disconnected or faulty spring. Replace.

5. Foot pedal sticks. Clean and lubricate. Check control linkages for binding from wear or loose connections.

6. Mounting bolts too tight. Loosen until toilet wobbles, then retighten only until toilet sits firmly. (NOTE: This problem occurs more frequently when toilet is mounted over a shag rug.)

B. Slide remains open
1. *Faulty spring. Replace.

C. Bowl won't hold water
1. See "A" and "B."

D. Water continues to run
1. Slide or foot pedal sticks. See "A."
2. Dirty or faulty vacuum breaker. Clean or replace.
3. Dirty or faulty water valve. Clean or replace ball. (Be sure something isn't holding valve open.)

E. Water leaks at base
1. Attachment nuts loose. Tighten, but be careful not to break the plastic toilet base.
2. Faulty flange seal. Replace.
3. Incorrect flange height. Check manufacturer's specifications and correct.
4. Cracked base. Consult manufacturer.
5. Internal problem. Check water supply line connection and visually scan observable areas to trace path of water.
6. Holding tank overflowing.

F. Toilet won't flush
1. Reservoir empty.
2. Pump inoperative. Check power supply and connections before attempting to repair or replace pump.
3. Faulty vacuum breaker. Clean or replace.
4. Faulty water valve. Clean or replace.
5. Faulty flush tube. Clean or replace.
6. Clogged flush tube. Remove and clean, or try reversing pump polarity briefly (check pump maker's manual first).
7. Holding tank full.

G. Weak flush
1. Low battery.
2. Low water pressure at toilet. Check main water supply and look for obstructions or kinks in supply line or valves.
3. **Faulty recirculating pump. Repair or replace.
4. Clogged filter. Remove and clean, or see F-6 above.

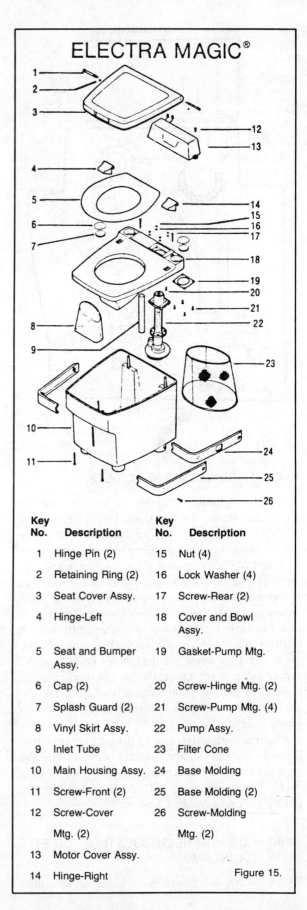

ELECTRA MAGIC®

Key No.	Description	Key No.	Description
1	Hinge Pin (2)	15	Nut (4)
2	Retaining Ring (2)	16	Lock Washer (4)
3	Seat Cover Assy.	17	Screw-Rear (2)
4	Hinge-Left	18	Cover and Bowl Assy.
5	Seat and Bumper Assy.	19	Gasket-Pump Mtg.
6	Cap (2)	20	Screw-Hinge Mtg. (2)
7	Splash Guard (2)	21	Screw-Pump Mtg. (4)
8	Vinyl Skirt Assy.	22	Pump Assy.
9	Inlet Tube	23	Filter Cone
10	Main Housing Assy.	24	Base Molding
11	Screw-Front (2)	25	Base Molding (2)
12	Screw-Cover Mtg. (2)	26	Screw-Molding Mtg. (2)
13	Motor Cover Assy.		
14	Hinge-Right		

Figure 15.

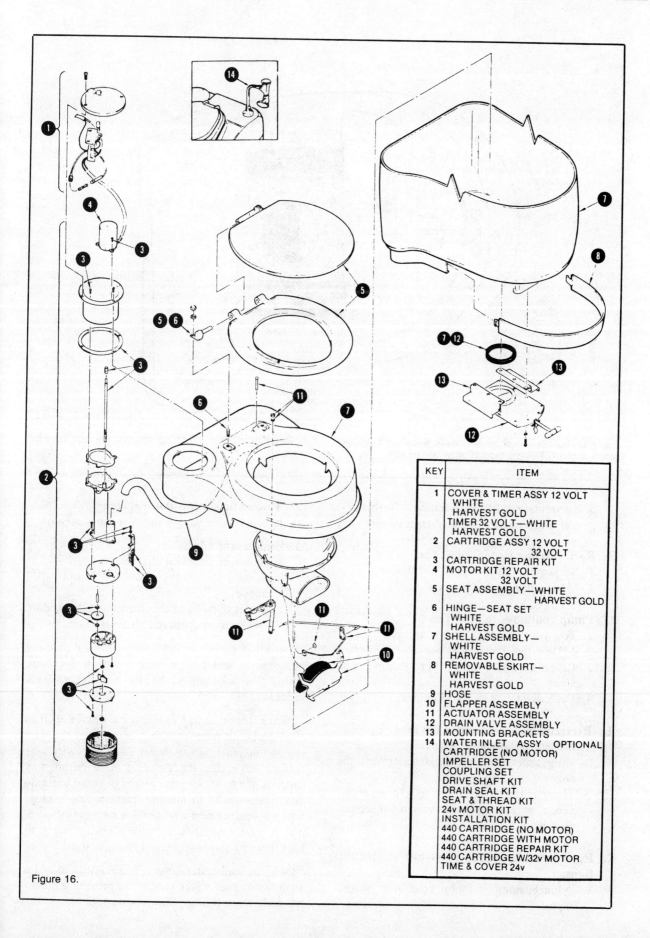

KEY	ITEM
1	COVER & TIMER ASSY 12 VOLT
	WHITE
	HARVEST GOLD
	TIMER 32 VOLT—WHITE
	HARVEST GOLD
2	CARTRIDGE ASSY 12 VOLT
	32 VOLT
3	CARTRIDGE REPAIR KIT
4	MOTOR KIT 12 VOLT
	32 VOLT
5	SEAT ASSEMBLY—WHITE
	HARVEST GOLD
6	HINGE—SEAT SET
	WHITE
	HARVEST GOLD
7	SHELL ASSEMBLY—
	WHITE
	HARVEST GOLD
8	REMOVABLE SKIRT—
	WHITE
	HARVEST GOLD
9	HOSE
10	FLAPPER ASSEMBLY
11	ACTUATOR ASSEMBLY
12	DRAIN VALVE ASSEMBLY
13	MOUNTING BRACKETS
14	WATER INLET ASSY OPTIONAL
	CARTRIDGE (NO MOTOR)
	IMPELLER SET
	COUPLING SET
	DRIVE SHAFT KIT
	DRAIN SEAL KIT
	SEAT & THREAD KIT
	24v MOTOR KIT
	INSTALLATION KIT
	440 CARTRIDGE (NO MOTOR)
	440 CARTRIDGE WITH MOTOR
	440 CARTRIDGE REPAIR KIT
	440 CARTRIDGE W/32v MOTOR
	TIME & COVER 24v

Figure 16.

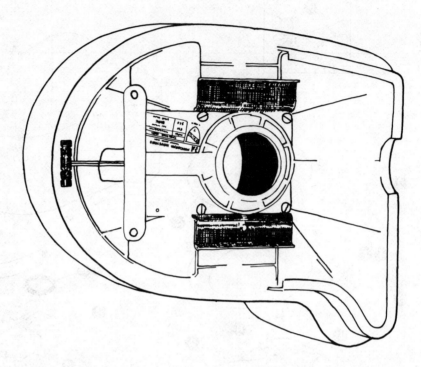

Figure 17. Bottom view of the Monomatic electric recirculating toilet shows the handle mechanism which opens the slide valve for waste disposal. This is typical of other brands also.

5. Recirculating filter cavitating. Flush several times to clear filter of trapped air.

H. **Recirculating motor won't run**
1. No power. Check supply and fuses.
2. **Defective pump. Replace.

I. **Pump continues to blow fuses**
1. Too much power. Check sources.
2. **Defective Pump. Replace.
3. Clogged recirculating filter. Remove and clean.
4. Defective timer switch. Replace.

J. **Recirculating motor runs too long.**
1. Not enough liquid in reservoir.
2. Pump timer wires are crossed. Reverse the polarity.
3. Timer is defective. Replace. (In an emergency, wire in a manual switch for temporary use.)

K. **Recirculating motor runs but no liquid flows**
1. Nylon bushing in motor coupler is worn. Replace.

L. **Automatic shutoff not working**
1. Motor wire caught in timer mechanism.

M. **Unpleasant odors**
1. Incorrect chemical charge.
2. Slide valve stuck. See ''A'' and ''B'' above.
3. Toilet parts have absorbed odor. Dismantle and soak in approved cleanser.

*Persistent pedal spring jump-off has plagued some users, and this is often traced to someone letting their foot slip so that the pedal snaps back suddenly.

**When disconnecting an electrical device such as a recirculating pump, make a diagram of the wiring and/or label each wire so you can rewire correctly. Reversing the polarity on a pump may cause it to run backwards, although some users do this intentionally to attempt breaking up a clog. Some manufacturers also build a moment of automatic reverse polarity into the flushing cycle to backflow the unit and keep it free of clogs.

NOTE: In hard water areas it is advisable to add a small amount of water softener to prevent a greenish scale from forming inside your toilet.

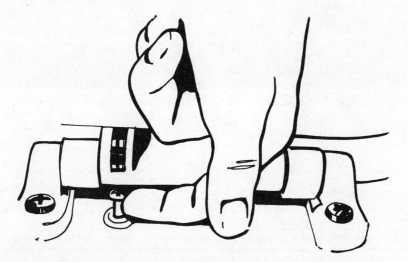

Figure 18. A feature on the Monogram electric recirculating toilet is the cam arm which is actuated by raising or lowering the toilet seat cover. In the fully extended position (toilet seat closed) it keeps an internal flapper mechanism sealed and prevents holding tank liquids from splashing upward.

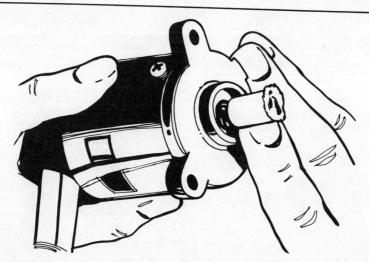

Figure 19. A common problem on recirculating toilets is that the motor runs but no water flows. This condition usually results from a worn nylon bushing on the motor; but it is both inexpensive and easily replaced.

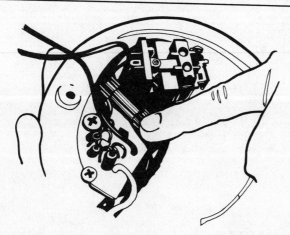

Figure 20. A blown fuse is the number-two reason why an electric recirculating toilet won't work. The first reason is that the RVs 12 volt power switch is OFF

Chapter Fourteen

The LP-Gas Systems

14.01 GENERAL CHARACTERISTICS OF LP-GAS AND THE LP-GAS SYSTEM.

The LP-gas system on your rig is basically a plumbing system. In this sense it's similar to the water plumbing, except that it carries gas between a reservoir and the point of use. This is a good analogy because it takes the mystery out of the subject, but the obvious differences between water and gas make additional preliminary understanding *very important*.

Why? Because if water leaks it makes a mess, but if gas leaks it is life threatening. Remember this dangerous aspect of LPG and develop a working respect for the material. In other words, *think safety*.

LPG is an acronymn meaning Liquified Petroleum Gas, and this marvelous substance has literally contributed the basic dimension of luxury to self-contained RVing. The characteristics which place LPG in this exhalted position are its high energy content and its *compressibility*. A huge quantity of butane and propane (the two types of gases which we lump under the "LPG" label) can be compressed into a small space and then released very slowly to fuel appliances. This means a relatively small tank will hold all the fuel you need for several days of camping. It also means that the tank contains very high internal pressures and this, combined with butane and propane's flammability, is why the system must be treated with respect.

14.02 THINK SAFETY

(1) Think safety means a faithfully-performed regime of inspection, maintenance and repair; (2) never applying direct heat (e.g., a welding torch) to a reservoir which contains *any* gas; (3) never exposing the system to flame or spark; (4) always bleeding the lines (releasing the gas held under pressure) before disconnecting anything; (5) never letting escaping LP-gas touch bare skin (it expands instantly and chills down to minus 40°F.); (6) using two wrenches to tighten connections in the manner pictured; (7) never overtightening a fitting; and (8) always testing the system for leaks immediately after working on it.

14.03 THE RESERVOIR.

Two types of tanks or cylinders are suitable for carrying LPG aboard an RV. The kind you generally see riding vertically on a trailer's tongue are called D.O.T. tanks because they are made under specifications established by the Department of Transportation. They are designed to handle less than 500 pounds of pressure, but a well-made D.O.T. should be able to withstand more than that (Figure 1).

You don't generally see the second type of tank because it is mounted horizontally underneath motorhomes. These are called ASME tanks because their manufacturing process is overseen by the American Society of Mechanical Engineers (Figure 2).

The functional differences between the two categories are simple: (1) D.O.T. tanks must ride vertically, while ASME tanks may be designed to ride either way; (2) All valves, fittings and brackets must be located on the ends of D.O.T. cylinders, while they can be on sides as well as ends of ASME tanks; (3) D.O.T. tanks must be filled by weight, while ASME tanks are filled by volume. Because the fitting location determines how the tank must be positioned, *never*, even temporarily, allow a tank to rest in a position it is not designed to be in. If this happens, the contents could escape and create an immediately hazardous situation.

Both types of reservoirs have some similar safety features, and you should study the illustrations which enumerate them and then find the counterparts on your rig's tank.

14.04 COMMON TERMS ASSOCIATED WITH ASME LP-GAS TANKS

Figure 3 shows:

1. POL vapor withdrawal service and relief valve. POL is an abbreviation for Prest-O-Lite, one of the early manufacturers of this device, but a more functional use of the letters would be as an acronymn to remind us that the threads in this valve are left-handed; therefore, "*Put On Left*." The POL spud and nut (10) fit this orifice.

2. Twenty percent fixed level gauge.

3. Filler valve.

4. Visible float gauge.

5. Pressure relief valve (part of the POL service valve) for venting gas if the internal tank pressure moves above 412 psi.

6. Vapor withdrawal tube (used on tanks where the POL valve is not located in the vapor space).

7. Eighty percent stop-fill tube (also called the "liquid level device" by some manufacturers) which syphons excess liquid if the tank is filled beyond 80% of its capacity. Be careful of this, though, as a filling attendant can pump gas in faster than this safety feature can release it.

8. Tank mounting brackets.

9. Typical gas regulator (see the description of

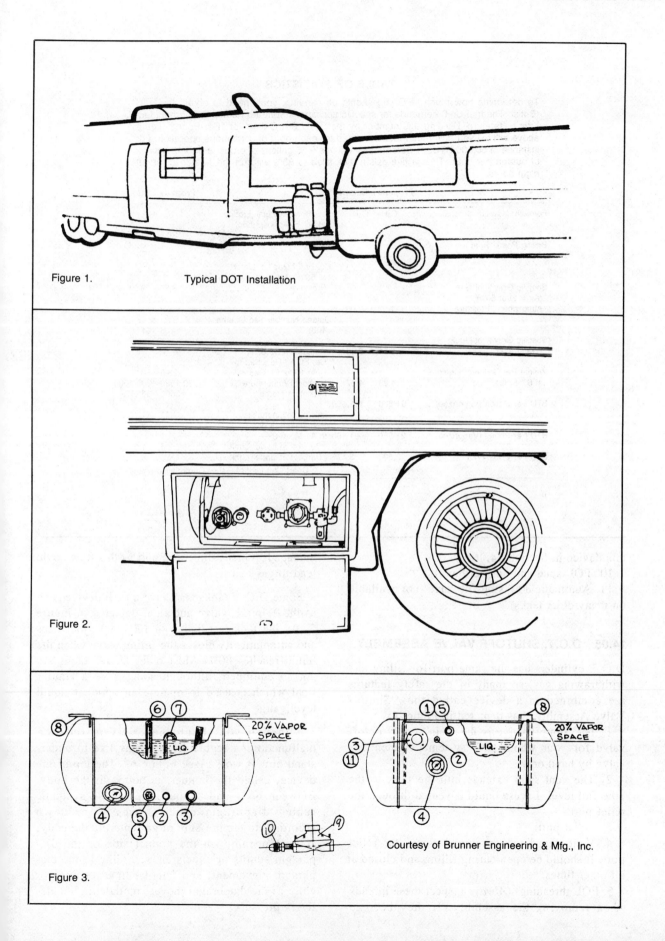

Figure 1.   Typical DOT Installation

Figure 2.

Figure 3.

20% VAPOR SPACE

LIQ.

20% VAPOR SPACE

LIQ.

Courtesy of Brunner Engineering & Mfg., Inc.

TABLE OF STATISTICS

To determine how much LPG you should be carrying, you'll need to obtain the BTU (British Thermal Unit) demands for specific appliances from the nameplate or manufacturer's literature. Dividing this number by the "BTU Per Gallon" or "Per Pound" figure above will tell you how much fuel is needed for each hour of continuous operation. For instance, a 50,000 BTU/hr. water heater will use 0.55 gallons of propane or 0.49 gallons of butane per hour. Thus a five-gallon tank filled to 80% will run the heater for about eight hours.

	Propane	Butane		Propane	Butane
Formula	C_3H_8	C_4H_{10}	Cu. Ft. of Gas/Gal. Liquid at 60° F, Atmospheric Pressure	36.5	31.0
Boiling Point, °F, at Atmospheric Pressure	−44	31			
			Cu. Ft. of Gas/Lb. Liquid at 60° F, Atmospheric Pressure	8.55	6.51
Specific Gravity of Gas (Air = 1) at 60° F, Atmospheric Pressure	1.53	2.00			
			Octane Number (Iso-Octane 100)	125	91
Specific Gravity of Liquid (Water = 1)	0.51	0.58	Combustion Date: Cu. Ft. Air Required to		
Weight Per Gallon of Liquid at 60° F, lbs.	4.23	4.87	Burn 1 Cu. Ft. Gas	23.5	30.0
			Ignition Temperature	920-1020	900-1000
BTU Per Gallon (Vaporized)	91,500	102,600	Maximum Flame	3600	3625
			Limits of Inflammability, Percentage of gas in Air Mixture —		
BTU Per Pound (Vaporized)	21,560	21,180	Percent at Lower Limit	2.4	1.9
BTU Per Cubic Foot	2,500	3,175	Percent at Upper Limit	9.5	8.5

Chart Courtesy of Fisher Controls Company

this device in Section 14.06).

10. POL spud and nut (lefthand).

11. Automatic 80% stop-fill valve (not available on many older tanks).

14.05   D.O.T. SHUTOFF VALVE ASSEMBLY.

D.O.T cylinders use the same port for filling and withdrawing gas, so many of the safety features are combined in a device called the "Shutoff Valve Assembly," as depicted in Figure 4:

1. The Shutoff valve is the main supply on/off valve for your whole LPG system. Tighten this valve by hand only.

2. The vent stem extends into the tank to the 80% full level. Excess liquid is vented through the relief port.

3. Relief port.

4. Vent stem knob opens and closes the relief port. It should be open during filling and closed at all other times.

5. POL threading. (*Always* inspect these threads when removing the assembly. If they become damaged, replace the entire unit as this flaw could lead to gas leaks.)

Some D.O.T tanks also have a float device such as the Triple-L valve and float depicted in Figure 5. As the tank is filled with LPG, the float rises and automatically closes the filling valve when the liquid reaches 80%. Most older D.O.T tanks are not so equipped, although some have a similar float which is used to operate an optional liquid level gauge.

Although you should never try to repair a malfunctioning regulator, you may like to understand how it works (see Figure 6). The top of the device, called the bonnet, is bolted to the body. Between body and bonnet is a flexible synthetic rubber diaphragm which moves up or down according to the pressure of gas entering the body. A vent opening on the bonnet side of the diaphragm admits or expels air according to the diaphragm movement, and internal linkages open or close as the diaphragm moves, modulating the delivery pressure.

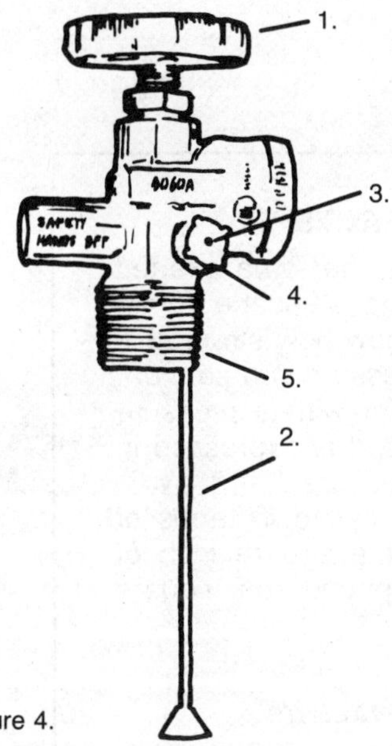

Figure 4.

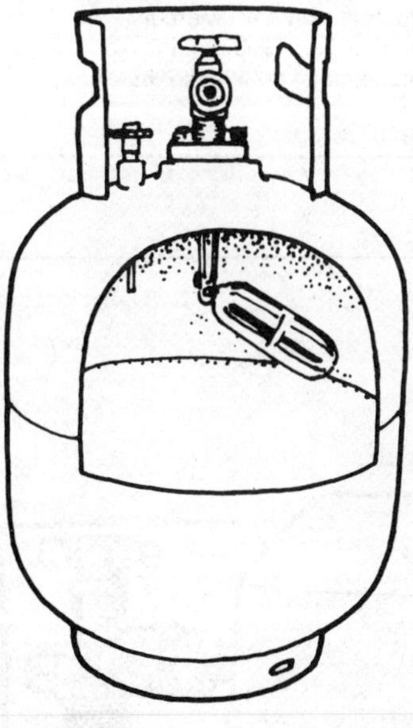

Figure 5.

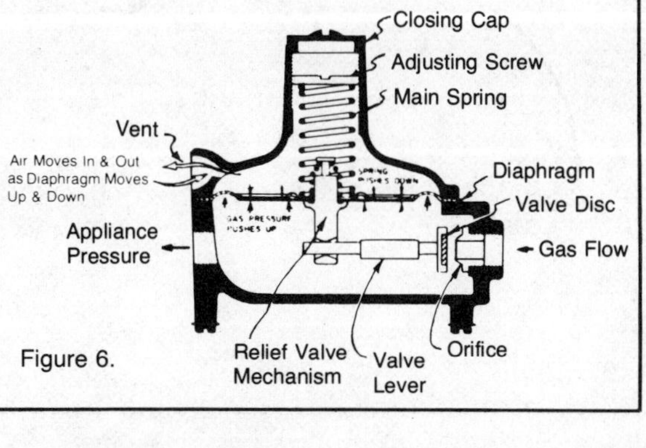

Closing Cap
Adjusting Screw
Main Spring
Vent
Air Moves In & Out
as Diaphragm Moves
Up & Down
Diaphragm
Valve Disc
Appliance
Pressure
Gas Flow
Relief Valve
Mechanism
Valve
Lever
Orifice

Figure 6.

14.06   THE REGULATOR.

High cylinder pressures of 100 to 200 psi keep LPG in its liquid or compact state, but appliances can't accept such force. The regulator protects your system by lowering gas pressure to 0.4 psi, and the magnitude of this reduction tells you how important a well-functioning regulator is. Because some instruments measure gas pressure by how high it lifts a column of water, 0.4 psi is often expressed as "11 inches water column." (See Pressure Conversion Chart, Figure 7.)

Regulators are rugged and trustworthy instruments, but insects or dirt which have entered the vent orifice can quickly put one out of business. A simple blockage will cause a pressure drop and perhaps extinguish pilots, but if debris obstructs the working mechanism, high-pressure gas may pass directly into your appliances. Both possibilities create a substantial safety problem. Most regulators brought to market after 1978 should have a fine-meshed vent covering which will alleviate much of this hazard (Figure 8).

But even a screen can be quickly clogged with road-splash, and protective covers are advised for exposed regulators (Figure 9). Frequent cleanings are highly recommended even when a cover is used.

A second source of vent clog is ice which forms quickly in a freezing rain. Tests conducted by both Fisher Controls Company and Underwriter's Laboratories show that vent openings which point to the ground and have a drip-lip construction are unlikely to freeze completely closed. (Figures 10 and 11.) Vents which must be aimed horizontally can be encased in a hood. But beware of carelessly installed hoods, as they may actually fill with water that can ultimately freeze the vent closed.

Water inside the LPG system is another cause of blockage, as it can freeze at the regulator entry port and stop the gas supply (Figure 12). Consumers usually create this problem by allowing moist air to enter empty tanks through an open valve, but even dealers' bulk supplies can become contaminated. Unless it's particularly severe, this problem seldom affects double stage regulators (see Figure 13). Should you experience this blockage, switch to a new supply and purge the system with dry gas. Methyl alcohol may be introduced into the system in severe cases, as it absorbs the moisture in a "wet" tank.

Regulators for RV use are either single or double-stage. The first type reduces pressure in one operation, while the double-stage is actually two regulators in one. The first reduces tank pres-

GAS PRESSURE

The greater the difference between these two water levels, the higher the pressure. Most LP-gas appliances work best when the pressure brought to them will cause a difference in level of 11 inches of water column.

MANOMETER

Figure 7.

PRESSURE FACTS

Simply stated, pressure is the force exerted by a gas or liquid attempting to escape from a container. It is useful to know how strong this "attempt to escape" is. Pressure can be measured with a manometer or with a pressure gauge. At the lower levels, it is expressed in "inches of water column," i.e., 11" W.C. Higher pressures are expressed in terms of the force exerted against a square inch of area. For example, "125 pounds per square inch" (125 psi).

PRESSURE EQUIVALENTS

1" Water Column ......equals........ .58 oz./sq. in.
11" Water Column ......equals........ 6.35 oz./sq. in.
11" Water Column ......equals........ .4 lb./sq. in.
1 lb./sq. in. ....equals........ 27.71" Water Column
1 lb./sq. in. ....equals........ 2.04" Mercury
1" Mercury ....equals........ .49 lb./sq. in.
1 Std. Atmosphere ......equals........14.73 lb./sq. in.

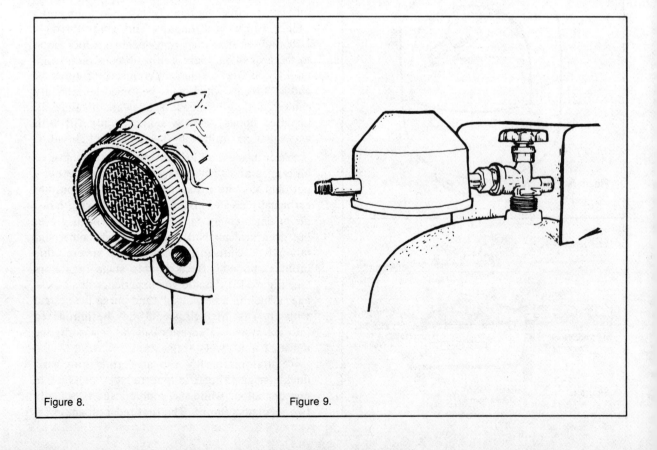

Figure 8.

Figure 9.

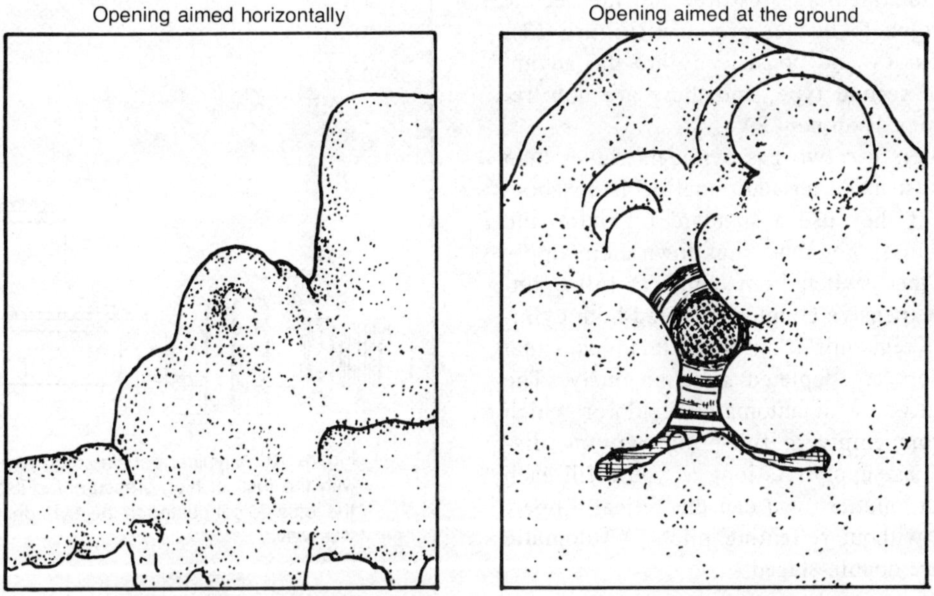

Opening aimed horizontally   Opening aimed at the ground

Figure 10.

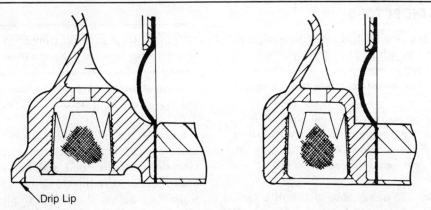

Drip Lip

Figure 11. The drawing on the left depicts drip lip vent construction which has a recessed vent opening, while the non-drip version on the right does not.

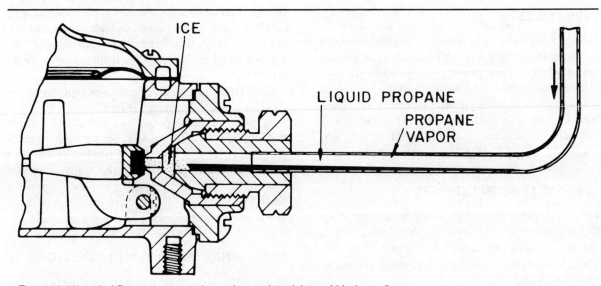

ICE

LIQUID PROPANE

PROPANE VAPOR

Figure 12. Water in LP-gas can turn to ice at the regulator inlet and block gas flow.

sure to an intermediate pressure, and the second brings it down to burner pressure (Figure 13). Greater accuracy and consistency are the advantages of the second type, and these are now required equipment on new RVs.

Many RVers use two gas cylinders rather than one, and must make an additional decision about regulators. If they use a standard regulator and POL connection, they must shut down their supply every time they switch from empty to full cylinders. An inexpensive coupler will feed both cylinders into the regulator at once, but this means that both cylinders are depleted simultaneously. The best alternative is an automatic regulator which switches from empty to full-bottle without disrupting the gas supply. As long as you refill each tank when it empties, you can theoretically operate forever without relighting pilots. (Automatic regulators are double-staged.)

14.07 LEAK DETECTORS.

Gas from the regulator feeds directly into the leak detector on the rigs which have this optional feature. If yours is not so equipped, it should be — as the price is a small investment in a large measure of safety.

Most leak detectors are non-repairable, at least by the consumer, so we won't explore their anatomy. The positive side of this is that they are simple devices and seldom need any kind of adjustment.

Figures 14 and 15 show how to install a leak detector and how a typical leak detector functions.

14.08 LINES.

From the regulator, gas is usually routed either directly to an appliance or, in larger rigs, to a main (often plastic) pipe running underneath the rig. Copper risers then lead to the various points of consumption. Rubber grommets protect the risers from chafing where they pass through flooring and cabinetry. Connections at the point of use are made with flared fittings (see Section 14.14).

14.09 STAYING IN SERVICE.

Because routine maintenance and troubleshooting techniques are almost identical, we'll lump them together — with the admonishment that doing the maintenance will eliminate the need for most troubleshooting.

Industry experts say that overfilled LPG cylinders are the largest single cause of accidents and

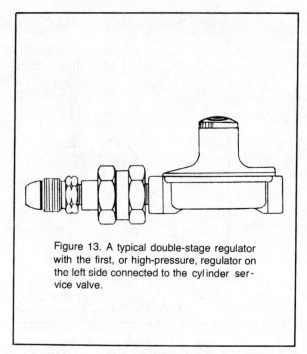

Figure 13. A typical double-stage regulator with the first, or high-pressure, regulator on the left side connected to the cylinder service valve.

malfunctions, thus good trouble-avoidance begins at the filling station. The cardinal filling rule is, "Only you are responsible for you;" so assume that the attendant is going to make a mistake and monitor everything he does. Never allow a cylinder to be filled beyong 80%.

Leaks in the LPG system are the second-largest cause of malfunctions. RVs experience substantial vibrations on the road and leaks are a normal occurrence, but failing to detect and correct them while they are small can lead to big troubles.

The time-honored method of discovering leaks is to prepare a container of soapy water (similar commercial substances can be purchased) and paint all lines, connections, cylinder parts and the regulator with this brew. Any leaks will immediately be evidenced by little bubbles (Figure 16).

CAUTION: It shouldn't need to be said, but *never* look for leaks with a match (Figure 17).

A mechanical leak detector (see Section 14.07) is one of the handiest troubleshooting (and trouble-preventing) devices available. Installed in the main gas transmission line, these devices tell you when a leak has developed. You may still need soap and a paint brush to find the specific leak, but at least you'll know you're looking for something real.

14.10 WHAT TO DO IF YOU SMELL GAS.

If the odor of leaking gas attracts your attention inside the rig, follow this procedure immediately: (1) Evacuate everyone from the interior and in-

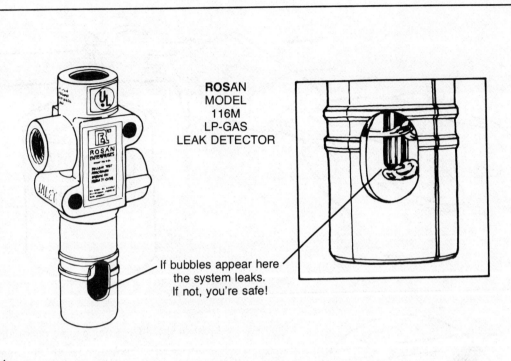

ROSAN
MODEL
116M
LP-GAS
LEAK DETECTOR

If bubbles appear here
the system leaks.
If not, you're safe!

Figure 14.

Figure 15.

MOUNTING INSTRUCTIONS

1. Turn off L.P.G. main gas valve, appliance and pilots.
2. Disconnect L.P. gas system tubing or hose from the regulator.
3. Mount leak detector on a rigid vertical surface or bracket as shown below. Locate detector such that the inlet port is accessible to the regulator by using straight fitting or elbows.
4. Remove plastic plugs and install appropriate 3/8 NPT fittings using the proper sealant.
5. After detector is mounted depress plunger 1/4 inch and hold it for a few moments to allow propylene glycol to return to glass container.
6. Assemble tubing or hose to the detector and regulator.
7. Assemble tubing or hose from the detector to the system inlet fitting.
8. Turn main gas valve on. Check joints worked on using soapy water. Bubbles indicate a leak. Tighten joints until bubbles stop.
9. See instruction manual installation test.

L.P. Gas flow

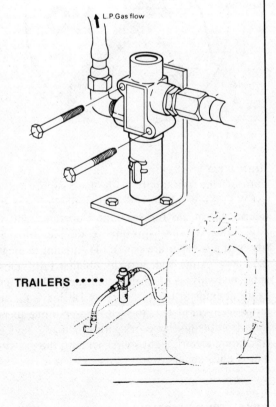

TYPICAL APPLICATIONS

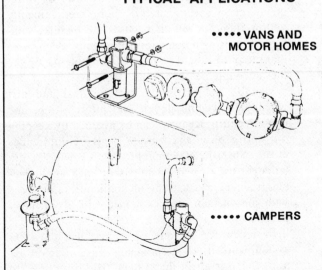

••••• VANS AND
MOTOR HOMES

TRAILERS •••••

••••• CAMPERS

MOUNT DETECTOR IN VERTICAL POSITION
WITH SIGHT GLASS AT THE BOTTOM.

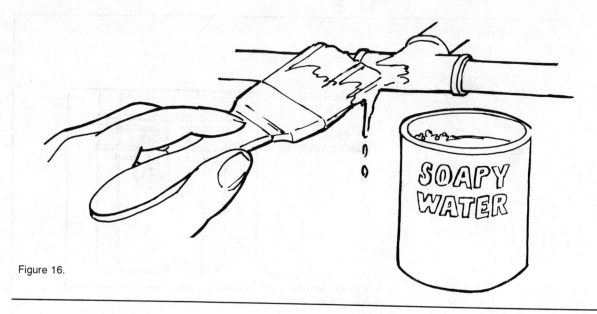

Figure 16.

Figure 17.

Most of the difficulties people encounter during the lighting sequence result from not reading the directions. Additionally, Duo-Therm offers this advice: ''Use a kitchen-type stick match, never a matchbook. Place the match in a holder, strike it and with a smooth but quick motion insert it through the lighter door while the phosphorous head is still blazing. If you hesitate, and wait until the flame stabilizes and is burning the wood, it can easily snuff out when you insert it through some lighter doors.'' As an alternative, this RV heater manufacturer suggests using a spark-type igniter available from RV supply houses.

Pilot lights are an excellent indicator of gas pressure irregularities. The ideal flame has a light blue base and a darker blue (sometimes violet or purple) top. Small amounts of yellow, or infrequent yellow specks, are OK; but a predominantly yellow flame or one that looses the pictured configuration is symptomatic of problems. Also, note that the pilot should be high enough to envelop the thermocouple device (Figure 19).

Usually the difficulty will be dust and dirt which has accumulated in the pilot orifice, and many repair procedures can be avoided by keeping the entire pilot and burner areas of appliances clean. Specific cleaning procedures will be detailed in the owners' manuals of each appliance, but frequent evacuations of appliance pilot areas with the vacuum cleaner nozzle will avoid many problems.

In a new rig, or one which has had the LPG system worked on, the probable cause of an erratic pilot flame is air in the system. The solution is to purge all lines by opening the pilot valves at the

struct them to assemble far away from the rig; (2) Turn off the gas supply at the tank supply valve; (3) Wait a few minutes, then thoroughly purge the interior air of gas fumes. (Don't operate lights or any flame or spark-producing device until all traces of gas vapor are gone); (4) Attempt to locate the cause of the leak visually. If that fails, close appliance valves, open the main supply valve and again attempt to locate the leak. Do leave the interior well-ventilated, though, and continue to refrain from using flame or spark-producing devices (including electric light switches) until the gas system is once again secure.

14.11   PILOT LIGHTS.

Most RV appliances which burn LP-gas use the pilot light system. Direction for lighting are found on the nameplate, as this is mandatory.

THE LP-GAS SYSTEM 179

Figure 18.

WARNING FLAMMABLE COMPRESSED GAS

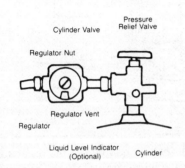

Cylinder Valve

Pressure
Relief Valve

Regulator Nut

Regulator Vent

Regulator

Liquid Level Indicator
(Optional)

Cylinder

WHEN YOU CONNECT THIS CYLINDER
- Close valves on pilot lights and appliance burners.
- Tighten regulator coupling nut into valve with wrench. Regulator nut has left hand thread.
- Open cylinder valve.
- Apply soapy water at areas marked X. If bubbles appear close valve and have leaks repaired.
- Relight pilots. Check pilots and burners for proper flames.
- Make sure regulator vent and pressure relief on valve are clean and protected from elements.
- Close cylinder valve when not in use.
- Do not use or store cylinder indoors or in an enclosed area.
- Secure cylinder in upright position at all times.

DO NOT ATTEMPT REPAIRS.
CALL YOUR LP-GAS DEALER.

These are a few safety suggestions. Read all manufacturers' instruction manuals carefully.

---

various appliances, and then running gas from a pure supply through the system until the air has been expelled.

Gas pressure may also drop or fall because of constrictions in the lines. Since appliances only perform optimally at prescribed pressures, have a serviceperson periodically test the supply at each outlet. (This takes just a few minutes with the proper tools and a special gauge.)

Persistent pilot flame-outs not attributable to dirt are generally wind-induced. This malady has plagued RVers ever since gas appliances were taken aboard, and some very ingenious baffles and protective shields have been developed by frustrated owners. Admittedly, it may be a difficult and patience-consuming chore, but try to determine where air is penetrating the pilot chamber and do whatever is necessary to plug the leak. Of course, the smaller the hole the harder it will be to find.

Automatic electronic pilot-lighting devices will generally take care of the occasional pilot outages which most RVs experience — and which aren't attributable to a sizable air leak. There are several such devices on the market, and they are easily installed as directed by the maker.

14.12   MOISTURE AND FREEZING.

A bothersome malfunction can develop if water has collected in the LPG system. Because the temperature of gas drops as it expands, the interior of the regulator may easily be below the freezing point of water. Water vapor passing through the unit will freeze and constrict the quantity of gas delivered to appliances. Industry people say that many dealers are dispensing water-contaminated gas, but consumers compound the problem by leaving empty cylinder valves open to moisture-laden air, or even by leaving their rig's gas lines uncapped while taking cylinders for refill.

If water is a problem, purging the system with gas (Section 14.06) may be sufficient. If this doesn't clear the system, an effective drying agent like methyl alcohol can be injected into the lines. This chemical absorbs moisture.

Another cold-related problem arises from the chemical difference between propane and butane. Although they are similar in performance characteristics, butane will not leave the liquid state in temperatures below 32 degrees F., while propane's lower limit is minus 44 degrees F. Most RVs carry a mixture of the two gases (although

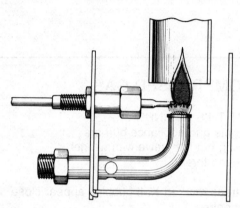

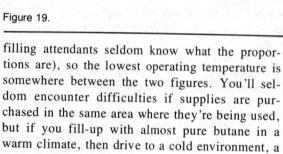

Figure 19.

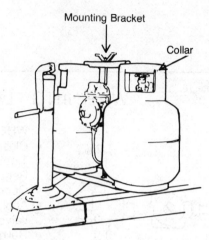

Figure 20.

filling attendants seldom know what the proportions are), so the lowest operating temperature is somewhere between the two figures. You'll seldom encounter difficulties if supplies are purchased in the same area where they're being used, but if you fill-up with almost pure butane in a warm climate, then drive to a cold environment, a gas outage may result.

14.13   SCHEDULED REGULAR MAINTENANCE.

Just like a good pilot methodically goes over his aircraft before every flight, you'll prevent most problems by giving your LPG system a good pretrip checkup every day. Habitually see that all appliances are turned off before opening the cylinder shutoff valve. Visually scan transmission lines, especially bends and corners, to detect cracks or abraded spots. Since most gas leaks result from connections working loose, finger-test them whenever your hand is near one, and periodically tighten all of them with wrenches used in the proper manner (Section 11.07).

Check the mounting brackets, too, as vibration can work them loose. And be sure that exposed D.O.T. tanks are turned so that the collar protects the controls from road splash (Figure 20).

While you're looking things over, learn to notice little things like chipped paint on the gas cylinder; if not touched up, these spots will rust and weaken the cylinder walls. Give serious attention to dents, because they also signal a weakening and should be inspected by an expert.

Every time you activate the system — especially after driving through inclement weather or over dusty roads — check the cylinder safety-relief valve and regulator-vent opening to be sure they

are clean. But don't try to do more to the regulator than clean it; these devices are precision-set at the factory and must never be adjusted by the consumer.

After operating for several years, LP-gas cylinders should be hydrostatically retested to make sure they are still able to withstand high pressures. The laws governing the frequency and methods of examination are complex, so ask an authorized serviceperson about your specific cylinder. Requalifying is not only inexpensive, but quickly pays for itself in terms of renewed confidence.

14.14   FLARED FITTINGS.

Flare connections will eventually wear out, but a variety of tools are available in trailer supply stores which enable you to make new ones. Illustrated is the Col-Flare tool and the procedure for making flared fittings with it (Figure 21 and 22.)

14.15   LP-GAS AS A MOTOR FUEL.

While not truly a subject for this manual, alternate fuels at least deserve mention because they are realities which many RVers are seriously considering. Of the available options, propane has proven to be so popular that it is being offered on several new RVs, but it does require substantial alteration to an existing vehicle. Most motorhomes will accept the additional equipment quite handily, but if you're thinking of adding this capacity to an automobile tow car, your decision may be out of your hands — there simply isn't enough room on or under most cars for the necessary storage tank.

Why should the LP-gas alternative even be considered? Propane burns at a lower temperature

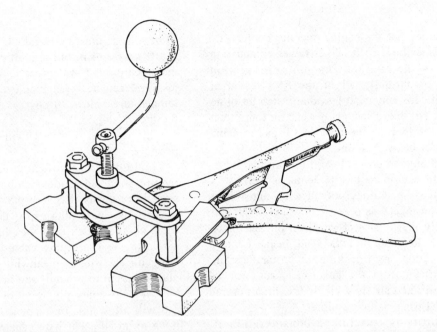

Figure 21.

Figure 22.

COL-FLARE TOOL
FLARING INSTRUCTIONS

1. Cut tubing to length, allowing slack for bends, snaking and ample working room. Cut end should be square and clean. Plastic tube cutter recommended.
2. Place tube nut over cut end and slide back out of the way.
3. Adjust jaws of Dan-de Col-Flare Tool to size of tubing to be flared.
4. Apply a small amount of lubricant inside end of tube to be flared. (Non-toxic oils or lubricants i.e. soap, cooking oil.)
5. Push lubricated tube end between Dan-de Col-Flare Tool vise jaws to fully retracted rotating head. Clamp securely in place.
6. Holding tool handle in one hand, slowly rotate flare head crank with other hand, screwing rotating head down against the tube end.
7. Continue rotating until flare is formed that will be snug in the tube nut seat. (See illu. I)
8. Unclamp Dan-de Col-Flare Tool and remove from flared tubing.
9. Pull tube nut up over flare so flare is seated in base of nut. (On a properly made flare, the edges will ripple against the threads of the nut.) (See illu. II) (Note: An undersized flare will not fill the flare nut seat.)
10. Make up joint by screwing tube nut onto desired fitting.
11. Take up hand-tight, then using appropriate wrench, TIGHTEN. (Recommend channel lock or crescent wrench.)
12. Use no lubricant or dope on tube nut or fitting. Use Teflon Tape on plastic to metal transition connections.
13. Concentric ridges on seat of Flaregrip fitting will uniformly indent into face of tubing flare providing a tight, leakproof, locked joint. (See illu. III)
14. Caution: Do not make an oversized flare which will "bell" when tubing is pulled down into nut (See illu. IV)

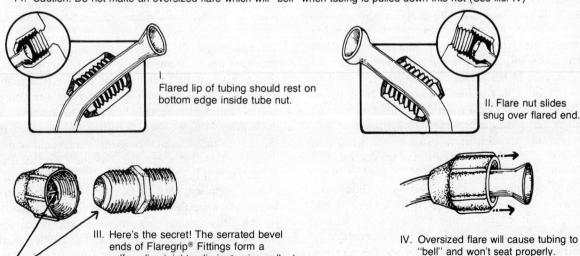

I.
Flared lip of tubing should rest on bottom edge inside tube nut.

II. Flare nut slides snug over flared end.

III. Here's the secret! The serrated bevel ends of Flaregrip® Fittings form a self-sealing joint to eliminate pipe pullout and fitting leakage.

IV. Oversized flare will cause tubing to "bell" and won't seat properly.

than gasoline, thus the engine operates cooler. It's also a cleaner fuel, so it leaves fewer combustion deposits in the engine. The miles per gallon achieved on virtually all of the RVs tested at Trailer Life are somewhat less than when gasoline is burned, but that disadvantage can be more than overcome as long as the cost of LP-gas remains substantially below gasoline.

But as though to prove the old maxim that nothing is perfect, propane has its debits as well as its credits. Because it does not have as much heat content, you'll get less power from LPG fuels, and that usually means slower acceleration and more time in the slow lane on hills. And, because many dual installations must position the propane carburetor upstream from the gasoline carburetor, a slightly restricted air flow yields less than normal mpg results when using gasoline.

Availability is certainly a consideration if you're considering the switch. Presently, LP-gas is widely sold throughout the nation, but unfortunately many dealers who are pumping it for general RV use are not licensed to sell it as motor fuel. This means that you may have trouble buying propane in some areas. Obviously, you're better off with the dual fuel capability in these situations, as you can burn gasoline until propane supplies are located. Remember, though, that you sacrifice some efficiency by retaining the dual option over a single fuel choice.

Other considerations when you switch to propane, either as a single or dual fuel, are numerous — and Bill Estes, Trailer Life's technical editor, offers these findings from his experiences with LPG-equipped vehicles:

"Cool morning starts," Estes observes, "will usually not be as quick as they were with gasoline. No choking is required with propane, though, and once started, the engine tends to keep running without the typical gasoline false starts. Below-zero starts will also be easier with propane.

"Operating temperatures with propane must be lower than with gasoline because the dry propane does not have the heat-quenching effect on exhaust valves that gasoline provides. Consequently, conversion kit manufacturers often recommend that stock engine coolant thermostats, usually rated in the 180- to 190-degree range, be changed to 160-degree thermostats. Also, fans with fluid-drive clutches usually are calibrated to actuate in the 220- to 230-degree range (water temperature), which is higher than desirable with propane. The thermostatic coils on the faces of the fan clutches sometimes can be adjusted for lower actuation. If adjustment isn't possible, a solid fan, which tends to be noiser, must be installed.

"It's wise to install a good coolant temperature gauge calibrated in degrees F. and a solid fan unless you can hear fan roar even with outside air temperature below 70 degrees, or you can adjust the thermostat on the fan so it will fully engage at not higher than about 190 degrees water temperature.

"Ignition is also critical with propane and may require some adjustment along with the conversion. Here's why: Because the ability of the spark to cross the spark plug gap is decreased, the electrical charge which fires the plug builds to higher levels in the spark-plug cables before the gap is bridged. The spark, meanwhile, is looking for a place to jump to ground, and faulty spark-plug cables, a leaky spark-plug boot or a worn distributor cap will allow this to happen. Or, the spark may jump to an adjacent wire causing out-of-sequence (premature) firing problems. Proper routing of the wires is important, therefore, and is specified in most service manuals for specific vehicles.

"Temperature of the air ingested by the carburetor also is important. A propane-fuel vehicle suffers more from hot intake air than does a gasoline engine and free breathing is necessary. Addition of cool-air induction to the air cleaner is a must. It's difficult in many older vehicles to find the room for a four-inch air tube leading from an air horn on the propane carburetor to an air filter ahead of the radiator, but where space permits, it's worthwhile. Cool-air intake appears critical only when ambient air conditions are above 70 degrees. Below that, air-conditioning normally is not used and the amount of heat thrown back into the engine compartment is reduced.

"Another mechanical consideration with propane is its effect on valves. Recession (wear) of exhaust valve seats has been a problem in some engines, especially in industrial usage where engines are operated under heavy throttle most of the time. This is not prevalent in the past several years since manufacturers have perfected the very hard valves and valve seats which are necessary for durability with lead-free gasoline. Lead often is thought to provide a lubricant to valves and seats, thereby extending their life, but the effect is different at least in regard to propane. The lead particles in gasoline perform a sort of shimming effect. They keep the face of the valve from actually resting fully on the seat; the distance is microscopic. Propane does not do this. The result is that the exhaust valve comes to rest fully on the seat. It's quite hot and in certain cases with specific metals, the valve welds itself to the seat at microscopic points. When it lifts, it takes particles of the seat with it, causing recession.

"When recession becomes a problem, the seats can be machined out and new hardened seats installed. Or, the heads can be replaced. It's not a prevalent problem in RVs, though.

"Safety with propane always has been of prime concern and some RV owners tend to distrust the fuel. It's a safe fuel if the owner will follow basic safety procedures, such as checking the fuel lines periodically for leaks with a soap and water solution. Actually, more hazard exists inside the coach with the propane appliance system than from a motor-fuel system, because the gas must grow in volume to a specific minimum mixture with air before it becomes explosive. Gas leaking from a motor-fuel system usually dissipates quickly because the lines and appliances usually are fully exposed. There are specific precautions, such as not parking a propane-fueled vehicle inside a closed garage that contains a water heater."

When considering LP-gas as a category you should remember that the label really encompasses both propane and butane. The two gases are quite similar and are sometimes sold for general RV appliance use as a mixture. However, there is one major difference between the two which you should be aware of: Propane will vaporize into usable form in temperatures as low as minus 40 degrees F., while butane's lower limit is 32 degrees F. That's a major difference if you're RVing in cold climates!

Your basic consideration in deciding whether or not to convert to propane will probably boil down to cost and availability. The cost of the conversion must certainly be weighed against the potential savings, and this directly relates to how many miles you put on your RV each year. The equipment involved in the conversion, though, is usually long-lasting and much of it can be transferred onto a new RV when you trade.

If all the ingredients make sense to you, by all means investigate the possibility of adding propane fuel capabilities to your vehicle. But do keep the facts in mind and do your homework *before* you go shopping, as too many conversion shops will only tell you about the benefits.

Chapter Fifteen

Ranges and Hot Plates

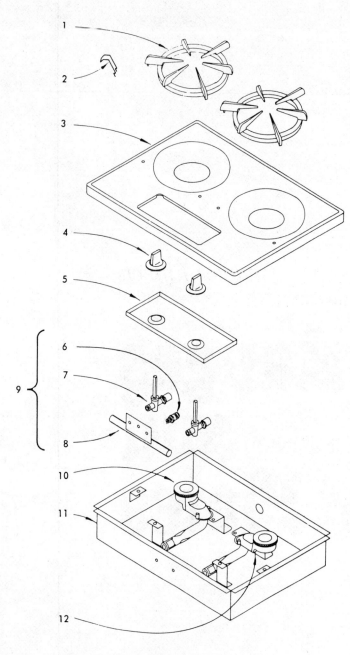

Figure 1. RANGE COUNTER UNIT

Key No.	Description
1	Grate
2	Grate Clip
3	Top Assembly (White)
4	Burner Knob
5	Valve Panel Assembly
6	Union Connection
7	Burner Valve Complete with Orifice Hood
8	Gas Manifold Only
9	Gas Manifold Complete with 2 Burner Valves, Orifice Hoods and Union Connection (6, 7, 8)
10	Left-Hand Burner
11	Burner Box Assembly (less Burners)
12	Right-Hand Burner
	Owners Manual (Not. Shown)

Everyone knows what a range is, right?

Wrong!

Technically, a range is a stove which contains one or more ovens and one or more burners. An appliance consisting only of burners is correctly called a hot plate. It's as simple as that, but the word "range" is commonly used to speak of burners alone, thus you'll hear about a range-and-oven combination. To banish confusion, we'll use the technical distinction first mentioned.

Ranges and hot plates are not complicated and don't require much fussing or adjusting. The ones on RVs are generally identical to home models, although smaller and lighter. And you'll find that most malfunctions will have their genesis in cleanliness or energy supply problems, rather than in parts failure.

15.01   PILOTLESS GAS BURNERS.

Very little explanation is necessary here, as these are such basic devices. Because they have no pilot flame, lighting simply requires placing a match next to the burner and turning the gas supply valve knob *on*. The height of the flame, and therefore its heat output, is regulated by twisting the knob to let more or less gas reach the burner. Pictured is the Elixer Trav'ler Model 800-212, which illustrates the typical components (Figure 1).

The Brown Stove three-burner model shows a basically similar anatomy (Figure 2).

Removing the top assembly (grate clips, grate and cover) exposes the easy-to-understand anatomy. The burner is removable for cleaning (see Section 15.02), and it's important that it be replaced so it is aligned with the venturi, or gas intake tube (Figure 3). If this alignment is not correct, it's possible for the gas supply to spin inside the venturi and "flash back" to ignite at the air intake hole. The solution is simply to center the burner.

Very rarely, you'll find that the burner isn't mounted correctly. In these cases the burner ring may appear off-center in the top assembly hole. While attempting alignment, you'll discover one of two situations: (1) the screw-in type (Harper-Wyman) valve, which is adjusted by turning slightly in either direction until alignment is achieved, and (2) the bolted valve (Robertshaw), wherein the manifold has been bent or misaligned and must be replaced to achieve correct burner placement.

The burner grates on several models are simply held in place with clips (see Figure 2), but you'll also sometimes find the grate itself is part of a locking mechanism (Figure 4). You'll see that the

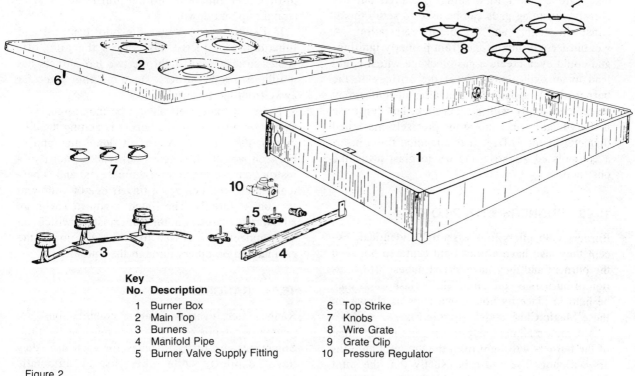

Key
No. Description

No.	Description	No.	Description
1	Burner Box	6	Top Strike
2	Main Top	7	Knobs
3	Burners	8	Wire Grate
4	Manifold Pipe	9	Grate Clip
5	Burner Valve Supply Fitting	10	Pressure Regulator

Figure 2.

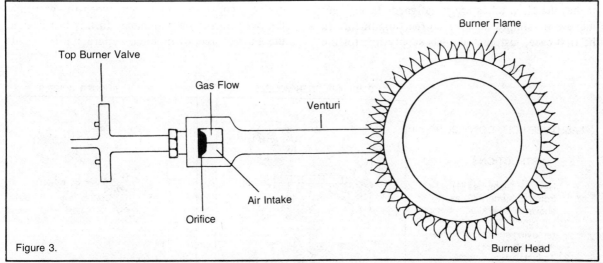

Figure 3.

ring of the grate has been cut to allow spring-back tension. This gap must always face toward the center of the top assembly (A). To remove these grates, first be sure they are cool, then grasp the grate with your thumb and fingers as shown (B), and compress the grate ring together while lifting it up.

15.02 CLEANING THE BURNERS.

To remove the burners, you must first take off the burner grates and the top assembly. On some units you'll also have to pull off the valve control knobs. Soaking the burner in hot soapy water will

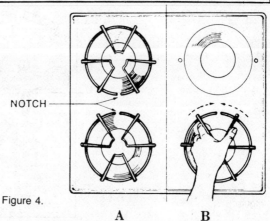

Figure 4.

A   B

take care of most food spills. Textured but not abrasive cleaning pads can be used to scrub them. Rinse thoroughly and dry before reinstalling. A wet burner will inhibit gas from properly igniting, and could even create a gas blockage which could lead to an explosion. Any of the orifices on the burner which appear clogged after cleaning may be reamed gently with a tooth pick, but don't use metal which could damage the precisely-machined diameter of the orifice. If this method fails, insert a compressed air hose and try to blast away the obstruction.

15.03   BURNERS WITH PILOTS.

Burners with pilots look essentially identical, except they also have a pilot light centered between the burners and they have "flash tubes" for ignition of burners by the pilot. These flash tubes may be held in place by hold-down clips as shown on these Magic Chef models (Figure 5):

A common ailment on pilot-lit units is that some of the burners will light from the top pilot but others will not. The cause is usually that the pilot flame is not centered in the pilot holder correctly, or that the flash tubes are misaligned. In the second event, simply achieve correct alignment. In the first case, just push the gas supply line for the pilot under the pilot holder until the pilot is straight up and down.

In Figure 6, (A) shows the pilot centered and functioning correctly. (B) shows the pilot off-center so that it will light the two left burners but not the two right burners, since the pilot is too far away from the flash tubes.

The pilot light itself should be monitored, as it shows whether or not the burner is getting the correct air-gas mixture. A perfect flame may appear between 5/8 and 1/8 inches tall (check your unit's instructions for the precise dimensions) and is basically blue with perhaps a tiny fringe of yellow at the top (Figure 7). The flame is adjusted with an adjustment screw on the thermostat, which on some models is accessed from the exterior of the cabinet and on others through the interior.

15.04   RANGES.

Ranges, i.e., oven and burner combinations, are generally categorized by their manner of ignition. Some must be lit by matches for each use (they have no pilot), while others use an automatic lighter (e.g., a built-in piezo device). Still others utilize a constant pilot which, when lit, will light the oven burner on command. In this last design, the burner and oven have separate pilot lights

FLASHTUBE HOLD-DOWN CLIPS

INSTRUCTIONS

1. Remove flashtubes (1) from top burners (2) as shown in illustration.
2. Lift clips (3) up carefully removing one end at a time from flashtube(1).
3. To install clips reverse procedure.

3 AND 4-BURNER MODELS

4-BURNER MODELS

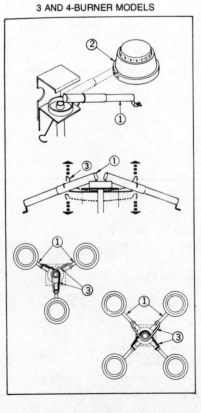
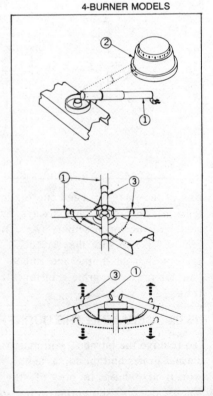

Figure 5.

which are fed by the same gas line, i.e., when the main gas valve is turned on *both* pilots must be lit. Burner operation from the constant pilot is simple and was discussed in Section 15.03. The oven function is somewhat more complex and is explained in the following sections.

15.05 GAS THERMOSTATS.

Gas thermostats have the job of controlling the quantity of gas flow to the oven system; it is usually operated directly by turning the thermostat knob which we usually call the oven temperature control knob. The thermostat is incapacitated by turning that knob to *off* or to *broil* — the first instance requiring no gas, and the second an unfluctuating quantity of gas. The thermostat knob also usually has a *pilot off* position separate from *off* when the unit utilizes a pilot light.

When the thermostat knob is dialed to a temperature setting which is higher than the existing oven temperature, it allows gas to flow through itself via the thermostat valve assembly that controls the gas supply to the mercury valve and the pilot assembly. But don't despair, it's all quite simple.

When the thermostat allows gas to pass, the constant pilot light (Section 15.06) ignites a separate pilot called the "heater pilot," and this second flame is located so that it warms a temperature-sensitive element containing mercury. The heat from the heater pilot boils the mercury, causing it to push against a mechanism which then opens a valve (called the mercury valve). When the mercury valve is open, gas flows to the oven burner and is ignited by the flame from the constant pilot. When the oven reaches the proper temperature (as sensed by the cylindrical sensing element usually attached to the sidewall of the oven),

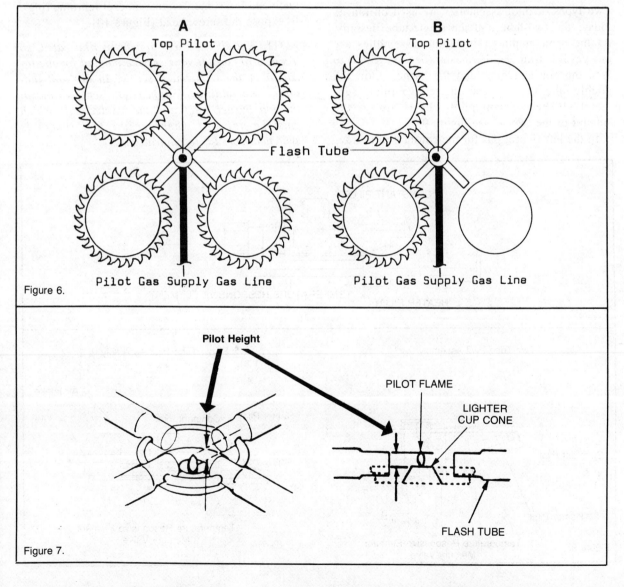

Figure 6.

Figure 7.

the thermostat cuts off the gas supply to the heater pilot. This allows the mercury in the sensing element to cool; it ceases to push against the bellows mechanism, and the mercury valve closes — shutting off the gas supply to the oven burner.

Understanding this sequence of events tells you why there is generally a delay between the time you command oven ignition and the actual lighting of the oven burner. Sometimes delays of up to 30 seconds are experienced, and this simply means that the mercury is taking that long to boil and open the mercury valve. This delay is not necessarily cause for repair action, but you may want to at least check to see that the sensing element is completely engulfed by flame and is thus receiving the full benefit of the heater pilot (Figure 8).

15.06   CONSTANT PILOT ASSEMBLIES.

Two types of pilot assemblies are used on ranges today: the two-tube and the single-tube designs. As the name implies, single-tube assemblies use one gas line from the thermostat (Section 15.05) to feed the constant pilot and the burner pilot; the double-tube variety feeds these two pilots separately. (The constant pilot tube is always the smaller of the two — see Figure 9).

In the left figure, gas for the constant pilot trav-

els through tube "A" to the pilot assembly. Gas for the heater pilot travels through tube "B." In the right figure, gas for both the constant and the heater pilot travel through the same gas line labeled "A." Observe also that the constant pilot and the heater pilot are really one and the same, i.e., the flame is the small constant pilot as long as the thermostat control knob is set to *off*. When a temperature is dialed, the gas supply through tube "A" increases and the pilot flame grows to become the heater pilot, as well, and it then encompasses the temperature responsive element. If this isn't immediately clear, look again at Figure 8 where you'll see these two pilot configurations outlined in dots.

It's vital that the size of the pilots be exactly as prescribed by the range's manufacturer. There is generally an adjustment screw on the thermostat which is accessed by removing the thermostat knob and, on some designs, a bezel (chrome ring), to expose the screw head (Figure 10).

NOTE: *Not all units will appear as illustrated, so it's best to consult your service manual for the location of the adjustment screw. In the unit pictured, the additional adjustment screws control the top burner pilot and the "selector," which must be adjusted whenever the fuel source is switched from LP to natural gas.*

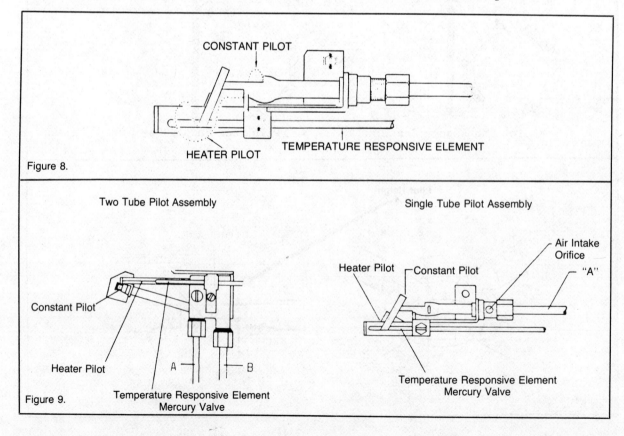

CONSTANT PILOT

HEATER PILOT

TEMPERATURE RESPONSIVE ELEMENT

Figure 8.

Two Tube Pilot Assembly

Constant Pilot

Heater Pilot

A   B

Temperature Responsive Element
Mercury Valve

Figure 9.

Single Tube Pilot Assembly

Heater Pilot   Constant Pilot

Air Intake Orifice

"A"

Temperature Responsive Element
Mercury Valve

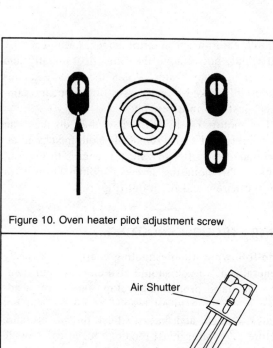

Figure 10. Oven heater pilot adjustment screw

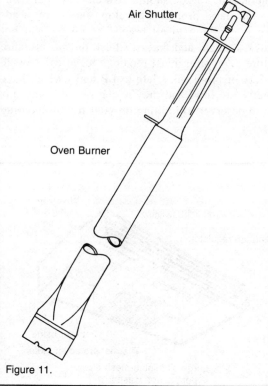

Air Shutter

Oven Burner

Figure 11.

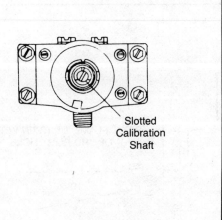

Slotted
Calibration
Shaft

Figure 12.

15.07   AIR SHUTTERS.

The size and behavior of a flame is controlled not only by the quantity of gas supplying it but also by how much air is mixed with that gas supply. A convenient method of adjusting this mixture of gas and air is through air shutters. These devices seldom need adjustment, but if the flame appears yellow, indicating insufficient oxygen, or if the burners won't ignite from the pilot and everything else (including gas pressure) is OK, or if the flame appears to lift away from the burner head as it tries to light, then the air shutter needs the appropriate adjustment to supply more or less oxygen (Figure 11).

15.08   CALIBRATING THE OVEN THERMOSTAT.

The oven thermostat is considered to be working perfectly if it is providing temperatures within 10 degrees on either side of the thermostat's temperature control knob. To check this, place an accurate oven thermometer on the rack in the center of the oven. Turn the oven on, set the temperature for 300 degrees and give the unit time to achieve that temperature. Note the temperature on the thermometer when you hear the burner cycling off. When the burner cycles on again, note that temperature. Now, compute the average temperature by adding to the low reading one-third of the difference between the low and high readings. The average temperature should be within 10 degrees of 300 degrees. (If the oven has no window and you must open the door to check the thermometer, do this quickly and be more forgiving of any discrepancies.)

If there is a significant discrepancy, be sure that the thermostat responsive element is in its proper place, see that the correct temperature (300 degrees) is set on the control knob, and check that aluminum foil or other materials aren't blocking heat in the oven.

If the thermostat does need adjustment, the screw is accessed by either removing the control knob or a little snap-out section in the middle of the control knob. Some thermostats are adjusted by holding the screw steady with a screwdriver while rotating the thermostat knob to the average temperature you calculated through the testing. Others are reset simply by turning the calibration screw (Figure 12).

15.09   FAULTY THERMOSTAT.

Oven thermostats are not repairable but they are easily replaced. If you suspect that a thermostat is not functional, test it when the oven is cold and the pilot is on. With the temperature control knob set to around 300 degrees F., the heater pilot should immediately light and, in a little while, the burner itself should ignite. If the heater pilot does not light, you have good reason to suspect the thermostat — and you should then consult a service technician.

15.10   GENERAL MAINTENANCE.

Commercial oven cleaners are still the best way to get rid of spills which weren't wiped up immediately and have caked on the walls. Do be careful, though, that these compounds don't contact the pilots or thermostats, as they can cause corrosion.

The burner or hot plate top should also be regularly cleaned, and warm water mixed with detergent will free most accumulations. Don't use abrasives on procelain or brush chrome — and be advised that many manufacturers suggest you don't use ammonia, as it can splash inside and cause damage.

Burner and oven grates can usually be cleaned with scouring pads in soapy water.

An interesting idea suggested by one manufacturer is to coat the hot plate cover with a light oil (e.g., Johnson's Baby Oil) which won't hold spills.

Range knobs can be easily removed and soaked in warm detergent solution to free dirt accumulations.

15.11   VENT AND FAN HOOD.

This easily understood device generally contains a fan motor, a filter and perhaps an electric light. Keep this area scrupulously clean, as grease builds here faster than anywhere else. Frequent wipings of both exterior and interior surfaces are generally sufficient, but remove the filter occasionally and soak it in soapy water. When the filter becomes impossibly caked with grease, or it appears damaged, just slip in a new one.

Fan motors rarely fail, but if they do they can be quickly and easily replaced. You must generally remove the filter to gain full access to the fan, remove the mounting screws, unplug the unit (or cut the wires) and lift it out (Figure 13.)

15.12   TROUBLESHOOTING.

The following troubleshooting chart is necessarily generalized, so you should also consult your owner's manual if problems develop. One word of advice is common to all brands of ranges and hot plates, though, and that is: Check the gas pressure before attempting most repair procedures. A wide variety of problems relate to LP tanks which have quietly run low, and they're the reasons why this motto deserves top billing on your troubleshooting list.

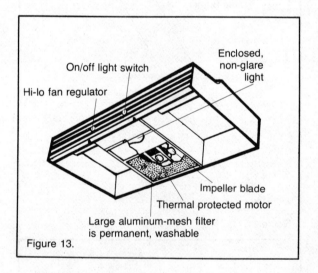

Figure 13.

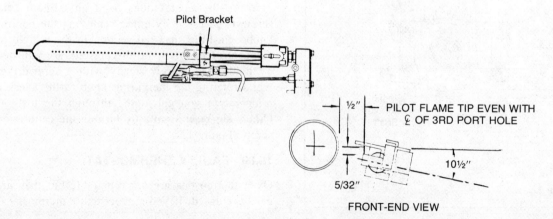

PILOT FLAME TIP EVEN WITH ℄ OF 3RD PORT HOLE

FRONT-END VIEW

What To Do To Save Unnecessary Service Calls

Covered here are some of the most common complaints together with their causes and corrections. By making a few simple checks, you may save the bother and expense of a service call.

CONDITION	CORRECTION
1. Oven too hot (burns food) Oven burner won't shut off No gas to oven pilots	A. Check the pilot Select-A-Gas Key cartridge to be sure it's for the type of gas being used. (See pilot adjustment for instructions.)
2. Oven slow heating up Poor baking Poor ignition of burners Pilots won't stay lit Popping sound from top burners Carbon on pilot shield Burner flame too low or too high	A. These conditions may be caused by a defective gas pressure regulator. Have the regulator tested by your gas dealer.
3. Oven pilots will not light or stay lit	A. Be sure the pilots are adjusted correctly for type of thermostat being used. B. Check pilot tubings: may be kinked, clogged or leaking at fittings. C. Have gas pressure regulator tested. D. Be sure oven control knob is not in the "Pilot Off" position.
4. Top burners won't light	A. Check and position top burners and flash tubing. B. Check pilot flame. C. Adjust air shutter, if equipped. See air shutter adjustment section. D. Clogged burner ports, clean with a toothpick.
5. Oven burner won't light Excessive oven temperature burns food Pilot outage	A. Check to see that the constant pilot is lit. B. Pilot assembly may be out of position. Position pilot assembly. See illustration. C. Oven pilot bracket not positioned properly could result in oven burner not cycling off at desired temperature. Bend pilot bracket to position pilot properly.
6. Gas smell	A. Check all connections with soapy water. This should be done at least every six months in recreational vehicles as vibrations due to travel may loosen connections.
7. Cake rises higher on one side	A. Pans set too close to side of oven. Allow two inches from side. B. Range not level.
8. Cakes burn on bottom	A. Oven too full for proper circulation. B. Using pan with dark bottom.
9. Oven door not closing properly	A. Because of expansion and contraction of metal, sometimes the oven door will slightly open at left or right hand corner. Adjustments can be made.

Chapter Sixteen

Furnaces

RVers who have had their furnaces malfunction during a winter trip readily agree that it's a misery. But we've learned that there are few legitimate reasons to be caught without heat if you've done your homework and are prepared to handle some elementary troubleshooting on the road.

16.01 FURNACE TYPES.

There are two primary furnace designs: radiant (also called *gravity*) and forced air. Radiant heaters warm the air immediately around themselves. As the warmer air rises and is replaced by cooler air, a natural pattern of circulation (convection) develops inside the RV.

Forced air heaters use an electric blower to distribute warmed air. In a large forced air installation, there may be several outlets (called registers) which are connected by flexible ducts, and the blower must be strong enough to service all of these points (Figure 1).

Theoretically, any source of energy can be converted into heat, but most RV furnaces take advantage of the LP-gas supply which is so easy to carry. Some models also contain electric heating elements which allow conservation of gas when campground power is available.

16.02 IGNITION.

The majority of RV furnaces use the pilot light system, and explicit directions for operating the pilot must appear on the nameplate. Section 14.11 in this manual also discusses lighting and adjusting pilots.

As an alternative to the match procedure, some furnaces feature a built-in peizo ignition. Pushing a lever on one end of the peizo device causes two crystals to contact each other with considerable force so that an electric spark results.

Simpler spark-type igniters and sophisticated electronic igniters (Section 16.05) are also used on furnaces. A glance at most RV supply house catalogs will illustrate the variety.

16.03 THERMOSTATS.

The best way to control a furnace's on/off cycling is with a thermostat, and models for RV use operate on the same principle as those in houses. In the simplest type, two different metals are joined together in a strip or coil. Because one of the metals contracts much faster when chilled, it will cause the strip to bend as the inside of your rig gets colder. When sufficiently bent, it will contact an electrode and complete an electrical circuit that

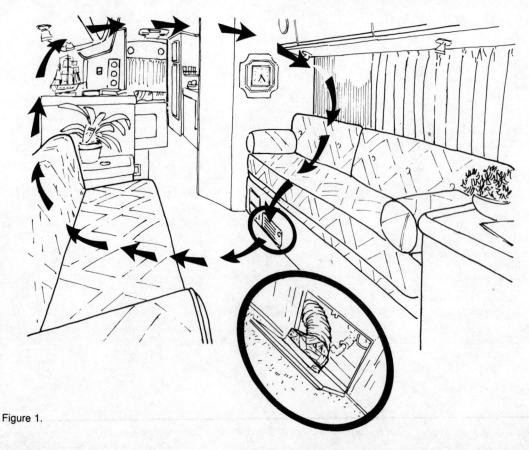

Figure 1.

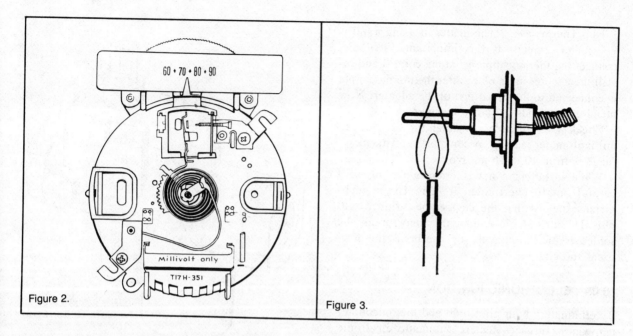

Figure 2.

Figure 3.

tells the heater to start working (Figure 2).

Most thermostats are relatively inexpensive and virtually trouble-free — but not suited to repair. When they do wear out, it's usually easier to replace the whole unit rather than trying to find the defunct part. One common cause of thermostat complaint should be noted, however, and it's this: Because the device can only measure the temperature where it is physically located, its reading does not necessarily reflect temperatures in other portions of the rig. If the thermostat is attached to a wall where there is a draft or where heat collects abnormally, it registers that reality — and RVers often think the unit is defective. If this is your situation, either relocate the thermostat or decide to use its numbered settings as reference points, not as degree markings. (CAUTION: If you replace a thermostat, be very sure that it is the proper design for your furnace. There are different mechanical designs and you won't be able to get incompatible components to work together.)

16.04 THERMOCOUPLE.

Integral with the pilot on most heaters is the thermocouple, a simple safety device which converts heat from the pilot light into very low voltage electricity (Figure 3). While the pilot burns, electricity generated by the thermocouple energizes the magnet that holds the pilot's gas supply valve open. If the pilot fails, electricity ceases to flow and a spring returns the valve to the closed position.

Thermocouples are replaced when they fail. When troubleshooting diagnosis points to the thermocouple, it must be tested with a millivolt meter and a special adapter. As this is a specialized device, most RVers leave the procedure to the experts. If you want to do-it-yourself, though, be very sure that you know how to use the meter.

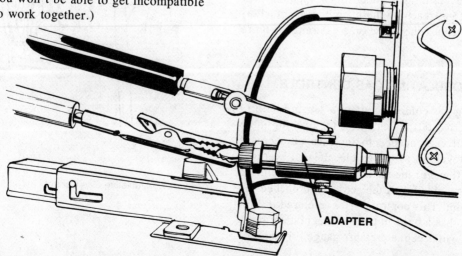

Figure 4.

ADAPTER

Duo-Therm says, ''The matter of using a milli-volt meter correctly is very important. First, dis-connect the thermocouple from the control and in-stall the adapter in its place after the thermocouple is connected to the upper end of the adapter. Now attach meter leads as shown in Figure 4.''

Check your furnace's manual for the desired millivolt meter reading. A common ''satisfactory'' range is from 10 to 16 millivolts.

When installing a new thermocouple, be very careful not to overtighten it. Duo-Therm tech-nicians suggest that the devices be ''finger-tight plus 1/4 turn.'' More than this may break the soldered connection at the tip and break the elec-trical curcuit.

16.05 ELECTRONIC IGNITION.

By eliminating both pilot light and thermocouple, many new furnaces feature automatic electronic ignition. On command from the thermostat con-trol, this device automatically turns on the main burner gas supply and offers it electrically-pro-duced sparks. And being an electronic device, it falls beyond the capabilities of most do-it-your-selfers to fix, although problems surrounding the device are covered in the Troubleshooting Section (16.17).

16.06 GAS CONTROLLERS.

In our war on cold, we might think of the thermo-stat as a forward observation post, while the gas control on the furnace itself is a command center. There are four types of control units, and each contain similar automatic safeguards which close the gas supply if the flame goes out.

Manual gas controls are the simplest type. Heat is varied by turning a knob which regulates the quantity of gas reaching the main burner, much as you would adjust the flame on a gas range (Figure 5).

16.07 MODULATING GAS CONTROLS.

Modulating gas controls contain a sensing bulb (a type of thermostat) which varies the opening in an internal valve as needed to increase or decrease the heat level in your vehicle. If you were to watch the flame of the main burner, you would see it slowly get smaller as the sensor approached the shutoff point. This control device (pictured in Fig-ure 6) also has a built-in pressure regulation and a tap which will accept a pressure gauge for testing.

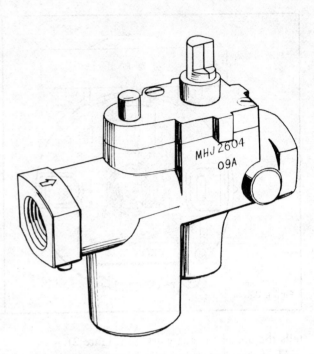

Figure 5. Manual Gas Control

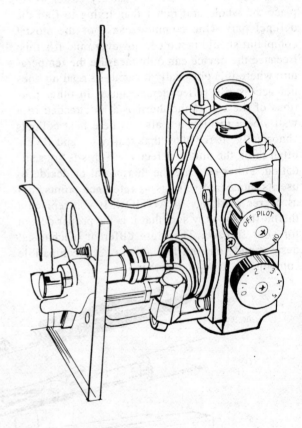

Figure 6. Modulating Gas Control

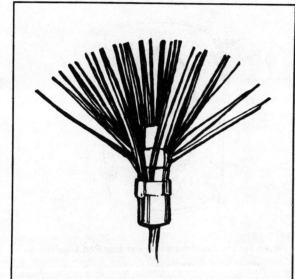

Figure 7. Shown here is the inside of a pilot generator used to power the millivolt system. The pilot generator is made up of 25 individual thermocouples wired in series. Each couple is made up of two dissimilar metals like nickel and iron that are joined together at one end. This is known as the hot junction because this is the end on which the pilot flame impinges. The heat on the hot junction generates a small amount of electricity. The open circuit output on each individual junction is in the range of about .025 volts more commonly spoken as 25 millivolts.

Courtesy of Duo Therm

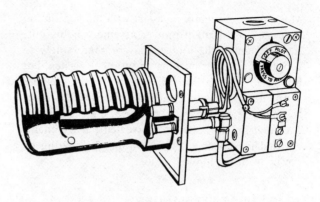

Figure 8. Millivolt Gas Control

16.08 MILLIVOLT CONTROL.

Next in complexity is the millivolt control, so-called because its bundle of thermocouples wired together in series produces as much as 750 millivolts when they are heated by the pilot flame (see Figure 7). This large quantity of self-generated electricity is used to operate the main burner gas supply valve on command from the wall thermostat. Like the modulating control, the millivolt control in Figure 8 has a built-in pressure regulator, a pressure tap for checking pressure and a pilot adjusting screw. In addition, there is a pilot filter to help keep dirt out of the system.

16.09 12-VOLT CONTROL.

Larger forced-air installations often use a 12-volt DC gas control. Power for all functions comes from the vehicle battery or the AC to DC convertor, and the system is usually regulated by a wall thermostat. The unit depicted in Figure 9 has a pilot filter and a pilot flame adjustment screw, but no internal pressure regulator.

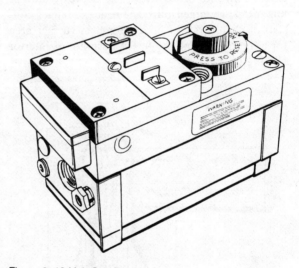

Figure 9. 12-Volt Gas Control

16.10 BURNER AND VENTING.

When things go wrong with a furnace, many people have an instinct to poke around in the main burner area, but you'll probably never be able to satisfy this urge. To protect your lungs rather than your fingers, all conventional units isolate the burning process. The sealed chamber draws the air necessary for combustion from the outside and vents the wastes outside. Again for safety reasons, the two ducts (intake and output) are separate, although they may appear to use the same port on the side of your rig (Figure 10).

16.11 BLOWER.

Most furnaces require an assist with the ventilation process, so the main blower assembly helps out. In small units, the blower may be there solely to supply oxygen for burning and to vent wastes, but forced-air models use the same motor to circulate warm air in the rig's interior. When the blower assembly serves this dual purpose, there is still no exchange of air between the sealed burner chamber and the coach's interior — only a sharing of power from the blower motor.

16.12 HEAT EXCHANGER.

The separateness between burner and heated air is made possible by the furnace's heat exchanger. In its simplest form, this is just a metal skin around the burner that is warmed by the burner flame. Cooler air from the RV's interior is warmed when it is drawn into contact with the opposite side of this metal. In larger units, the heat exchanger consists of chambers which create greater surface area for a more efficient and faster warming of interior air (Figure 11).

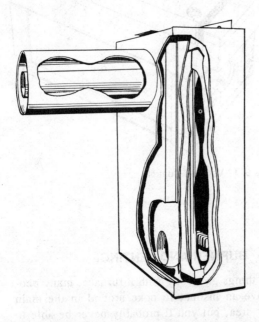

Figure 11. In this Duo-Therm Series H heat exchanger, combustion air enters through the large tube surrounding the vent pipe. Air goes down through the box on the back, through the tube in the bottom and into the heat chamber in the area surrounding the burner.

The products of combustion are vented to the outside through the small tube. Properly installed there are no chances of products of combustion getting into the living area.

Figure 10. Furnace Intake and Exhaust Port Mounted on the Exterior Wall of an RV.

16.13 ADDITIONAL SAFETY FEATURES.

In addition to those already mentioned, your furnace also contains several safety devices. While you may never see them (and most RVers should definitely avoid tinkering with them), knowing about their presence and function may help you understand the genesis of a problem. In the order of operation, these remaining features are: the overload switch, which monitors the AC or DC input and automatically shuts down the supply if voltage exceeds safe limits; the sail switch, which monitors the quantity of air flowing into the sealed burner chamber and turns off the gas supply if there is insufficient oxygen for good combustion; and the limit switch, which also controls the main gas valve and closes it if the heater's temperature exceeds a preset limit.

16.14 INTERNAL POWER CONVERTOR.

Furnaces designed to use either vehicle or campground power supplies may contain their own convertor for reducing 115-volt AC to 12-volt DC. In these cases, an automatic switch "senses" the power input and either channels it directly into the furnace electrical system or into the convertor.

16.15 OPERATIONAL SEQUENCE.

Before moving into maintenance and troubleshooting techniques, it's useful to understand the sequence of events as they occur in a well-functioning furnace. Even if you don't do your own work, this knowledge will give you the "language" you need to specifically describe a problem and thus lower your repair bill. The account which follows

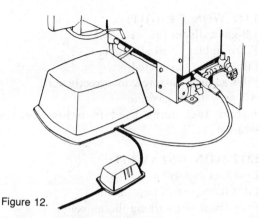

Figure 12.

fits most units (your owner's manual will give specific information):

(1) When the temperature reaches the designated setting, the wall thermostat contacts close. (2) The fan relay coil is energized, completing the circuit to the blower motor (some models have a five- to 25-second delay after the thermostat contacts close). (3) The motor starts, turning the combustion and circulating air blower wheels. (4) When the blower reaches the rpm necessary to close the air-operated sail switch (approximately one to two seconds), current is supplied through the temperature limit switch to the direct spark ignition control module. If yours is a conventional pilot furnace, skip steps five through nine as the sail switch would supply current through a temperature limit switch and the gas valve would open. (Some models incorporate a built-in delay so the fan can purge the combustion chamber before the gas valve opens.) Gas would be ignited by the pilot light, and you'd be in business. (5) When energized, the module delays 15 seconds while the blower purges the combustion chamber. (6) The direct-spark ignition system module supplies a high voltage spark through high tension leads to the igniter. (7) The gas valve opens. (8) Burner ignites. (9) A sensor signals the presence of flame and the spark stops. (If flame is not established in seven seconds, the system closes the gas valve and locks out.) (10) Temperature rise causes a fan switch to close, but this does not affect the fan's operation since it is already receiving power through the fan relay in step two. (This is not applicable to time-delay models, or to radiant heaters that don't have a forced air blower.) (11) Gas valve opens when either the limit switch or the thermostat contacts open (i.e., the desired temperature is reached). (12) The blower continues operating for a short period because it is still receiving power through the fan switch (Step 10 above). When the heater has cooled sufficiently, the fan

switch opens (or the time-delay relay opens) and the blower shuts down.

16.16 MAINTENANCE.

Actual maintenance of your heating system is rather simple, because many of its components shouldn't be touched. This isn't a conspiracy on the part of organized technicians, either. It is an acknowledgement of two facts: Many parts are far too intricate to be understood by anyone but an expert with specialized tools; plus, you're dealing with a system that is potentially dangerous — and any little goof on your part could result in a lethal situation. The best advice is to understand your own skills and be guided by them. For most of us, the maintenance functions, which can (and should) be performed, fall into the categories of cleanliness, monitoring and testing.

Simple dirt in its many forms is by far the largest source of burner problems. Make it a habit to vacuum the accessible part of your unit whenever you clean the rest of your rig. Also, check in the pilot area after the coach has been stored for even just a week; spiders love to set up housekeeping in there (it's doubtful that they catch anything in their webs, but instinct tells them to try). Other stowaways include a variety of insects and sometimes even birds that have built their homes in the vent on the side of your rig. Particularly notorious are mud daubers, little wasps who will methodically choke the whole duct with mud.

Monitoring means being aware of how the unit is functioning on a daily basis. Watch the pilot light (if you have one) and see that it's always in correct adjustment (see Section 14.11). The adjustment screw on most models lets you control its functioning. Also, notice the burner flame and use an adjustment screw to modify it. (Simplistically, when gas ignites at the burner orifice and rises off of the burner, there is too much air in the system; a yellow flame means too little air, incomplete combustion and a burner chamber which loses efficiency as it becomes coated with soot.) In addition, monitor the condition of the heater's supply systems, the LP-gas and the electric supply, including the various ducts and lines, and see that these are in good condition.

Testing should be a periodic concern, and most manufacturers recommend that this be accomplished along with more detailed cleaning and servicing (by a technician, of course) once each year. If you have the appropriate equipment, you can do some testing, such as measuring the LP-gas pressure both at the cylinder and at the heater gas valve, and checking the electric supply at the battery and at the heater for correct and consistent voltage.

Like almost every other aspect of your rig, it's simple to keep tabs on condition and functioning if you develop habitual routines. It may be difficult to organize yourself at first, but the time you spend in learning good habits pays off handsomely in lower repair bills and greater equipment reliability.

16.17   TROUBLESHOOTING

Assuming regular maintenance by yourself, and timely inspection by an authorized serviceman, it's highly unlikely that serious problems will develop on the road. If malfunctions do occur, the accompanying troubleshooting chart will help you locate and rectify the disruption.

In checking for probable causes, always suspect the supply system first. Like the proverbial appliance that won't operate because someone didn't plug it in, a large number of furnace malfunctions are simply due to an empty LP-gas tank, a closed gas supply valve, or lack of electricity. (Please don't feel that we're being condescending in suggesting these obvious solutions; repair personnel consistently find that the little things lead directly to abrupt equipment failures.)

One problem which deserves special mention simply because it teaches many RVers how to curse is *flame-out*, i.e., the pilot light goes out, often while the rig is traveling or parked in a windy environment. Infrequent flame-outs may just be an exercise in patience, but chronic pilot failures have led to a fascinating assortment of homemade remedies, some of which actually work. If all immediate efforts to locate and close or baffle an air leak fail, there are electronic pilot lighting accessories (such as pictured in Figure 12) which have solved the problem for many RVers. Before installing one of these devices, though, be sure that your trouble really *is* the wind — and not something within the furnace.

From a safety standpoint, furnaces are just like any other gas and/or electric appliance in that they require thoughtful treatment. So don't smoke or use flames near gas lines. Be wary of hot surfaces. Always double-check everything you do. And don't attempt any repairs that you aren't competent to complete.

The following troubleshooting chart is a compilation from several manufacturers. It will be obvious which symptoms and probable causes are appropriate to your unit.

PILOT WON'T LIGHT:
- LP-gas cylinder low or empty
- Peizo lighter (if used) inoperative
- Pilot orifice obstructed
- Pilot adjustment screw incorrectly set
- Air or water in gas line
- Butane fuel being used in below freezing weather

PILOT WON'T STAY LIT:
- Low fuel supply
- Pilot flame out of adjustment
- Pilot flame not striking thermocouple
- Thermocouple loose or faulty
- Outside vent grill not securely fastened
- Faulty gas valve

PILOT OK BUT BURNER WON'T LIGHT:
If blower motor runs:
- Low fuel supply
- Fuel lines obstructed
- Faulty gas valve
- Faulty sail or limit switches

If blower motor won't run:
- No electricity
- Faulty thermostat
- Faulty convertor
- Faulty system or overload switch
- Faulty blower motor

INSUFFICIENT HEAT:
- Gas supply low
- Faulty gas regulator
- Using butane in below freezing weather
- Burner flame out of adjustment
- Blocked return air ducts
- Sealed burner chamber coated with soot
- Blower running backwards due to reversed polarity in circuit from battery

ON AC/DC MODELS, FURNACE RUNS BATTERY DOWN WHEN USED ON 115 VAC SUPPLY:
- Faulty convertor or convertor wiring

BLOWER CYCLES WHEN WALL THERMOSTAT IS IN "OFF" POSITION:
- In mild weather, heat from the pilot may energize fan switch, causing blower to operate. If pilot is properly adjusted, the correction is to turn system switch to "off" during mild weather.

FURNACE BLOWER SHUTS OFF IMMEDIATELY WHEN FURNACE SHUTS OFF:
- Faulty fan switch.

BLOWER RUNS SMOOTHLY ON 12 VOLTS BUT VIBRATES (MAKES NOISE) ON 115 VOLTS:

- Faulty capacitor in furnace

FURNACE BURNS CONTINUOUSLY:

- Thermostat wires shorted together

BLOWER VIBRATES ON EITHER 12-VOLT OPERATION OR 115-VOLT OPERATION:

- Blower impeller out of balance
- Motor mounts deteriorated
- Motor shaft bent

METALLIC "SCRAPING" NOISE WHEN BLOWER OPERATES:

- Either combustion or blower impeller improperly centered on motor shaft causing impeller to hit blower housing.

TROUBLESHOOTING SPECIFICALLY APPLICABLE TO ELECTRONIC IGNITION SYSTEMS*

CAUTIONS:

1. Never operate the furnace with the electrode wire disconnected nor with the electrode assembly removed from the furnace.
2. Never use a battery charger to check an electric ignition furnace — use a 12-volt battery only.
3. Never use a screwdriver on any part of the electrode assembly while the furnace is in operation.
4. Be sure the electrode assembly screws are tight at all times, especially after the electrode has been removed and reinstalled.
5. Electrodes and module boards are not field repairable.

A. Electrode not sparking
  a. Low voltage — must be 12-volt DC at module board
  b. Loose wire at connector plug
  c. Faulty electrode
  d. Broken electrode wire
  e. Wire off electrode or module board
  f. Faulty module board

B. Valve not opening
  a. Low voltage
  b. Faulty valve
  c. Loose or broken wire
  d. Faulty micro switch
  e. Faulty limit switch
  f. Faulty module board

C. No ignition (electrode sparking and valve opening)
  a. Low gas pressure
  b. Electrode out of position
  c. Air adjustment to burner
  d. Air leak around gaskets

D. Burner will not stay on (goes into lockout)
  a. Flame sensor out of position
  b. Loose or broken sensor wire
  c. Faulty electrode assembly
  d. Faulty module board

*(courtesy of Suburban Manufacturing)

16.18 REPLACING A FURNACE.

The furnace size which is appropriate to a particular recreational vehicle is determined through actual tests. After building and insulating a rig, many manufacturers work with equipment suppliers to determine how quickly heat is lost through the layers of material in the coach. When this can be measured in BTUs per hour, it is a simple matter to install a furnace which replaces the heat during a 50% duty cycle, i.e., the heater works and rests an equivalent amount of time. A lesser duty cycle is even more advantageous from the standpoint of noise, power drain and blower life.

While the tests mentioned are undoubtedly accurate, they don't necessarily measure what you're interested in. Frankly, it's one thing to park a rig in a temperature-controlled laboratory and measure heat loss — but it's something else again when you're traveling down a wintery highway at 55 mph. A quick glance at a chill factor table will show you how moving air affects temperatures, and this obviously relates to how well your equipment can maintain an interior environment.

The purpose of saying these things is to suggest that the unit which is recommended for your rig may not necessarily be the best buy. If you're replacing a furnace, you know what the old unit's rating was and how effective it was, so you can upgrade or not based upon experience. Adding to a new rig is at best a guessing game — but at least you can make your guess an educated one.

Chapter Seventeen

Water Heaters

When you talk about all the comforts of home being aboard an RV, hot water must certainly lead the list. "Roughing it" with a hot shower to start the day or doing the dishes in warm suds is hard to beat, and the water heaters which make these luxuries possible are relatively trouble-free devices.

17.01   GAS WATER HEATERS.

An overwhelming number of RVers choose a gas heater simply because it gives them the flexibility to camp where campground power isn't available (Figure 1). Some of these units may also offer an electric capability, but they tend to heat the water in the same manner.

Basically, a gas water heater consists of a glass or metal-lined container for the water, a layer of insulation (often fiberglass) and an outer skin to tie it all together.

The burner assembly is familiar to anyone who has investigated their furnace or absorption refrigerator. It consists of a pilot light (unless the unit has an automatic electronic lighting device), the burner and a thermostat-thermocouple package. The by-products of combustion are vented to the outside world, and fresh air to feed the flame is drawn in from the same source. The heat created by the burner flame travels through a conduit that passes through the interior of the storage or reservoir tank, and the water is heated as it contacts this source (see Figure 2).

A sensing element within the water tank monitors the water temperature and mechanically transmits this information to the thermostat. When the temperature is within a few degrees of the setting on the external control knob, the thermostat shuts off the gas supply to the main burner and the heating operation ceases. Likewise, when the temperature drops a few degrees below the manually controlled setting, the thermostat opens the gas control valve and lets gas flow through to the main burner, where it is ignited by either the continuously-burning pilot or an electronic lighting device.

Because there is an obvious danger of gas not being lit at the burner, and thus escaping into the environment, every pilot must be equipped with a thermocouple. The thermocouple is a heat sensing element which remains in physical contact with the pilot flame. If the pilot should be accidentally extinguished by a vagrant air current, the thermocouple cools and quickly shuts off the gas supply to both main burner and pilot light. Relighting of the pilot then requires a special procedure which is described in the instructions attached to the water heater.

17.02   ELECTRIC HEATING ELEMENTS.

Electric heating elements are a useful dimension, as they allow preservation of LPG supplies whenever generator or inexpensive campground power is available. On most RV models the element itself is a simple U-shaped structure attached to a baseplate which is easily screwed into place. (See Figure 3.) Gas and electric combination units may employ separate thermostats, so be careful that

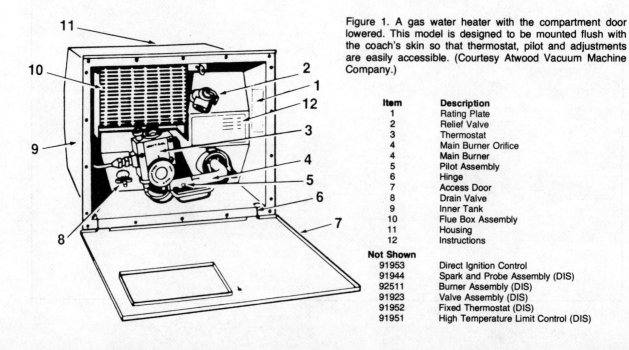

Figure 1. A gas water heater with the compartment door lowered. This model is designed to be mounted flush with the coach's skin so that thermostat, pilot and adjustments are easily accessible. (Courtesy Atwood Vacuum Machine Company.)

Item	Description
1	Rating Plate
2	Relief Valve
3	Thermostat
4	Main Burner Orifice
4	Main Burner
5	Pilot Assembly
6	Hinge
7	Access Door
8	Drain Valve
9	Inner Tank
10	Flue Box Assembly
11	Housing
12	Instructions
Not Shown	
91953	Direct Ignition Control
91944	Spark and Probe Assembly (DIS)
92511	Burner Assembly (DIS)
91923	Valve Assembly (DIS)
91952	Fixed Thermostat (DIS)
91951	High Temperature Limit Control (DIS)

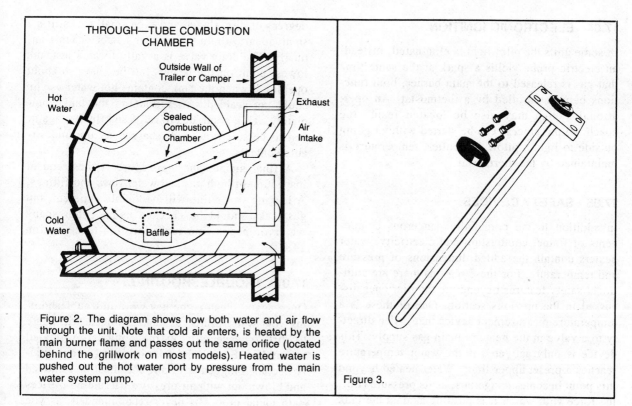

Figure 2. The diagram shows how both water and air flow through the unit. Note that cold air enters, is heated by the main burner flame and passes out the same orifice (located behind the grillwork on most models). Heated water is pushed out the hot water port by pressure from the main water system pump.

Figure 3.

you are checking the correct one when trouble-shooting. CAUTION: Never turn on the power to an electric heating element when the water tank is not filled. Even momentary operation with a dry tank can destroy the element.

17.03 HEAT EXCHANGERS.

Another useful device for the traveling RVer is a heat exchanger on the water heater. Sometimes called by other trade names, the units work similarly on all brands in that they connect the engine heater to the water heater with hoses. This connection allows the heat generated by the engine to be used for warming the water in the reservoir. Obviously, the device only works when the vehicle is operating, with the advantage being that after a long drive you arrive with your water fully heated.

There is nothing complex about heat exchangers, as they consist primarily of hoses which conduct the hot engine coolant to the heat exchanger entry port on the water heater. Within the heater, the warmth is extracted from the coolant and applied to water in the reservoir, then the coolant cycles out of the heater and back through another set of hoses to the engine. (See Figure 4.)

Because of its simplicity, the repairs you will most likely encounter will be the necessity of installing new hoses when the old ones age, and periodically checking the clamps and fittings for tightness.

A TYPICAL HEAT EXCHANGING SYSTEM

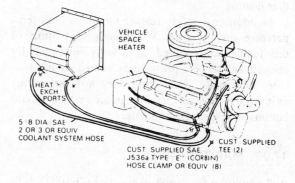

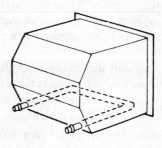

Figure 4. Drawing shows how hot coolant from the vehicle engine flows through the water heater and back into the engine cooling system.

17.04 ELECTRONIC IGNITION.

In some units the pilot light is eliminated. Instead, an electric probe yields a spark at the same time that gas is released to the main burner, both functions being controlled by a thermostat. An operational switch may also be located inside the coach, so the process can be started without going outside to light a pilot. Thereafter, temperature is maintained by the thermostat.

17.05 SAFETY DEVICES.

In addition to the potentially dangerous components of flame, combustion and electricity, water heaters contain the added dimensions of pressure and temperature. For these reasons there are additional safety features beyond the familiar ones discussed in the previous section. One of these is a temperature measurement device that is tied directly to a valve in the heater's main gas supply. This device is only activated if the water temperature reaches a preset upper limit. Water heated beyond this point becomes dangerous, as its pressure (i.e., the force with which it is pushing against the tank walls) also increases with increased temperature. When this upper limit is reached, the safety device automatically closes the gas supply to prohibit further heating.

An additional safety feature measures both temperature and pressure. When the preset limits of this feature are reached, a valve is automatically opened and excess pressure is vented to the outside. Obviously, steam and very hot water may exit through this port, so it is an area which should command respect from the user.

17.06 MAINTENANCE.

Maintaining a gas water heater is a relatively simple procedure. The working parts of the appliance are generally accessed from the exterior of the coach and, as with most other mechanical features of your rig, the basic maintenance is a good cleaning regimen.

Because dust and dirt easily enter the louvered compartment door which protects the water heater, regular wipe-downs and vacuumings will literally do wonders in prolonging efficient operation.

The outside vent/air intake port must also be kept clean and free of any kind of obstruction. Be especially critical about inspecting this area after storing your RV, as insects find this a desirable place to set up housekeeping.

Because most water supplies contain varying degrees of dirt, sludge and even small rocks, it's a smart idea to drain your water heater at least annually. The drain valve is usually located near the lowest point on the heater, but be cautious about opening it when the tank contains hot water as you could get scalded. After draining the tank completely, it's a good idea to refill and flush it again, just to be sure you've discharged all the undesirable contents.

A final maintenance procedure is the frequent inspection of both gas and water lines and fittings. A leaking water line will be visibly apparent, but gas leaks should be checked using either soapy water or a gas line leak detector (see Section 14.07).

17.07 TROUBLESHOOTING.

Once again, clean is the key word in troubleshooting your water heater, as most problems will relate to dirt — especially in the combustion-related assemblies. Burner and pilot orifices can eventually become clogged with dirt and must be removed and blown out with air pressure. (Reaming orifices with metal probes is never recommended, as you can easily alter the precisely tooled diameter.)

Pilot flames are an especially useful index of proper operation. A healthy flame is basically a deep blue or purple with a small upper fringe of yellow. Occasional yellow flecks in the flame are simply pieces of dust being burned. (A proper flame is illustrated in Section 14.11.)

A flame which is not stable or which differs from the ideal often indicates low gas pressure, but improper air shutter adjustment may also be the culprit. If you are sure that the gas supply to the heater is adequate, and that dirt isn't clogging the orifice, the shutter can be adjusted on most models. Open it for more air supply to the combustion process or close it for less (you should consult your owner's manual for specifics pertinent to your model, although the process will probably be similar to those shown in Figure 5).

The inevitable carbon deposits in flues must be cleaned periodically. This is usually a good chore to leave for the professional, however, as it involves disconnecting the thermostat and gas lines — and sometimes even dismounting the entire unit.

As with your other gas appliances, thermostats usually contain adjustment screws for controlling flame characteristics, but the units themselves are generally unrepairable. The thermocouple devices, considered part of the thermostat assembly, are likewise unrepairable — but problems with them

Figure 5.

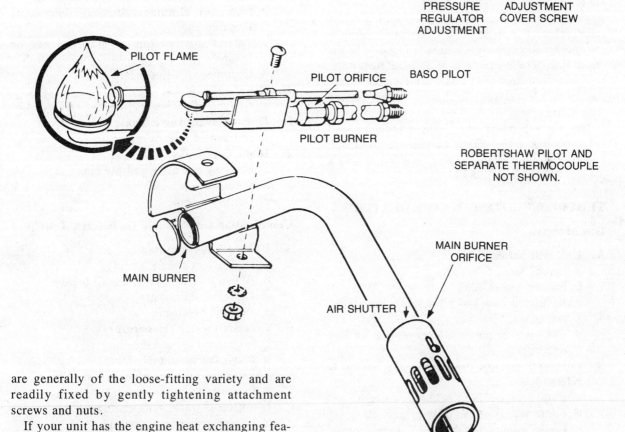

ITT GENERAL CONTROL

TEMPERATURE
SELECTION
LEVER

LIGHTING/CONTROL
(RESET) DIAL

ECO
SWITCH
LOCATION

PILOT BURNER ADJUSTMENT
ITT General Control:
Pilot adjustment located directly below pilot on/off knob.
1. Remove pilot gas adjustment cover screw.
2. Adjust pilot key directly inside to provide proper size flame. (½-inch high or until a slight yellow tip appears in pilot flame.)
3. Replace pilot gas adjustment cover screw.

PRESSURE
REGULATOR
ADJUSTMENT

PILOT GAS
ADJUSTMENT
COVER SCREW

PILOT FLAME

PILOT ORIFICE

BASO PILOT

PILOT BURNER

ROBERTSHAW PILOT AND
SEPARATE THERMOCOUPLE
NOT SHOWN.

MAIN BURNER
ORIFICE

MAIN BURNER

AIR SHUTTER

are generally of the loose-fitting variety and are readily fixed by gently tightening attachment screws and nuts.

If your unit has the engine heat exchanging feature, inefficiencies are usually traceable to cracked hoses or loose hose attachments.

Problems in units with electric heating elements generally arise from low or non-existent voltage. Always check this possibility before considering further troubleshooting explorations.

Loose wiring connections are the next most common electric malfunction, and you can often trace these problems by simply hand-testing each junction. Do be sure to shut off the power supply before putting your hands into the unit.

BURNER ADJUSTMENT: Slide main burner air shutter to the right enough for yellow tip to appear in flame, then slowly slide shutter to the left until yellow tip disappears and lock with set screw.

SPECIAL CAUTION: ALL GAS APPLIANCES MUST BE SHUT OFF WHEN REFUELING. THIS ALSO INCLUDES PILOT LIGHTS.

A defective heating element is also a possibility with electric units, and these are often simply placed so that they can be exchanged by the consumer. But before you go to the bother and expense of doing this, check the power supply to the heating element with an electrical metering device. (Again, be careful, because you're dealing with high-voltage live power when you make these tests. Don't attempt it if you aren't familiar with, and comfortable around, electricity.)

Temperature and pressure relief valves are designed to open at or around 210 degrees F., or 125 psi. A properly functioning heater will not reach the temperature limits of the relief valve, but if this should occur you can suspect a thermostat problem. Pressure, though, especially in demand water systems, can briefly reach the 125 psi setting, and this may cause a slight dripping at the relief valve. The cause of this pressure buildup is the check valve, which is normally installed in the water line between the heater and the freshwater reservoir (see Section 11.05). Unless this symptom proves excessive, it should not be viewed with alarm.

The accompanying troubleshooting chart will help you locate the source of specific problems, but always check your findings with your unit's manual before proceeding further.

TROUBLESHOOTING WATER HEATERS

Gas Models:

A. Unit will not light.
   a. Insufficient gas supply.
   b. Incorrect pilot adjustment.
   c. Restricted travel of pilot button (needs lubrication).
   d. Complete or partial blockage of pilot line or orifice.

B. Pilot extinguishes itself when the button is released.
   a. Button has not been held long enough.
   b. Loose wafers at end of thermocouple.
   c. Loose connection between thermocouple and control.
   d. Weak or defective thermocouple, magnet or ECO.

C. Main burner will not ignite.
   a. Partial or complete orifice obstruction.
   b. Main burner obstruction.
   c. Improper air shutter adjustment.

D. Pilot outage.
   a. Improper pilot adjustment.
   b. Improper main burner edjustment.
   c. Obstruction in the air intake.
   d. Dirt in pilot orifice or between the two wafers at end of thermocouple.
   e. Defective thermocouple magnet or ECO.

E. Smoking.
   a. Improper pilot adjustment.
   b. Improper main burner adjustment.
   c. Improper alignment of main burner tube.
   d. Obstructions in U-tube or main burner.
   e. Improper alignment of flame spreaders.
   f. Bad gas supply.

F. Main burner continues to hold a small flame after unit has been shut down.
   a. Improper seat of the main burner valve contained with the control.

G. Sporadic or "popping" main burner.
   a. Partial blockage of main burner orifice.
   b. Improper alignment of main burner of flame spreader.
   c. Partial obstruction of main burner or U-tube.
   d. Improper air adjustment.

H. Relief valve leaks.
   a. Buildup of sediments in relief valve seal.

I. Petcock drain valve leaks.
   a. Buildup of foreign materials.

J. Inner tank leaks.
   a. Freezing has destroyed the tank.
   b. Welding leak.
   c. Corrosive leak.

Combination Gas/Electric Or Electric Units:

A. Unit will not operate.
   a. Insufficient electric supply.
   b. Blown fuse or tripped circuit breaker.
   c. Defective thermostat.
   d. Defective element.

B. Excessive water temperatures.
   a. Improper thermostat setting.
   b. Loose thermostat mounting.
   c. Fallen insulation blocking sensitivity of thermostat.

C. Insufficient water temperatures.
   a. Improper thermostat setting.
   b. Excessive lime buildup on heating element (element must be replaced).

(Courtesy Atwood Mobile Products Division)

Chapter Eighteen

Air Conditioners

Air-conditioners belong in one of two categories: evaporative or compressor types. Both are easily understood and lend themselves to some basic maintenance and troubleshooting procedures, but many of the more complex repairs must be left to professionals. Yet even when the problem is beyond your skills, it pays to understand enough air-conditioner anatomy to pinpoint the trouble for the technician, thus saving his time and your money.

18.01 EVAPORATIVE COOLERS.

Of the two types of air-conditioners, evaporatives are the simplest as well as the oldest — the principle having evolved thousands of years ago in India, where water-soaked mats were hung over open windows to filter hot winds and breezes.

The idea behind an evaporative cooler is easily understood if you'll dip one of your hands into water and compare it with your dry hand. Of course, the wet hand almost instantly feels colder because the water is evaporating. Holding your wet and dry hands to a breeze enhances the difference because moving air hastens evaporation.

The simple physics behind this cooling effect is that when any substance changes from liquid to vapor it absorbs heat energy. The water molecules on your wet hand were escaping; they were moving from a liquid to a vapor state — and they absorbed your body's heat in the process. If you'll remember this simple principle, you'll always understand how air-conditioners function.

Evaporative RV coolers add modern efficiencies to the Indian mat idea (Figure 1). These units usu-ally have an internal reservoir filled with water, and liquid-level is maintained by periodic replenishment or through a tie-in with the RV water supply. In the latter case, a valve, similar to a toilet ball valve, maintains appropriate levels.

From the reservoir, a 12-volt DC electric pump (1) pushes the water through pipes which eventually distribute it over an absorbent filter or pad (2). Exterior air is pushed through this filter either by a fan (3) or the movement of the vehicle against outside air. The moving air quickens the evaporation, and thus removes heat energy from the air. Now this cooler air passes into the RV interior to keep you comfortable (4), and the unevaporated water drips back into the reservoir. Because the chilled air also contains water vapor, your rig's humidity may rise, but most users either enjoy the moisture or keep a vent open to let the damp air escape.

18.02 EVAPORATIVE MAINTENANCE.

The most important maintenance, and usually the most neglected, is cleaning and inspection. Although the procedure is simple, ''out of sight, out of mind'' is the general rule with most people. As a result, dirt builds in gargantuan proportions, followed by breakdown.

On most models, the filter or pad slips out easily and can be washed in soapy water, dried and replaced. New filters are inexpensive and should be installed at the first sign of deterioration. Also, cleanliness can be enhanced by vacuuming the unit frequently (just hold the hose against air vents and let the suction draw out dirt).

The cooler's water reservoir should receive periodic cleanings with a mild detergent. In addi-

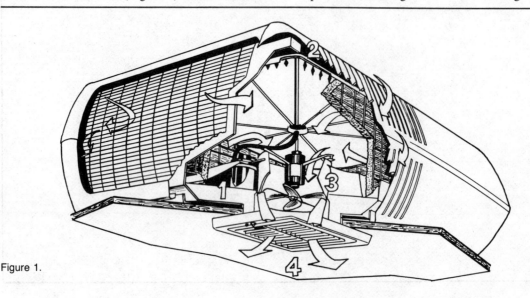

Figure 1.

tion, the distribution system should be flushed and checked to be sure that all valves are open and flowing, and that lime deposits are not preventing the valve from seating securely. Failing to clean thoroughly will allow dirt and algae to accumulate.

Periodically remove the shroud (the exterior roof cover is called the shroud, while the interior cover is the plenum) and gently wipe off grime which has accumulated inside. Then give the interior a thorough vacuuming.

Visually inspect the shroud frequently, as it can crack with age or abuse. Small cracks may be temporarily bandaged (see Section 12.04, Figure 5), but the shroud should be replaced as soon as possible when it is not in perfect condition.

A canvas or fabric air-conditioner cover is a smart idea if there are long periods of time during which you don't use the unit; they both prolong the shroud's life and keep dirt and dust out of the interior.

18.03   TROUBLESHOOTING.

In keeping with the simplicity of operation, troubleshooting is quite easy and straightforward:

TROUBLESHOOTING EVAPORATIVE COOLERS

SYMPTOM: UNIT FAILS TO OPERATE

REMEDY:
1. Check switches for proper positions.
2. Check battery for charge and electrolyte level.
3. Check all electrical connections, including grounds, and be sure that they all make good contact and that there are no broken or frayed wires.
4. Check fuse and replace, if necessary, with recommended type.
5. Check the fan motor shaft to be sure that the motor turns freely.

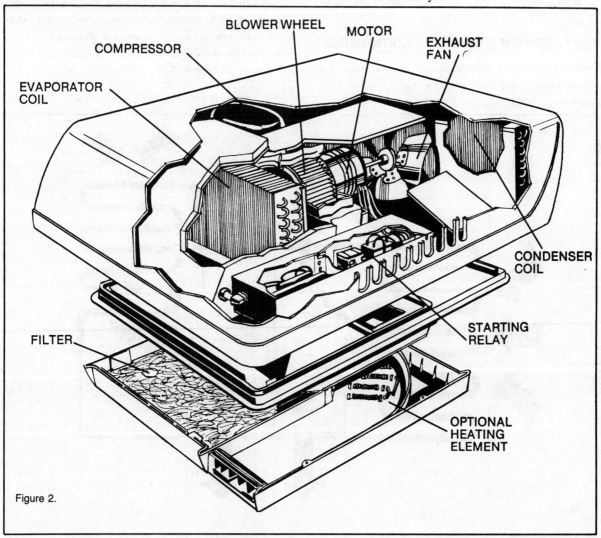

Figure 2.

SYMPTOM: UNIT DOESN'T COOL

REMEDY:

1. Remember that as outside relative humidity increases, the cooling efficiency decreases. There is no cure.
2. If the fan motor is operating, check to see if the water pump is operating.
3. If the water pump is running but not delivering water, briefly disconnect the inlet and outlet sides independently to see if the problem is in the pump or is an obstruction in the lines. Blowing through distribution lines may help locate the problem, and blowing hard in a direction opposite to the water flow may dislodge the blockage.
4. Check that water is actually reaching the absorbent mat and be sure it becomes sufficiently saturated during the cooling operations, that it is not blocked with foreign materials, and that the inlet air does not bypass the pad in any manner.

18.04 COMPRESSOR AIR-CONDITIONERS.

Although compressor-type air-conditioners are much more complex than evaporative units (see Figure 2), they employ the same physics. Keep this in mind as we explore what the experts call an "air-conditioner refrigeration cycle."

Figure 3 shows the pipes and coils running throughout the compressor-type unit. This closed system contains a refrigerant, usually Freon, which is in a gaseous state under normal temperatures and pressures.

The compressor (labeled A) is literally the heart of the system; it pumps the refrigerant, which at this point is quite hot, into the condenser coil (B). The fan motor (E) operates the condenser fan which pushes air across the coil. Because the refrigerant is rapidly losing heat to the passing air stream, and because it is being compacted in the coil, its natural tendency is to condense into the liquid state.

The pressure within the condenser coil pushes on the cool, liquid refrigerant and forces it through a tiny orifice into the capillary tube (C) and then into the evaporator coil (D). (Sometimes a fine-mesh strainer is positioned at the entrance to the capillary tube to catch stray particles.) Note that the capillary tube has a smaller diameter, which restricts the quantity of liquid that flows and helps maintain pressure in the condenser coil. But the pipe diameter increases about 25 times at the evaporator unit and this, combined with the

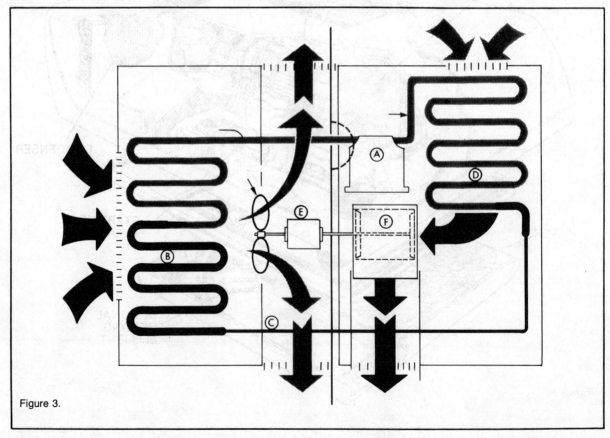

Figure 3.

"sucking" action of the compressor, lets the refrigerant quickly expand back into its gaseous state. The effect is just like taking the lid off of a pressure cooker and, as the evaporation occurs throughout the evaporation coil, the refrigerant *absorbs* heat from the air flowing over the coil. The air is sucked from the living area by the spinning evaporator blower wheel (F) which also passes the cooled air back into the RV.

That's a complete cycle in its rather elegant simplicity: The refrigerant picked the heat out of the interior air (where it was objectionable) through the heat absorption and released properties of evaporation and condensation. Note that in this process the refrigerant must completely evaporate, as the compressor isn't designed to pump liquid. To ensure this total evaporation, a sufficient quantity of heat energy (air flow from the vehicle interior) must always be passing over the coils. (That's why instruction manuals caution you to never obstruct the intake vent.) Also note that the blower and condenser fan are both operated by the same fan motor. This last fact contributes to problems in some air-conditioners under some circumstances, but we'll explore that in a moment.

One side-benefit of the compressor refrigeration cycle is that interior air loses some of its moisture content as it contacts the evaporator coils. This dehumidifying action means that the unit can be used during winter camping to combat the RVer's nemesis, condensation.

18.05   POWER REQUIREMENTS.

Unlike evaporative coolers which require only 12 volts, compressor air-conditioners need roughly 15 amps of 110 VDC to run the powerful internal motors. This is a sizable withdrawal on top of other electrical needs, so when two units are used, the second is often wired through a two-way switch which designates either the air-conditioner or some other power-hungry appliance (e.g., microwave oven) — never both simultaneously.

Adequate power is also important, because compressor motors can suffer costly damage when operated at less than specified voltage. The best insurance against such problems is a built-in voltage meter. The next best determination is through other appliances, i.e., when lights and small appliances don't perform adequately, or when your TV picture is smaller than normal, immediately suspect low voltage and shut everything down while you investigate. Don't be lured into complacency just because you're on campground pow-

er, either, as some areas have exceedingly unreliable supplies.

18.06   DELAY SWITCH.

As you may have observed from other appliances, most electric motors require a greater quantity of power to get started than they do to keep going. This start-up excess is called surge power, and air-conditioners use a fair amount of it. To both reduce the immediate need and to protect everything from momentary starvation, some air-conditioners have an internal delay switch which activates the components in sequence rather than all at once. You can also do your part to reduce low-voltage damage by always turning the operating switches to *off* when you're through with the unit.

18.07   CONTROLS AND OPERATION PROCEDURE.

Air-conditioners are fairly simple to operate, but do read the instruction pamphlet as it is possible to inadvertently harm them. The controls usually consist of louvered vents for directing air flow, a multi-positioned switch to give you a choice of blower speeds and a temperature selector switch for setting the internal thermostat — although this is not usually marked in degrees of temperature. Simply speaking, when air temperature climbs above the thermostat setting, the unit's compressor is switched on and the cooling process begins. When the air is sufficiently chilled, the thermostat automatically cuts power to the compressor — while allowing the fan motor to continue circulating air through the RV. And if you prefer, the fan alone can be operated just to circulate air.

Because compressors can be damaged by rapid-fire on/off cycling, many units contain a built-in delay switch that provides a minimum rest period for equalization of system pressure. It is sometimes possible to override this delay by repetitively operating the manual on/off controls, so beware of doing this. Additionally, be cautious about evaporator icing which can occur when temperature is set to the coldest position and the fan is on low speed. This is especially possible in humid climates, because large quantities of water are extracted from the air and deposited on the evaporator coils. The condition also arises when users want to reduce fan noise at night and fail to reduce the thermostat setting. The cure is simply to operate the fan on "high" with the temperature setting at "warm" or "off."

18.08   MAINTENANCE.

As with evaporative coolers, dirt is a leading cause of trouble in air-conditioners. Make a habit of gently placing the vacuum cleaner hose against vent openings as often as you can. Also, remove the shroud (roof cover) and wipe out accumulated road grime. Check the shroud for damage, too; cracks can be temporarily repaired as in Section 12.04, but a new piece should be installed as soon as possible. Using an external cover during the off-season is a good way to prevent both damage and dirt entry.

The compressor and/or fan motors in newer units are usually the sealed "self-lubricating" type, and odds are you won't have to bother with them. When lubrication is called for, never deviate from the manufacturer's recommended quantity and type of lubricant, and be sure you insert it through all of the lubrication ports.

As stressed earlier, all of your appliances will benefit if you monitor your power supply closely. The air-conditioner should have a low voltage cutoff switch to protect the sensitive compressor, but don't rely on its accuracy — metering devices are inexpensive and useful for many projects. If a deficiency is found, trace back to the cause (usually a bad or low battery). With the problem corrected, check your instruments again to be sure there is not an additional problem.

Further preventative maintenance which should be accomplished periodically, and especially when taking your rig out of winter storage, includes:

1. Check all wiring for loose connections, wear or worn insulation.
2. Check all tubing connections for good solder joints.
3. Check all tubing for cracks, kinks or breaks.
4. Clean condenser and evaporator coils with a vacuum hose. CAUTION: The fins are delicate, so don't do anything that would bend them.
5. Remove the control panel and clean the filter with soapy water (if it is the cleanable type), or replace it if it appears worn.
6. Be sure all hardware is securely fastened in place.
7. Check fans and motor for free turning without excess wobble.
8. Look around and remove any dirt or grime you can find.

18.09   TROUBLESHOOTING COMPRESSOR UNITS.

Many compressor repairs are beyond the scope of consumer attention simply because they involve the complexities of electric motors or the dangers of high-pressure coolant. The second factor should be especially appreciated, because refrigerant is indeed under high pressure and can come at you with terrific force if you tinker with the lines. (That's why air-conditioner technicians wear face shields.) Additionally, any nearby open flame can convert released refrigerant into phosgene gas — which causes severe respiratory irritation.

Recognizing that consumers are sometimes lured into attempting repairs that are beyond their scope, the Coleman Company offers this advice to their technicians:

"Always be alert for a consumer who has been working on his own equipment, or whose neighbor has been helping him 'fix it.' The air-conditioner is probably now suffering from 'tinkeritis' — probably the most deadly malady that it can catch. If you suspect that anybody has been working on the equipment, don't trust him to have done a good job. Compare all wiring with the diagram. Visually inspect all motors, fans, capacitors, dampers, tubing, etc. First repair the damage that has been done by the self-proclaimed experts — then proceed to identify and correct the initial problem."

But don't despair if you're a do-it-yourselfer, as there is still a great deal you can accomplish in checking out or clearing small problems.

Troubleshooting the compressor-type unit is firstly a matter of isolating where the problem is occurring. If this isn't obvious from the symptoms, a systematic run-through will help you locate it.

A good source-detection starting point is a quick visual inspection along the same lines as your maintenance procedures, because many problems are traceable to dirt, shroud impact or low voltage. If the unit simply fails to operate, the power portion of your check is the place to begin.

Starting with the obvious, be sure a circuit breaker hasn't been tripped. If power is definitely reaching the unit, check your voltage — the internal cutoff switch may have detected insufficient power. More times than not, these two simple steps will clear the difficulty.

One final note regarding low voltage: Duo-Therm, in their excellent dealer service manual, says, "Watch out for customers who have extra-long line cords. Many times they are undersize and result in a drastic voltage drop. This can account for the unit working for you but not for him on the last time he was out.'' Figure 4, taken from this manual, shows how this drop works.

Maximum Cable Length for 2% Voltage Drop			
Current in Amperes	Wire Size		
	10	12	14
5	234	147	93
10	117	74	46
15	78	49	31
20	59	37	23
25	47	29	—
30	39	25	—
35	33	—	—

Figure 4.

When the unit will function, putting it through its paces in an operational test will help isolate the problem. This should be a sequential procedure, and as you take each step *listen* to what's happening; clinks, howls and other strange sounds are important to note. Also, if there is any hint of strain, shut everything off before the problem is compounded.

18.10 OPERATIONAL SEQUENCE.

Here is the operational sequence suggested by Frigiking's servicepeople: (1) Verify proper unit fusing and adequate power supply. (2) Turn temperature control off. Cycle the air control between high and low fan settings. The blower should function and change speeds accordingly while the compressor remains off. (3) Turn the air control and the temperature control to low. The compressor should start and the blower should run at low speed. Now turn the air control to high. The compressor should continue to run and the blower should change speed. Air from the compressor vent should be cold and crisp. (4) Set the air control to low. Slowly turn the temperature control from low to high. The compressor should cut off when the thermostat passes the RV's interior temperature. (Remember that thermostats have operational limits — minimum and maximum temperatures — so consider the room temperature before blaming the thermostat.)

If this procedure tells you where the problem is, try referring to the accompanying troubleshooting chart, but definitely don't attempt something you aren't qualified to do. The well-intentioned ''Mr. Fixit'' is probably the number-one reason why service personnel work longer hours than most of us. So don't add to their problems, or your bill, by presenting them with a botched job. Remember, if your problem is thoroughly diagnosed but uncured, you'll stand a chance of quicker service and, in our book, that means more time to go fishing!

SERVICE DIAGNOSIS
SYMPTONS AND CAUSES:

A. Blower running slow
1. Loose connection or high resistance circuit.
2. Motor shaft binding — fan blade or blower misaligned.
3. Poor contact in switch.
4. Improper voltage.
5. Condenser fan or blower wheel misaligned.

B. Fan Motor Inoperative
1. Open or defective circuit breaker.
2. Bad wiring connections. (Including ground.)
3. Tight or burnt motor bearings.
4. Switch open or defective.
5. Open winding.

C. Compressor will not start — no run
1. Disconnect switch open.
2. Blown fuse or circuit breaker open.
3. Defective wiring.
4. Tripped or defective overload.
5. Open switch contacts.
6. Defective thermostat or evaporator air below thermostat setting.
7. Compressor motor winding open.
8. External power overload.

D. Compressor will not start — hums but cycles on overload
1. Low voltage.
2. Unit wired incorrectly.
3. Starting capacitor defective.
4. Starting relay contacts not closed.
5. Compressor motor defective.
6. High head pressure (refer to L).
7. Bearings or pistons tight — low oil charge.

E. Compressor starts but starting winding remains in circuit
1. Low voltage.
2. Unit wired incorrectly.
3. Starting relay defective.
4. Starting capacitor weak.

5. Running capacitor defective.
6. Compressor motor defective.
7. High head pressure (refer to L).
8. Bearings or pistons tight — low oil charge.

F. Compressor starts and runs but cycles on overload
1. Low voltage.
2. Running capacitor defective.
3. Overload defective.
4. High head pressure (refer to L).
5. Fan motor, etc., wired to wrong side of overload.
6. Compressor motor partially grounded.
7. Bearings or pistons tight — low oil charge.
8. Mechanical damage in compressor.

G. Compressor tries to start when thermostat closes but cuts out on overload: Finally starts after several attempts
1. Low voltage.
2. Thermostat capillary tube not positioned properly in evaporator input air flow. (Probably inserted into evaporator and touching coil.)
3. Starting relay contacts badly pitted.
4. Starting capacitor weak.
5. Slight restriction in strainer or drier.
6. Air or non-condensable gases in system.

H. Compressor starts but cuts out on overload
1. Starting relay contacts welded together.
2. Starting relay coil open.
3. Starting capacitor defective.
4. Low voltage.

I. Starting relay burns out
1. Low voltage.
2. High voltage.
3. Compressor short cycling (refer to N).
4. Incorrect running capacitor used.
5. Incorrect relay being used.

J. Starting capacitors burn out
1. Compressor short cycling (refer to N).
2. Incorrect starting capacitor being used.
3. Relay contacts sticking.
4. Start winding remaining in circuit for prolonged period.

K. Running capacitors burn out
1. High line voltage.
2. Capacitor voltage rating too low.
3. Capacitor terminals shorted by water.

L. Head pressure too high
1. Unit overcharged.
2. Air or non-condensable gases in system.
3. Clogged condenser.
4. Defective fan motor.
5. Restriction in strainer or drier.
6. Restriction in liquid line.
7. High air temperature entering condenser.

M. Head pressure too low
1. Insufficient refrigerant charge.
2. Leak in system.
3. Low ambient temperature.

N. Compressor short cycles
1. Thermostat set too close to outside air temperature.
2. Refrigerant undercharge.
3. Refrigerant overcharge.
4. Cutting out on overload because of tight bearing, tight piston, high head pressure, or restricted air.
5. External power overload.
6. Bad start relay.
7. Cold air mixing with return air.

O. Running cycle too long or compressor operates continuously
1. Insufficient refrigerant charge and/or leak in system.
2. Dirty or restricted condenser.
3. Too much load on system. (Unit too small for application.)
4. Control contacts stuck.
5. Air or non-condensable gases in system.
6. Restricted capillary tube.
7. Vehicle doors or windows left open.
8. Evaporator coil plugged with ice or dirt.
9. Compressor valves bad.
10. Air filter or evaporator fins dirty.
11. Thermostat stuck.

P. Cooled space too warm
1. Shortage of refrigerant or leak in system.
2. Restricted capillary tube, strainer, or drier.
3. Iced or dirty evaporator coil.
4. Compressor malfunctioning (See O.)

Q. Noisy unit
1. Fan blades bent, covered with accumulated dirt, or blower dirty.
2. Motor shafts bent.
3. Fan or blower loose on shaft.
4. Fan motor mounting loose.
5. Fan motor bearings loose or worn.

6. Tube rattle.
7. Loose parts in unit.
8. Compressor oil charge low.

R. Evaporator freezes but defrosts while unit is running
1. Moisture in system.

S. Liquid line too hot
1. Unit overcharged or air in system.
2. See L.

T. Liquid line frosted
1. Restriction in line such as drier (if used).

U. Heat strip does not come on
1. Fuse link burnt out.
2. Loose wire connection.
3. Defective fan switch.

Chapter Nineteen

Absorption Refrigerators

Manufacturers of absorption-type refrigerators like to boast that their products have "no moving parts." Of course they're right in one sense, but wrong in another — most RVers give that refrigerator door a very moving workout, especially on hot days.

But "no moving parts" really means that many of the parts-fatigue problems which afflict other appliances simply won't happen to these refrigerators. In fact, if it weren't for a few common ailments these units could function virtually trouble-free.

The common ailments? Consumer neglect and abuse.

Not all RV refrigerators belong to the "no moving parts" category, but enough do to make them the most popular type on the road. The major advantage to the RVer is that these units function on either LP-gas or electricity, and that choice lets you decide where you'll camp. But there are some disadvantages, too, and we'll look at both sides in this chapter.

19.01 THE INSIDE VIEW.

Outside of cosmetic differences, older refrigerators are similar to new. Similar isn't "identical," though, and some brands have experienced important engineering upgrading in recent years — the most notable achievements being greater tolerance for non-level operation, fewer flame-outs, and better performance in hot climates. But improvement doesn't mean either perfection or indestructibility. So let's take a closer look at the absorption refrigerator's anatomy in order to better understand reality.

19.02 THE COOLING UNIT.

The cooling unit is the heart of absorption refrigerators and the principles of operation will be identical regardless of who makes it. To prove the point, two major manufacturers use identical schematic diagrams of the cooling unit in their service manuals, while another two firms have copied each other's description of how the unit functions!

The cooling unit contains a precisely measured amount of ammonia and water solution, plus some hydrogen gas. It functions on the simple physics of condensation and evaporation. Here's how that works:

19.03 EVAPORATION AND CONDENSATION.

Theoretically, any substance can exist in a solid, liquid or gaseous state, dependent entirely upon its temperature. Ammonia, for instance, boils at minus 33 degrees centigrade. Water moves from solid (ice) to liquid at zero degrees C., and from liquid to gas (steam) at 100 degrees C. In each step, the substance absorbs heat in order to accomplish its transformation.

To experience this heat absorption phenomenon, just dampen your hand and hold it in a breeze; the chill you immediately feel is caused when the water molecules absorb heat from your hand as they escape into gaseous form.

Reversing the process, take enough heat away from a gas and it will liquify; subtract the heat from a liquid and it solidifies.

19.04 PRESSURE.

But pressure also affects a substance's boiling and melting points. RVers immediately notice that water boils very fast in the mountains, but they also find that it takes longer to cook things in that boiling water. This phenomenon occurs because lowering the pressure around a liquid also lowers its boiling point, and atmospheric pressure diminishes as altitude increases. Your water is boiling at something less than 100 degrees C., which accounts for the longer cooking times. Pressure cookers, on the other hand, increase the pressure and raise the liquid's boiling point well above 100 degrees, so food cooks quite rapidly.

19.05 MIXING EVAPORATION, CONDENSATION AND PRESSURE CHARACTERISTICS.

Now you can understand that the mixture of hydrogen and water is in the cooling unit because the two substances combined have an exactly predetermined boiling point. The hydrogen gas contained in part of the system alters the pressure in that section, and also affects the boiling point. The result is a system which will absorb or release heat exactly when we want it to; it will capture heat from the cooling and freezing compartments and release that heat to the outside environment. That's the easy physics behind an absorption refrigerator. The mechanics are equally simple.

19.06 THE ABSORPTION PRINCIPLE IN PRACTICE.

The absorption cooling unit (see Figure 1) is basically a closed system of interconnecting tubes whose sole purpose is to transfer heat from one

Figure 1. Absorption Cooling Unit Diagram

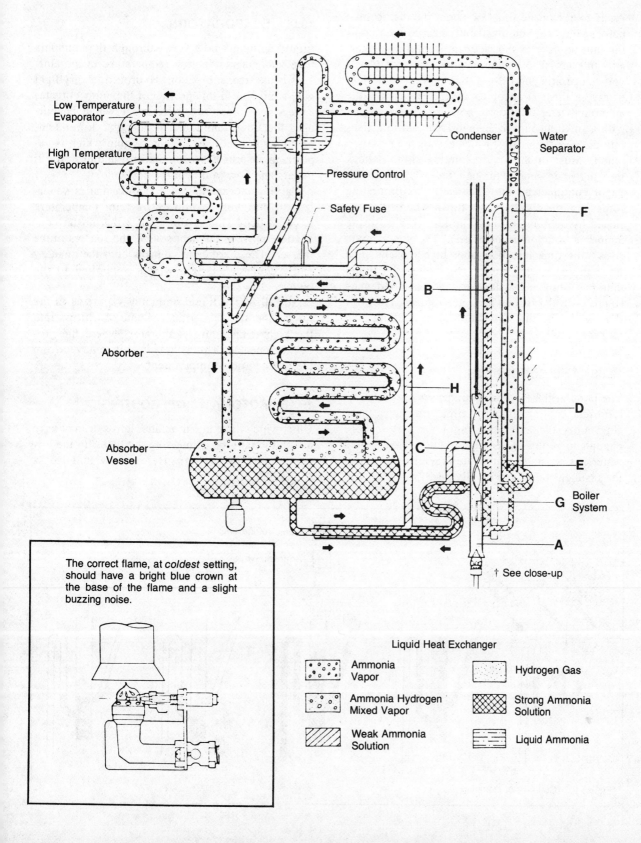

Low Temperature Evaporator

High Temperature Evaporator

Pressure Control

Safety Fuse

Absorber

Absorber Vessel

Condenser

Water Separator

F

B

H

D

C

E

G Boiler System

A

† See close-up

The correct flame, at *coldest* setting, should have a bright blue crown at the base of the flame and a slight buzzing noise.

Liquid Heat Exchanger

	Ammonia Vapor		Hydrogen Gas
	Ammonia Hydrogen Mixed Vapor		Strong Ammonia Solution
	Weak Ammonia Solution		Liquid Ammonia

place to another. It does this through four basic internal sections:

19.07 THE GENERATOR OR BOILER.

As if to prove the old saw about having to give before you take, you must apply heat to your cooling unit in order to subtract heat from the refrigerator interior. The heat is applied at point (A) if you're operating on LP-gas, or at point (G) if electricity is the source of energy. Heat causes the ammonia/water solution to boil. The vapor, along with a small amount of unvaporized solution, rises into the percolator, (B), which acts as the system's pump. Most of the rising solution siphons back into the main supply through tube (C) while the vapor continues up into tube (D). The propelling force now pushes the vapor down where it is enriched by bubbling through the reservoir of strong ammonia solution at point (E). The vapor again rises, this time into the vapor pipe (F) and then into the water separator. At this point, any liquid that has remained with the vapor is condensed (liquified), and it runs back down to the reservoir (E), while the dry ammonia vapor continues on into the condenser.

19.08 THE CONDENSER.

The parallel lines over the condenser (in Figure 1) represent cooling fins. Air circulating over these fins cools the ammonia vapor until it is cold enough to return to its liquid state. Because the water has separated-out in the previous processes, the resultant liquid is virtually pure ammonia.

Notice that the condenser is the highest point in the system. We needed the heat in the boiler to get the ammonia up to the condenser, but from now on gravity will propel the refrigerant.

19.09 EVAPORATORS.

Liquid ammonia now flows through the ammonia tube and enters the low temperature evaporator. This is the freezer box coil. Hydrogen, a very light gas, is present in this portion of the unit; it creates a very low pressure environment which encourages the liquid ammonia to boil at a lower temperature. If you'll recall that a liquid which is vaporizing absorbs heat from its surroundings, you'll understand how your freezer gets cold.

Varying the amount of ammonia that is vaporized at this point is how refrigerator temperature is controlled. This is done via a thermostat connection between the heat source and sensors in the freezer. The thermostat controls both the quantity and frequency of heat which is applied to the boiler.

Not all of the liquid ammonia vaporizes in the low temperature evaporator. Some of it flows into the high temperature evaporator, where the process is repeated. This is how heat is removed from the refrigeration compartment.

19.10 AUTOMATIC DEFROSTING.

Units which have an automatic defroster may have an additional tube connecting the boiler to the low temperature evaporator. Here's how that works (Figure 2):

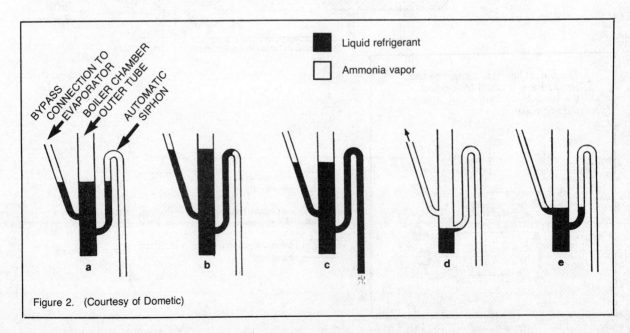

Liquid refrigerant

Ammonia vapor

BYPASS CONNECTION TO EVAPORATOR
BOILER CHAMBER
OUTER TUBE
AUTOMATIC SIPHON

a   b   c   d   e

Figure 2.   (Courtesy of Dometic)

During the normal refrigeration cycle (a) the bypass outlet from the central tube is closed by condensed liquid. As vapor continues to condense, the liquid level rises slowly (the process may take 20 to 30 hours) until it reaches the top of the siphon tube (b). Liquid moves down the siphon tube (c) and creates a vacuum which drains the boiler chamber tube to the point where the bypass connection is uncovered (d). Now, hot ammonia vapor travels through the bypass connection to the evaporator coil, where it melts the ice which has formed on the outside of that coil. After perhaps a half-hour, condensing vapor again rises and seals the bypass entrance (e). As vapor can no longer enter the bypass tube, the defrosting ceases and the cycle begins anew.

19.11   THE ABSORBER.

Hydrogen by itself is quite light, but the heavier ammonia vapor pulls the hydrogen gas down through the evaporators and into the absorber coils. A continuous trickle of strong ammonia solution enters the absorber coil through tube (H); upon contacting this strong solution the ammonia vapor is absorbed into a liquid state. The hydrogen gas, freed of the ammonia, rises back up to the evaporators. Heat, which the ammonia picked up when it vaporized in the evaporators, is now released as the ammonia liquifies. This heat is picked up by the absorber coils and carried away by outside air passing over the coils.

The absorber vessel catches the liquified ammonia from the coils and feeds it out to the boiler system, where the refrigeration cycle is started anew. This simple process is how all absorption refrigerators "keep their cool" — and explains what the manufacturers' claim, "no moving parts," is all about. But as you'll soon see, the unit is not without its limitations.

19.12   SOME POTENTIAL PROBLEMS.

Consider three things about the absorption principle: (1) It depends upon gravity for the liquid circulation portion of the cycle. (2) The condenser and absorber coils depend upon outside air circulation to remove heat from their contents. (3) The quantity of ammonia, vapor entering the system is dependent upon both the amount and duration of heat applied to the boiler system. These three items directly relate to the greatest majority of problems which an absorption refrigerator will encounter in its lifetime. They are also behind the earlier comment that consumer abuse and neglect

are at the root of most absorption problems. Let's look at this a little closer.

19.13   THE IMPORTANCE OF LEVELING.

Because gravity is essential for proper liquid circulation, it's obvious that a unit which is positioned at an angle will not operate efficiently (Figure 3).

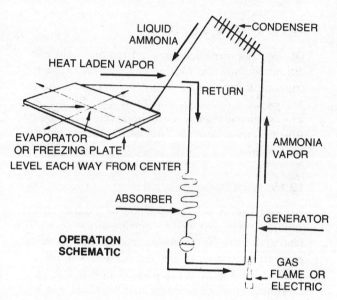

Figure 3.

What happens, here, is that the system becomes clogged by liquid which hasn't drained through to the absorber. As a result, the unit will cease chilling when there is a complete blockage, because heat isn't being carried away by the vapor. More seriously, these circumstances promote the formation of chromate crystals (chromate is in the system to prevent pipe rusting). The cooling unit then becomes progressively less effective, until the crystals completely block internal orifices. At this point, the cooling unit is non-functional and must be replaced. At a cost of several hundred dollars, that's an expensive mishap — and reason enough to remember that absorption refrigerators must always be leveled before they are turned on. Also remember that crystalization is cumulative, so it's possible to ruin a cooling unit by short off-level operations over a long period.

The "on the level" rule is so well-known to RVers that there is no excuse for violating it. What has happened in recent years, though, is that some absorption refrigerators have been improved to the point where they will tolerate larger deviations from absolute level. This doesn't mean that they will be efficient (in fact, they squander gas supplies and yield less cooling when off level), but at least they won't malfunction. Consumers tend to get sloppy about leveling when they know of this improvement and, misjudging the tolerance, they too frequently operate their units at extreme angles (e.g., letting the refrigerator run while parked on a hill). If your unit is one of those which has been upgraded in this manner, it's wiser to treat the improvement as a safety feature and continue to level your rig as usual.

19.14   ON-THE-ROAD.

On-the-road operation does not require level conditions because the rocking motion forces the refrigerant to move quite freely. Movement also improves air circulation, and these two factors are why absorption units work best while traveling. But the question of air circulation also raises the next point.

19.15   VENTING.

Because heat is subtracted from the system at the condenser and absorbed by outside air, it's important that there be ample air circulation to these points. Shutting off the circulation would, of course, leave heat in the cooling unit and negate its functioning. This means that adequate venting must be part of the installation.

Manufacturers sell their refrigerators complete with ventilation kits and explicit instructions for installing them. The customary configuration consists of a flue, roof vent, louvered access door and precisely-measured free space around the refrigerator (Figure 4).

Because measurements are specific for each individual model, no figures are shown in the illustration. It's imperative that you consult the service manual for the unit in question if you plan on doing anything which would affect or change that configuration. There are usually no alternate vents, doors or installation techniques which would not endanger both the refrigerator and, possibly, yourself.

19.16   THE EFFECTS OF HEAT.

This matter of air is also the source of a weak point inherent in the absorption principle. Most units become progressively less effective as the outside temperatures rise, and as the thermostat senses higher refrigeration compartment temperatures it calls for more refrigerating action and thus burns more fuel. In extreme heat, the process can be quite wasteful, and the unit may even develop a problem known as "vapor lock" (see Section

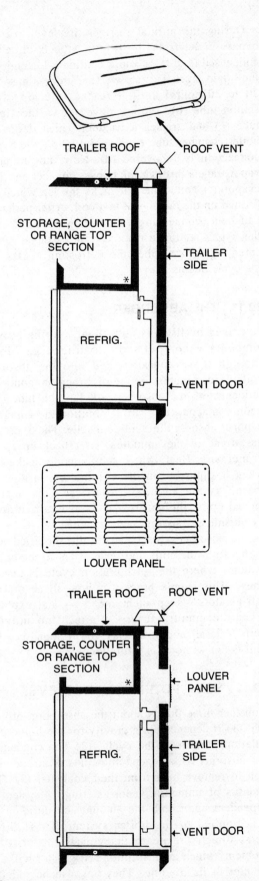

Figure 4.

19.34). Of course, a few refrigerators are designed with greater tolerance for these conditions, and they perform comparatively well in heat.

But hot weather operation asks any refrigerator to work harder, so be kind to your unit by opening the door as infrequently as possible. Also, be careful not to overstuff the refrigerator compartment or cover the shelves with large containers, as the interior must have space for good circulation.

Let's take a closer look at circulation in a refrigeration compartment (Figure 5).

19.17 CIRCULATION.

As the air around the evaporator coil is cooled it gets heavier and literally falls downward. As it passes over foods on the shelves, the air absorbs heat and becomes lighter — eventually reversing its course and rising to the top, where it gives up that heat to the evaporator. This is called convection current, and knowing about it also tells you that the coldest place in the refrigerator is immediately below the evaporator.

19.18 MAINTENANCE.

When it comes to refrigerators, "cleanliness" and "trouble-free" are almost synonymous. It's not too difficult to remember that the inside of the refrigerator needs periodic cleansings, because if you forget your nose will soon remind you. But who thinks about cleaning *around* the unit?

The basic external cleanings can be done with a vacuum cleaner. Whenever you're vacumming the RV, just stick the hose into the areas around the refrigerator and capture the accumulated dust which could work its way into the mechanical portions of the unit. And don't forget to open the outside access door and vacuum in there, too — it gets mighty dusty after a few trips.

The importance of simple cleaning procedures will be confirmed by any service technician; the dirt which isn't removed is the source of much of their business!

Starting with the inside, a good occasion for a thorough cleansing is whenever all the food is out of the box — at the end of a trip or at defrosting time. Use lukewarm water laced with unscented household detergent. Rinse and dry thoroughly. Shelves and drawers may be removed and soaked in the same cleanser, but be careful about exposing some of the plastic parts to heat, as most of these pieces wouldn't survive a session in a home dishwasher.

Incidental spills in the box can be wiped away

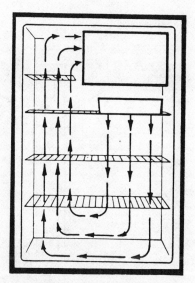

Figure 5. Air Circulation

with a sponge containing warm water and baking soda. And whenever the unit is not being used, let it stand with the door ajar.

On the exterior, both side and roof vents must obviously be kept free of obstructions. Because these spots are popular with some species of animals and insects, an inspection after a rig has been parked for some time is definitely in order.

The flue assembly also needs periodic attention. Like a chimney, the flue sits over the burner assembly and provides a draft for pulling the products of combustion up and out through the roof vent. Many flues also contain a baffle which is suspended in the flue tube to both distribute the burner heat and enhance the draft. After many hours of operation, the interior walls and baffle become thoroughly coated with soot (Figure 6).

Disassembling the flue for cleaning is complex on some models, and may require removing the refrigerator from its mountings if access to the rear panel isn't otherwise available. Some units also require dismantling the burner unit to free the flue (sec Section 19.23).

Once the flue is available, lift out the baffle (if your unit has one) and gently scrub the tube with the type of brush recommended by the manufacturer. Usually they will also suggest using an alchohol-based cleanser.

The burner is another place where insects like to take up residence. But if insects don't eventually clog the orifice, dirt will — although faithful vacuuming will substantially delay this problem. (Removing the burner unit for cleaning is treated in Section 19.23.) Testing for LP-gas leaks, correct gas pressure and proper electrical input is also important.

Figure 6. Flue Assembly

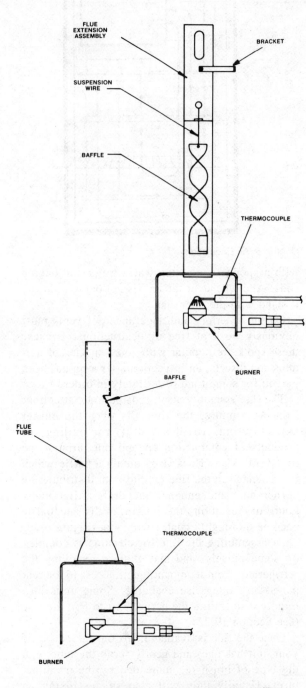

The dimensions of the flue and the flue baffle have been engineered to give best possible efficiency and meet AGA and CSA standards.

The baffle distributes the heat produced by the burner and enhances the draft, providing primary and secondary air to the burner.

The sizes and distances differ with each cooling unit. It is important that these factory dimensions be maintained to ensure proper performance and safety.

Burner must be perfectly aligned so that flame never impinges on any part of the flue tube or burner box assembly.

19.19   TROUBLESHOOTING CAUTION:

While absorption refrigerators function on simple principles and are easy to understand, they are also delicate instruments. Many parts of the unit shouldn't be bothered by anyone who hasn't been specifically trained to work with them. Consumers, for instance, should never attempt to add or subtract refrigerant from the unit, nor should they attempt to remove the refrigerator from its mountings. You must judge for yourself the extent of repairs you're willing and able to undertake — remembering all the while that mistakes can cost more than the services of a professional. It's a good idea, though, to trace problems as thoroughly as you can, using both your unit's service manual and this troubleshooting section. Understanding a problem and its probable cause will often get you better service, and cut down the time which the technician would have devoted to research.

19.20   TROUBLESHOOTING: THE FIRST STEP.

When your absorption refrigerator isn't functioning correctly, don't rush for the tool kit. Instead, first make certain that there isn't an external problem. Here's a check list to go through before determining that the unit is faulty; the steps which aren't appropriate to your suspected problem will be evident.

1. Refrigerator is level.
2. Ventilation is adequate.
3. Flame height is correct.
4. Gas pressure is correct.
5. Baffle is positioned correctly.
6. Burner orifice is clean.
7. Bypass screw is clean.
8. Supply voltage corresponds to voltage stamped on heating element.
9. Voltage supply is not fluctuating.
10. No loose electrical connections.
11. Heating element is not burned out.
12. Heating element is in correct position.
13. No leaks.
14. Thermostat(s) is (are) intact.
15. Thermostat valve is clean.

If the problem persists and the cause is not apparent, try tracing its origin in the following troubleshooting chart. Use the troubleshooting suggestions in your owner's manual, too!

19.21 OPERATION ANALYSIS FOR REFRIGERATORS OPERATING ON ELECTRICITY.

SYMPTOM					CAUSE
REFRIGERATOR TOO COLD	REFRIGERATOR NOT COLD ENOUGH	NO REFRIGERATION	FROST FORMS RAPIDLY	ODOR INSIDE CABINET	Note: It will be seen in this tabulation that several causes can be responsible for one effect. The real cause or causes should be determined through a process of elimination, starting at the top of the tabulation and proceeding to the bottom.
	X	X			Not adequate ventilation
	X	X			Refrigerating unit not level
	X	X			Heater faulty, wrong voltage or type
	X	X			Voltage not constant
		X			Electric connections loose
	X	X			Heater not inserted correctly in its pocket
	X	X			Improper food storage
X	X	X			The thermostat incorrectly used
			X		Improper storage of liquids and moist foods
	X	X	X		Leaky cabinet seals
				X	Infrequent cleaning of food compartment
				X	Refrigerator shut off with closed door
				X	Unwrapped odorous food
X			X		Incomplete contact of thermostat capillary tube
	X	X			Lost thermostat charge
	X	X			Failed refrigeration unit
X					Room temperature too low

19.22 OPERATION ANALYSIS FOR LP GAS REFRIGERATORS.

SYMPTOM							CAUSE
REFRIGERATOR TOO COLD	REFRIGERATOR NOT COLD ENOUGH	NO REFRIGERATION	FROST FORMS RAPIDLY	BURNER FLAME GOES OUT	ODOR INSIDE CABINET	ODOR OUTSIDE CABINET	Note: It will be seen in this tabulation that several causes can be responsible for one effect. The real cause or causes should be determined through a process of elimination, investigating each possible cause, proceeding to the bottom.
						X	Gas leaks
	X	X					No adequate ventilation
	X	X					Refrigerating unit not level
	X	X		X			Jet orifice clogged
				X			The thermocouple tip not in position
				X			No contact between thermocouple and safety valve magnet
				X			Faulty safety valve magnet
	X	X					Improper maximum flame
	X	X		X			Bypass flame too small
	X	X		X			Gauze in burner head clogged
X			X				Dirt in thermostat or valve seat
X			X				Bypass flame too large
	X	X		X			Improper position of the flue baffle
	X	X					Unstable burner flame
	X	X					Improper food storage
X	X	X					The thermostat incorrectly used
			X				Improper storage of liquid and moist foods
	X	X	X				Leaky cabinet seals
	X	X	X			X	Obstructed flue
						X	Flame contacts central tube
						X	Insufficient primary air
					X		Infrequent cleaning of food compartment
					X		Refrigerator shut off with closed door
					X		Unwrapped odorous food
X			X				Incomplete contact of thermostat capillary tube
	X	X					Lost thermostat charge
	X	X					Failed refrigerating unit
X							Room temperature too low

19.23 BURNER AND BURNER ASSEMBLY.

The size of the burner orifices, or jets, precisely dictates the maximum amount of gas which can pass through. Occasionally, they get clogged — and must either be cleaned or replaced. It's inadvisable to try reaming out an orifice because it is fragile and such treatment would alter the size of the opening. The customary approach is to soak the orifice in an alcohol solution and/or blow the obstruction free with compressed air.

The burner orifice is in the burner assembly. Typical configurations are shown below in Figures 7 through 12.

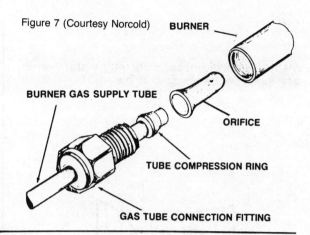

Figure 7 (Courtesy Norcold)

BURNER

BURNER GAS SUPPLY TUBE

ORIFICE

TUBE COMPRESSION RING

GAS TUBE CONNECTION FITTING

Figure 8. Some popular Dometic models will appear as follows:

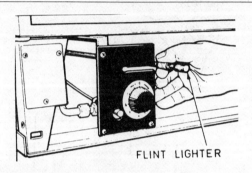

FLINT LIGHTER

(1) Remove flint lighter assembly from the refrigerator by unscrewing the knurled nut, behind the black thermostat bracket.

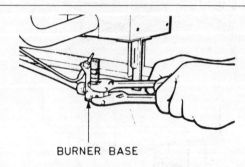

BURNER BASE

(4) Pull the base assembly to the left and with two crescent wrenches remove the jet and burner barrel from the burner base.

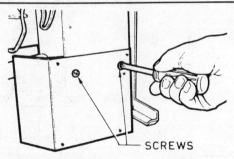

SCREWS

(2) From the rear of the refrigerator, through the access door of trailer, remove the two screws holding the flame guard.

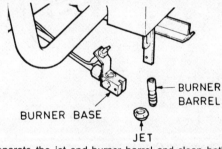

BURNER BASE

BURNER BARREL

JET

(5) Separate the jet and burner barrel and clean both with alcohol and air pressure *only*. Do not use wires or other objects to clean the jet. If the jet is obstructed, replace it.

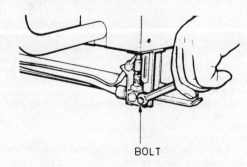

BOLT

(3) Remove the chrome-plated bolt from the left side of the burner base and let the base drop down from the holder.

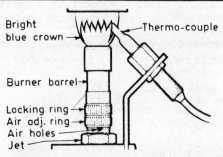

Bright blue crown

Thermo-couple

Burner barrel

Locking ring
Air adj. ring
Air holes
Jet

(6) The air-intake of the burner should be adjusted by means of the air adjustment rings so that a slight roaring sound is heard and so that the flame has a bright blue crown at its base.

Figure 9.

Many Instamatic absorption refrigerator burner assemblies will be accessed in this way:

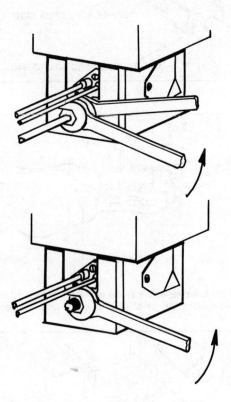

How to Change an Orifice

1. Hold the orifice with a 12-millimeter open-end wrench and disconnect the gas line flair nut with a 13-millimeter wrench. *Be careful!* Any sharp bends in the aluminum gas line will result in the aluminim gas line will result in leaks and necessitate its replacement.

2. Back the orifice out of the burner with a 12mm wrench.

3. Thread the new orifice into the burner and tighten securely.

4. Carefully reposition the gas line and thread the 13mm flair nut onto the orifice. Make sure that the gas line is in a straight line with the burner, and, while holding the orifice in place with a wrench, tighten the flair nut firmly.

NOTE

Whenever making any repairs involving gas connections, always check for leaks when repairs are completed.

Any attempt to clean a ruby orifice with a wire-like device will crack the ruby and result in extreme malfunction!

Figure 10. GAS BURNER   (courtesy Elixir)

The gas burner consists of the following parts:
1. Mixture tube
2. Burner Orifice
3. Burner Filter
4. Burner Joint
5. Spacer

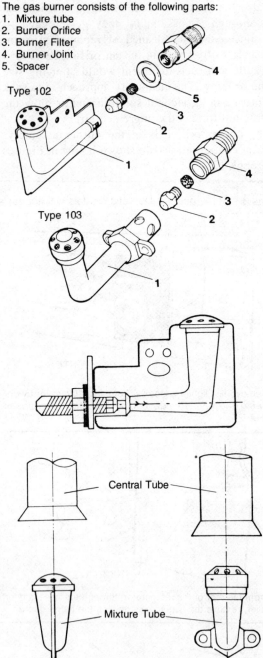

It is most important to ensure the following conditions when setting up the burner.
1. The mixture tube is firmly screwed with the burner joint and bracket.
2. When the burner orifice is screwed to the burner joint, be sure that it is clean.
3. Position the mixture tube in such a way that its center line should be aligned center-to-center with the central tube axis.
4. Look for spiders in burners.

Figure 11.

Elixir Trav'ler models may appear as in the following two sets of illustrations:

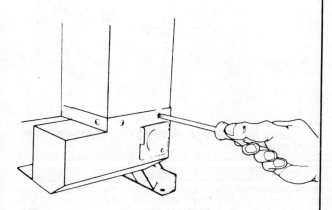

1

Remove the flame blow-out guard from the refrigerator by unscrewing three screws.

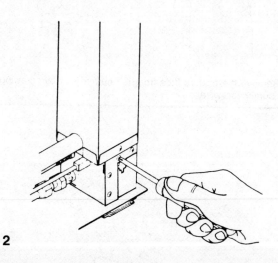

2

Remove the flame blow-out guard from the refrigerator by unscrewing two screws. (For Model 2 and 2TW.)

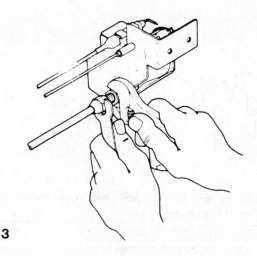

3

Remove the box nut of the gas pipe from the burner joint. (Turn the nut counterclockwise.)

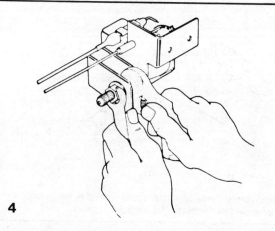

4

Take off the burner joint out of the burner bracket. (Turn the nut counterclockwise.)

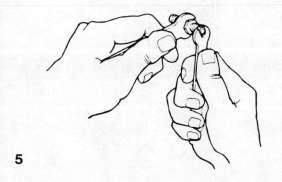

5

Take out the orifice from the burner joint. (Turn the nut counterclockwise.)

Figure 12.

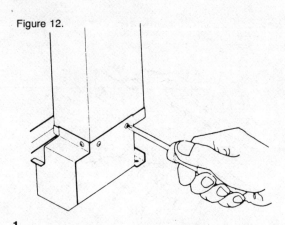

1

Remove the flame blow-out guard from the refrigerator by unscrewing three screws.

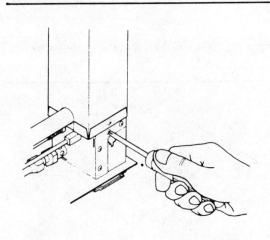

2

Remove the flame blow-out guard from the refrigerator by unscrewing two screws. (For Model 2.)

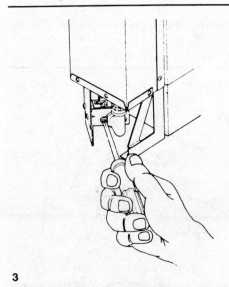

3

Unscrew two screws which hold the mixture tube.

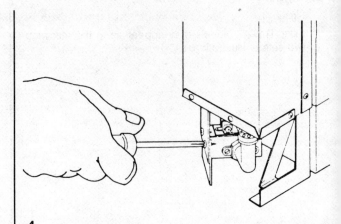

4

Unscrew two screws of the burner bracket which hold the mixture tube.

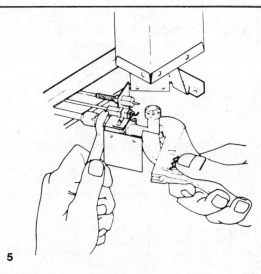

5

Remove the mixture tube from the burner joint by screwing counterclockwise.

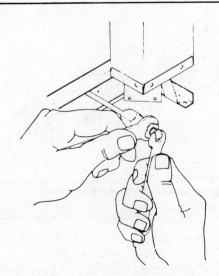

6

Take out the burner joint with the gas pipe, then remove the orifice from the burner joint.

Figure 13.

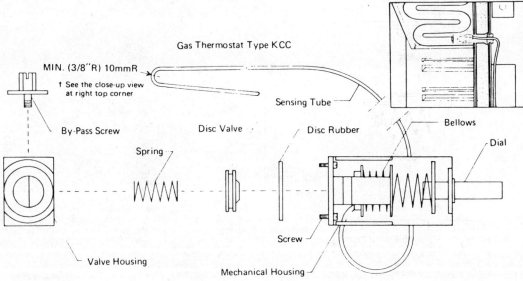

19.24 THERMOSTATS.

Some refrigerators have two thermostats, one for gas operation and the other for electric. Manufacturers strongly advise that you don't tinker with these devices and that you allow an authorized service technician to replace them when it's necessary. But it may help your thinking to understand how the thermostats do their job. The type KCC gas thermostat found in some models illustrates the thermostat principle (Figure 13):

The bellows system consists of a spring-loaded bellows and a sensing tube (called a capillary tube by some manufacturers). The sensing tube is bent about three inches from its free end and terminates in the refrigerator compartment. The tube is filled with gas which expands or contracts in response to temperature changes, and these movements either apply or release pressure against the bellows.

Within the mechanism section, turning the thermostat dial alters the amount of tension applied against the bellows by the spring, thus making it easier or more difficult for the bellows to move in response to the gas pressure in the sensing tube. The bellows movement is transmitted to the disc valve which governs the flow of gas.

The valve housing contains the disc rubber, disc valve, a spring and the bypass screw (see Section 19.26). The disc rubber acts like a washer in a hose, preventing gas from leaking. The bypass screw allows a small quantity of gas to keep a pilot-type flame going whenever the disc valve is closed. The valve housing is attached to the mechanical housing with four screws.

Very rarely, dirt will accumulate on the thermostat gas valve or valve seat, preventing it from closing tightly. When this happens some gas continues to pass, causing the burner flame to be higher than necessary and resulting in cabinet temperatures which are too low. This condition can be easily detected by turning the thermostat to the "defrost" position. If more than just the bypass flame continues to burn, it will be necessary to have the valve and seat cleaned.

The Ranco-type electric thermostat on some Trav'ler units is similar to the gas thermostat, except the bellows operate a switch which makes or breaks a connection to control the burner flame (Figure 14).

When a refrigerator performs satisfactorily on the "maximum" setting, but not on other settings, you can suspect a faulty thermostat.

19.25 THERMOSTAT CAPILLARY TUBE.

A small capillary tube connects the thermostat to the sensor on the evaporator. This sensor can be located either in the high or low temperature compartment. The capillary tube contains a gas which expands or contracts as the sensor is exposed to warmer or colder compartment temperature. This expansion or contraction is transmitted to the thermostat as explained in Section 19.24.

Occasionally, the sensing (capillary) tube in any type of thermostat will lose its charge and, in effect, become non-functional. To test for this condition, turn the thermostat to a high setting, then warm the sensing element or bulb with your hand.

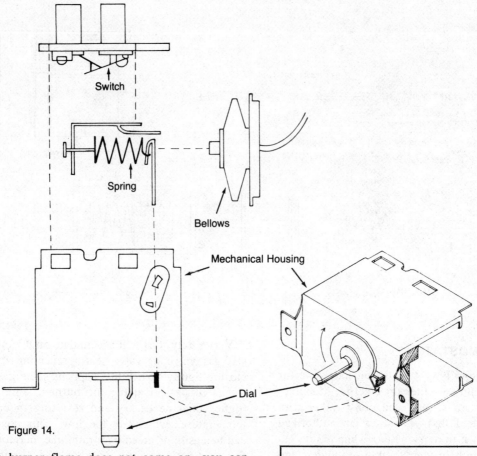

Figure 14.

If the burner flame does not come on, you can strongly suspect that the charge is deficient. The cure with most units is to replace the entire thermostat assembly.

If the end of the capillary tube is not properly inserted into the sleeve of the sensor, it will erroneously tell the thermostat that the temperature is too hot and the thermostat will operate the burner continuously. Cabinet temperatures which are too low will result.

19.26   BYPASS SCREW.

During those periods when the thermostat tells the burner not to boil ammonia, a pilot light must remain to start the burner again later. The bypass screw performs this function by allowing a small amount of gas to "bypass" the main gas supply valve (enough to keep the flame failure device's thermocouple heated and light the full burner). On rare occasions, the small hole in this screw will clog and *must* be cleaned. It is generally located in the gas thermostat housing. Cleaning is easily accomplished by soaking in alcohol or MEK (methyl-ethyl-keytone) and/or blowing out with air (Figure 15). (Also see Section 19.24 re: thermostats.)

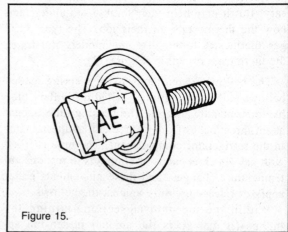

Figure 15.

19.27   REPLACING THE HEATING ELEMENT.

CAUTION: Disconnect power supply before investigating the heating element.

Many refrigerator heating elements have two windings: one for 12-volt DC power and the other for 120-volt AC. Access to the element will be from the rear of the refrigerator.

The instructions for changing the heating element on most brands of refrigerators are similar, so they are generalized here (see Figure 16):

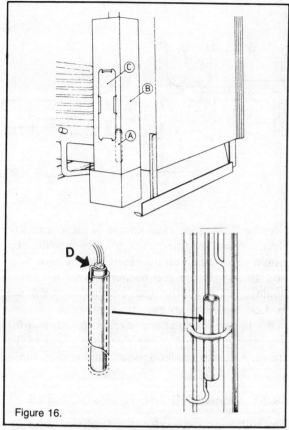

Figure 16.

The heater (A) is accessible for replacement after removal of shutter (C) and some of the rockwool insulation inside the compartment (B). Be careful; the edges of the opening are sharp!

1. Check that the size and wattage of the replacement heater are correct for the unit. Don't substitute!
2. Check that the supply voltage corresponds to the voltage stamped on the heating element.
3. Make sure that the heater is inserted to its full length at the bottom of the well pocket. If the heating element requires screws, be sure they are fixed in place.
4. Some heaters are held in position by a hook on the heater pocket (D); be sure this is properly used.
5. Be very careful to replace the insulation properly.

Some refrigerators, such as the Instamatic IM-40 C pictured below, may have double heating elements. These are accessed and replaced in a similar manner (Figure 17).

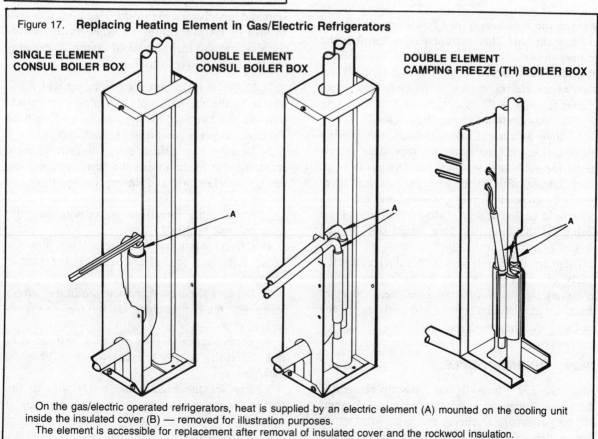

Figure 17.   **Replacing Heating Element in Gas/Electric Refrigerators**

SINGLE ELEMENT CONSUL BOILER BOX

DOUBLE ELEMENT CONSUL BOILER BOX

DOUBLE ELEMENT CAMPING FREEZE (TH) BOILER BOX

On the gas/electric operated refrigerators, heat is supplied by an electric element (A) mounted on the cooling unit inside the insulated cover (B) — removed for illustration purposes.
The element is accessible for replacement after removal of insulated cover and the rockwool insulation.

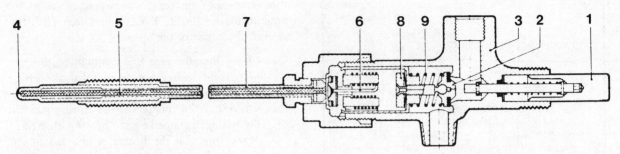

Figure 18.

19.28   FLAME FAILURE SAFETY DEVICE.

The purpose of this feature is to prevent gas from being dispensed to the burner when there is no flame. A typical Flame Failure Safety Device functions as follows (Figure 18):

By pressing the spring-loaded push button (1) the gas valve (2) is opened and the gas can pass the housing (3) and proceed to the burner. If this gas is then ignited by a match or ignition device at the burner, the sensing element within the feeler (thermocouple) tips (4) (see Section 19.29) and senses the presence of flame. The thermocouple absorbs the heat energy and transforms it into an electric current. This current passes through the enamel-insulated copper wire (5) to the electromagnet (6) and back through the outer tube (7). As soon as the electric current is generated, the electromagnet attracts the armature (8) with the valve (2). The push button can then be released.

As long as current flows through the sensing element (i.e., as long as the thermocouple detects heat), the valve remains open and lets gas through to the burner. If the flame were extinguished there would be no more current generated and the valve (2) would be forced into a closed position by the spring (9). Shutting the valve would stop the gas flow.

There are other variations of this device, but it's really of academic interest because you should *never* attempt to make repairs on them. Most of these installations can be removed fairly easily and replaced with new units.

19.29   THERMOCOUPLE.

Also called a ''feeler'' and ''thermo-element,'' the thermocouple is a safety device which shuts off the gas supply whenever the flame goes out. It accomplishes its job by sitting above the flame and ''feeling'' the heat. Heat energy is transformed to electrical and magnetic energy at its opposite end within the Flame Failure Safety Device (see Section 19.28). If the thermocouple were not functioning, you would be unable to maintain a flame as there would be no gas.

It's imperative to check your service manual for the exact placement of the thermocouple over the flame. A few examples appear in the next section.

19.30   CHANGING THE THERMOCOUPLE.

The following steps refer specifically to some Instamatic models (see Figure 19), but they also give an idea of the procedures for other makes. Additionally, see the instructions in Figure 20 pertaining to Dometic's refrigerators.

1. Removal of the burner box cover will make access to the thermocouple retaining clip easier. Remove the two Phillips-head screws which hold the cover in place, then slide it back and out.

2. Remove the igniter electrode-thermocouple retaining clip by removing the screw and pulling the igniter electrode and thermocouple out of the burner.

3. Remove the blue flame meter wire from the thermocouple terminal.

4. Carefully remove the 5/16-inch nut from the back of the gas control and remove the thermocouple.

5. Replace the new thermocouple in the burner along with the igniter electrode and replace the retaining clip.

6. Thread the 5/16-inch nut back into the control. Carefully torque this nut down to 20 to 50 inch/pounds.

7. Replace the blue flame meter wire in the thermocouple interrupter (terminal), and tape if necessary.

8. Replace the burner box cover.

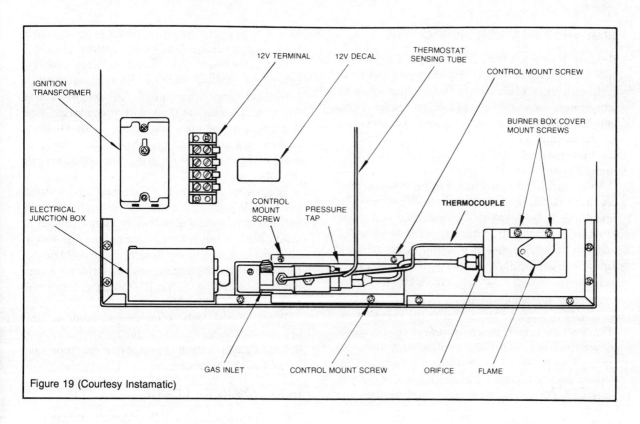

Figure 19 (Courtesy Instamatic)

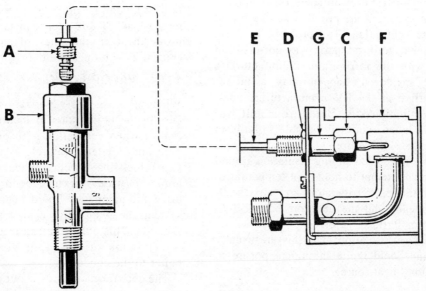

Figure 20. How to replace the thermoelement of the thermoelectric flame failure safety device on some Dometic refrigerators.

1. Unscrew plug (A) from the valve housing (B).
2. Loosen the position nut (C) and lock nut (D).
3. Screw off nut (C), remove spacer (G) and nut (D). Release the thermoelement (E) from burner housing (F).
4. Bend the new thermoelement to the same shape as the old one. Screw nut (D) into the new element.
5. Put the feeler through the hole in the burner housing (F), refit the spacer (G) and screw the position nut (C) tight against the shoulder on the feeler, making sure the nut

(D) is free during this operation.
6. Tighten the lock nut (D) against the burner housing with a small spanner, if necessary holding nut (C) with another spanner. Make sure the feeler is located as in figure.
7. Screw plug (A) onto the valve housing (B), taking care not to damage the threaded hole in the aluminum cap of the housing. Plug (A) must be properly tightened to the valve housing to ensure contact between the thermoelement and the magnetic coil within the housing.

19.31   HOT WEATHER INEFFICIENCY.

Because absorption refrigerators depend upon outside air to remove heat from their coils and fins, their efficiency decreases in direct proportion to temperature increases beyond a certain point. Each unit has different characteristics and tolerances, so no generalities can be made except, perhaps, to say that most units are struggling when their surroundings are over 100 degrees F.

Very little troubleshooting can be done to correct hot weather inefficiencies, but RVers can do a few things to help. If you'll be camping in hot environments frequently, you may want to consider installing a small fan which would direct moving air at the appropriate part of your refrigerator. Remember, though, that fans use electricity.

Another sometimes-used "emergency" measure is simply to place a block of ice in the refrigerator. The ice will help keep compartment temperatures down, and thus allow the cooling unit some respite. The drawback is that many absorption refrigerators can't handle the melting water, so you must put the ice in a container and periodically empty it.

Hot weather inefficiency in some older units is curable to an extent, if the problem can be traced to inadequate ventilation. The problem in these older rigs is that the installation was not made in conformity with the refrigerator manufacturer's instructions. This doesn't happen today, as the refrigerators arrive at the RV manufacturers complete with ventilation kits. But if your unit was improperly installed, you may be able to build-in new and adequate ventilation.

Some RVers have tried adding insulation around their units in an attempt to hold cool temperatures inside the unit. Most refrigerators are fairly well-insulated, though, and the addition will accomplish but little. Further, safety experts frown on this idea because insulation materials are usually flammable and could ignite through exposure to the refrigerator's heat source.

19.32   FLAME-OUT.

Sometimes RVers are plagued with a problem called flame-out, which simply means that a vagrant air current blows out the flame. The problem was more prevalent on older models, and a common but sometimes disastrous remedy was to place furnace filters over vents to prevent drafts. Needless to say, the filters gradually collected dirt and progressively restricted air flow to the point of damaging the cooling unit. Modern units seldom have this problem, however, and kits are available for correcting flame-outs on some older models.

Flame-outs can also be a temporary problem caused by peculiar specific circumstances where you're camping. When this is the case, just facing the rig a different direction will often suffice. And don't forget that these temporary drafts could be "down drafts" entering through the vents, so moving these away from prevailing winds may do the job.

Occasional flame-outs sometimes send a do-it-your-self-minded RVer on an exploration of the entire burner area, and parts like thermocouples or safety devices are needlessly replaced. The moral, obviously, is to be very sure of your problem before taking action. Sometimes just building a simple non-obstructive baffle to stop air currents will be sufficient.

When all else fails, some people advocate simply turning the thermostat to the maximum setting, but the danger with this remedy is that food may get too cold or even freeze.

19.33   AMMONIA LEAKS.

Whenever you notice a yellow deposit on any portion of a cooling unit, you should suspect an ammonia leak. If this occurs in the evaporation coil inside the unit, the smell of ammonia should be evident as you open the door.

19.34   VAPOR LOCK.

When an excessive vaporization of ammonia occurs in the boiler, due to incorrect heat distribution or when ventilation is inadequate (e.g., very high ambient temperature), a situation known as vapor lock may occur. When this happens, the ammonia/water mixture becomes too weak to drive the pump. As liquid begins forming in the system, the evaporation cannot achieve its cooling function. This condition can lead to blistering and discoloration of the vapor pipe connecting the boiler to the condenser.

The cure for most units is not easy — it requires removing the cooling unit or the entire refrigerator and turning it upside down several times to mix the liquid in the absorber with that in the boiler, thus restoring balance. After reinstallation, the unit is operated for a few minutes on maximum setting. Not all makes utilize this procedure, so check your service manual first.

19.35   CHANGING ABSORPTION COOLING UNITS.

One important piece of troubleshooting advice is

to check the cooling unit's operation on both sources of power before deciding what the problem might be. One manufacturer candidly told us that many perfectly good cooling units have been replaced, even by their own service centers, because the technician failed to do this. If the unit operates on one heat source but not on the other, you'll know with certainty that your problem isn't in the cooling unit.

Installing a new cooling unit should in most cases be accomplished by a professional. But this is not to say that a patient and careful RVer can't do the job. Here are a few examples:

Instructions For Some Dometic models

To remove refrigerator – proceed as follows:

1. Check that refrigerator is empty and remove ice tray.
2. Turn off gas bottle.
3. Disconnect gas line to inlet valve (see C Figure 25).
   CAUTION: Use a backup wrench to prevent undue rotation.
4. On gas/electric models, unplug the electric line from the coach outlet.
5. Remove the four screws in rear cabinet base.
6. Check for any additional screws which the coach manufacturer may have used to fasten the refrigerator in place.
7. Carefully slide refrigerator straight out of its recess.

To replace refrigerator in its recess:

1. Reverse above procedure.
   CAUTION: Check all gas connections for leaks with soapy water, not with an open flame.
   At test the refrigerator gas equipment must not be subjected to internal pressure exceeding 22 inches (560 mm) pressure of water column.

Replacement of absorption unit on models RM36/45/60, RA34/44/59

When replacing the absorption unit it will be necessary to remove the refrigerator from its recess.

To remove the absorption unit – proceed as follows:

1. Put the refrigerator on a test bench of suitable height.
2. Remove the thermostat capillary tube(s), (two on gas/electric models) by loosening the two screws (A) on the evaporator flange (Figure 21).
   CAUTION: The locations of the thermostat capillary tube(s) should be noted at this time for relocation later on. The tube(s) must be replaced in the right position, otherwise improper performance may result.
3. Remove the two sealing plugs for capillary tube(s), one on the back and one inside the cabinet, and straighten the tube(s) out.
4. Remove the capillary tube(s) by going to the back of the refrigerator and gently pulling the tube(s) straight out.
5. Remove the four screws (B) and take away (C) the evaporator flange(s). (On RM45/60, RA44/59, six screws and two screws in the freezer compartment).
6. Remove the plastic cover (A) [Figure 22] by means of pulling it upwards on the right-hand side which will release it from the cabinet liner (only on RM36, RA34).
7. Remove the connection block cover on the side of the boiler case and disconnect the two electrical wires where they join the heater leads in the connection block. (New electric heater is normally installed in new absorption units at factory.)
8. Remove the earth-screws (A) [see Figure 25]

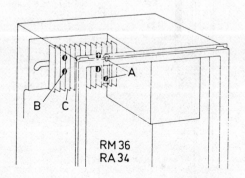

RM 36
RA 34

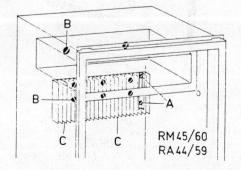

RM 45/60
RA 44/59

Figure 21.

on the lower part of the boiler case.

9. Remove the flue top and the flue baffle by means of bending the flue top holder upwards.

10. Remove the screws (B) [see Figure 25] holding the absorption unit onto the back of the cabinet.

11. Release the flint lighter by pressing the guide pin upwards and push the lighter towards the back of the refrigerator [Figure 23].

12. Remove the fastening screw (A) [Figure 23] on the burner housing and release the burner housing from the boiler case.

13. Carefully slide absorption unit straight out of cabinet.

    CAUTION: Be careful not to damage the inner liner of the cabinet.

14. To replace absorption unit reverse above procedure.

    CAUTION:

    1. Be sure to apply sealing permagum (A) [Figure 24] on the unit mounting plate and on the high evaporator inlet tube (B).

    2. Be sure to fit insulation pad (C), part No. 200 23 90-00/9 and insulation sleeve (D), part No. 200 23 59-00/4 (only on RM36, RA34).

    3. Be sure to apply proper amount of "Thermal Mastic" on the evaporator coil (E) [Figure 24].

    4. When fitting the evaporator flange(s) be sure to tighten the screws properly in order to obtain a perfect contact between the evaporator coil and evaporator flange, otherwise improper cabinet performance may result.

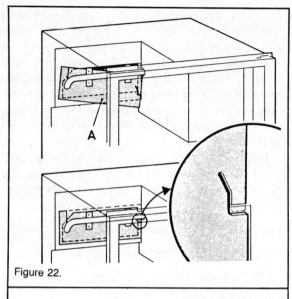

Figure 22.

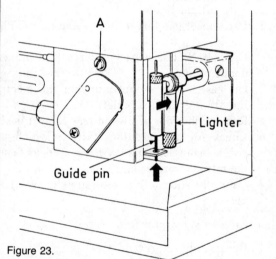

Figure 23.

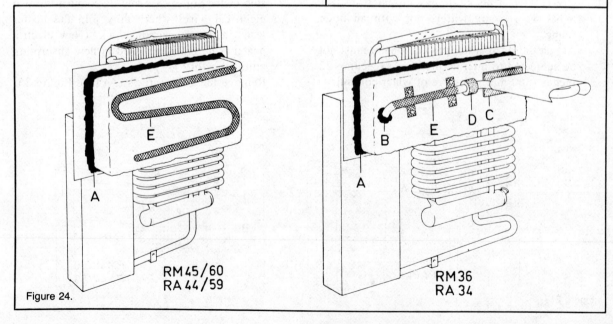

Figure 24.

RM 45/60
RA 44/59

RM 36
RA 34

Replacement of absorption unit on Dometic Models RM75, RA74

When replacing the absorption unit it will be necessary to remove the refrigerator from its recess.

1. Remove the six screws at the bottom of the freezer compartment (A) [Figure 26].
2. Remove the thermostat capillary tubes by loosening the two screws (B) on the evaporator fins [Figure 26].
   CAUTION: The locations of the thermostat capillary tubes should be noted at this time for relocation later on. The tubes must be replaced in the right position, otherwise improper performance may result.
3. Remove the two sealing plugs for capillary tubes, one on the back and one inside the cabinet, and straighten the tubes out.
4. Remove the capillary tubes by going to the back of the refrigerator and gently pulling the tubes straight out.
5. Remove the connection block cover on the side of the boiler case and disconnect the two electrical wires where they join the heater leads in the connection block (new electric heater is normally installed in new absorption units at factory).

6. Remove the earth-screws (A) [Figure 25] on the lower part of the boiler case.
7. Remove the flue and the flue baffle.
8. Remove the screws (B) holding the absorption unit onto the back of the refrigerator [Figure 25].
9. Release the flint lighter by pressing the retainer pin upwards and push the lighter towards the back of the cabinet [Figure 23].
10. Remove the fastening screw (A) [Figure 23] on the burner housing and release the burner housing from the boiler case.
11. Carefully slide absorption unit straight out of the cabinet.
    CAUTION: Be careful not to damage the inner liner and the locations of the fastening strips (A) [Figure 27] on the evaporator should be noted at this time as they have to be fitted on the new unit.
12. To replace absorption unit, reverse above procedure.

CAUTION: Be sure to apply sealing permagum (B) [Figure 27] on the unit mounting plate. Be sure to fit the fastening brackets (A) on the evaporator coils in the right positions, otherwise it will be difficult to refit the six fastening screws inside the freezer.

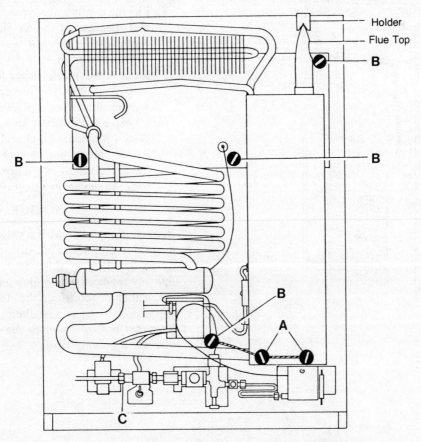

Figure 25.

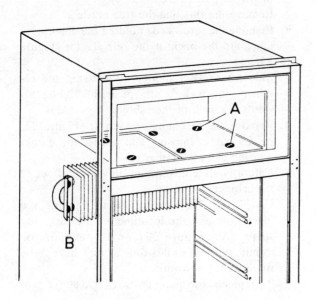

Figure 26.

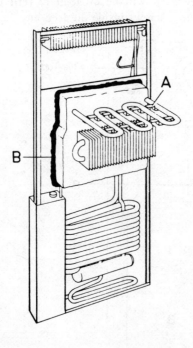

Figure 27.

Replacing a Cooling Unit on Some Instamatic Models

1. With the refrigerator in the upright position, remove the mounting screws in freezer box and cut the 12V interior lamp wires behind the spade connectors. (See Figure 28.)

2. Remove the protective grill from refrigerator cooling coil.

3. Loosen capillary tube from the retainer (Figure 29) by backing the Phillips-head screws in the plate retainer out about two turns. Straighten the capillary tubes, being careful not to crimp or break them. Pull tubes out from back of cabinet. Carefully coil to prevent kinks or breaks.

4. Lay the refrigerator face down. Remove the two Phillips-head screws holding the burner box cover and slide the cover off *(toward the bottom of the refrigerator)*. Remove both machine bolts holding the box to the bottom of the cooling unit.

5. Pull the electrical spade connectors apart in the insulating sleeve to free the electrical heating element.

6. Remove all self-tapping metal screws holding the cooling unit to the cabinet of the refrigerator.

7. Lift the cooling unit from the refrigerator cabinet. Because of the weight and the hydraulic action of the thermal mastic, this is often a job for two people.

8. Remove the plastic inner lid *(if your unit has one)* from behind the secondary evaporator and install on the replacement unit. If liquid adhesive is available, spraying the plate lightly will provide a good seal to the new unit.

9. Perfect freezer box contact is essential. Therefore, use all of the thermal mastic supplied with the replacement cooling unit.

NOTICE:

Because a cooling unit is a delicate instrument and a major component which sometimes sustains rough handling in shipment, it is recommended that any replacement cooling unit be hung level on the wall and operated on the electric element about eight hours prior to installation on a refrigerator. Such a "run-in" assures the quality of the replacement cooling unit.

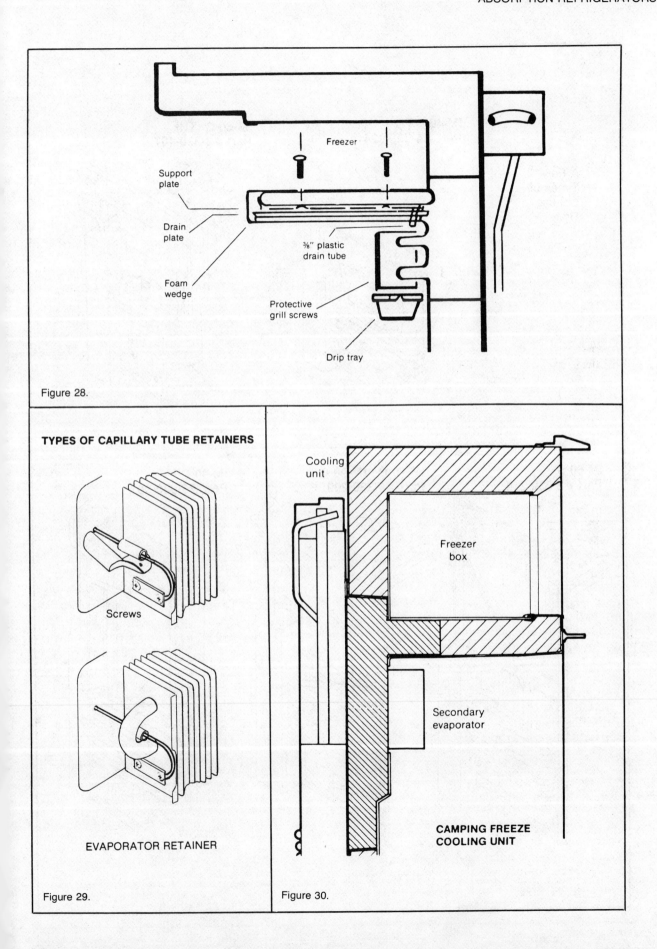

Freezer

Support
plate

Drain
plate

Foam
wedge

⅜″ plastic
drain tube

Protective
grill screws

Drip tray

Figure 28.

TYPES OF CAPILLARY TUBE RETAINERS

Screws

EVAPORATOR RETAINER

Figure 29.

Cooling
unit

Freezer
box

Secondary
evaporator

**CAMPING FREEZE
COOLING UNIT**

Figure 30.

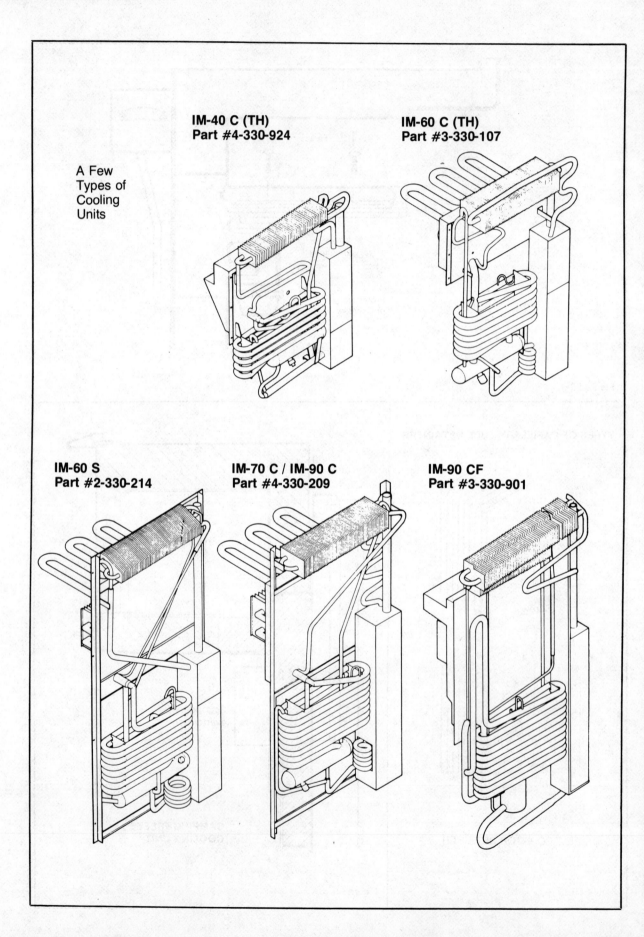

A Few
Types of
Cooling
Units

IM-40 C (TH)
Part #4-330-924

IM-60 C (TH)
Part #3-330-107

IM-60 S
Part #2-330-214

IM-70 C / IM-90 C
Part #4-330-209

IM-90 CF
Part #3-330-901

19.36 DOOR GASKET.

A common non-mechanical problem is a worn or dried door gasket. If the gasket doesn't fit tightly, it's letting cold air escape. To test the fit, insert a thin sheet of paper (a dollar bill is fine) against the portion of the gasket which you suspect to be unsound, then close the door. A good gasket will hold the paper firmly. If the gasket does need replacing, the job is simple — the new part will slide, screw or glue into place very quickly.

19.37 BUYING A NEW REFRIGERATOR.

When the time comes to get a new refrigerator, you'll want to remember that absorption units are not the only kind on the market. They are the most popular with RVers simply because they can operate from electricity *or* gas, thus they are functional in wilderness or full-service campground environments. But regular compressor-type refrigerators are also available. These units are small versions of the kind found in homes, and they have their own advantages and disadvantages. The important features for the RVer are that compressor units aren't bothered by off-level, and they work more efficiently than absorption types in hot weather. The disadvantage is that they use only electricity and will draw down a battery too quickly if you like to camp self-contained for long periods.

The next consideration in buying a new refrigerator is the space available in your rig. It's not just the hole in the wall that matters; you must also consider the ventilation system.

We've mentioned earlier that manufacturers are very specific about the ventilation requirements for their units. If you replace a refrigerator with a similar unit, it's probable that the existing ventilation will be adequate — but it's also likely that you'll need new ventilation for a larger refrigerator. Installing larger vents on an existing rig can be a major undertaking, including lowering a section of the floor or cutting holes in the skin — and that's why this job is usually left to an authorized service center. Again, this doesn't mean you can't do an installation yourself — just that you should be completely aware of what's needed before tackling the job.

Other considerations in replacement units are the features on today's models. Some larger units, for instance, now offer the frost-free option we mentioned earlier. Freezers are available on many units, piezo lighters make lighting pilots easier, and different shelf and drawer configurations offer a latitude of choice which can come closer to matching your particular needs. For smaller installations, Dometic has introduced a unit which has a sealed combustion chamber and doesn't need a side vent.

Workmanship is one of the prime considerations when inspecting a new refrigerator, but it's often the hardest quality to judge. Do look for the obvious, though. See that drawers slide easily and fit tightly; check the sturdiness of shelves; make sure the door closes squarely; see if the construction has a substantial "feel;" check that the cooling unit looks well-attached; compare insulation; and ask other RVers about their experience with various brands, particularly the quality of service they've received at authorized service centers.

Portable units may be a useful idea when you need increased capacity in the rig, or when a small unit in your car or boat would be a welcome addition.

19.38 ICELESS ICEBOXES.

These appliances are new to the market and are relatively simple to explain and troubleshoot. The devices are not true refrigerators, but they will cool down to the temperature of a conventional icebox or, using their simplified heat withdrawal system, they'll make a cube of ice last a long time.

The actual refrigeration mechanism is solid state, i.e., no moving parts. It depends on a chemical bonding reaction, which is catalyzed by 12-volt current, to absorb heat from the box interior and release it to the outside. A small electric fan generally assists the process.

One frequent "problem" with these units is that the interior fins get caked with food and grime, and the unit's efficiency gradually diminishes. It's the old story again — there is a very practical value in cleanliness.

An equally common cause of poor cooling is low voltage — the same problem that plagues other electrical appliances on an RV.

Another electrical problem is experienced when polarity is accidentally reversed. This causes the unit to heat rather than chill the interior compartment.

The very rare incurable problems which involve the preset thermostat or the chemistry of the unit are corrected by the manufacturer. If it becomes necessary to seek such remedies, the good news is that the repairable parts are all contained in the door — and this can be shipped separately to a service center. But before you do so, contact the

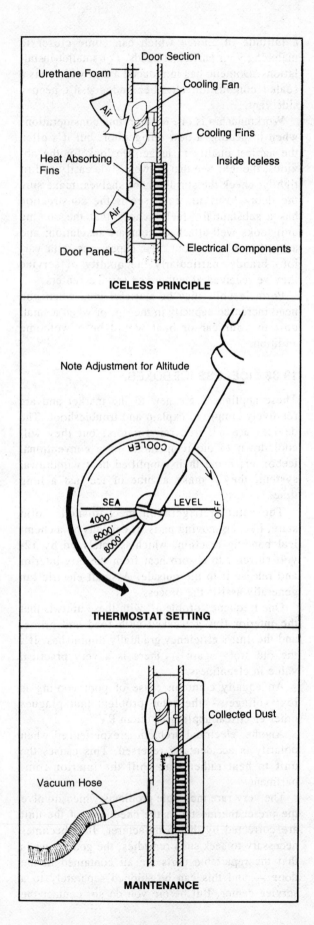

ICELESS PRINCIPLE

THERMOSTAT SETTING

MAINTENANCE

manufacturer for specific instructions.

A&E ICELESS ICEBOX
ICELESS PRINCIPLE

In principle, the fins, which are evident on the inside of the door, absorb the heat from within the box, thereby cooling the box interior. Heat is thermoelectrically pumped from these fins to another set of fins located within the door. The cooling fan, which is the only moving part in the box, blows room air over these fins to keep them cool and to dissipate the heat that they accumulate. The fan sucks the air in through the circular opening and discharges through the grill near the handle. This discharged air will give off heat at about the same rate as a 50-watt light bulb.

Controlling the temperature within the box is done automatically with a preset thermostat. The thermostat will control the icebox temperature to the same level as if ice were in the box and causes the fan to cycle on and off as the internal temperatures warrant. After cycling off, the fan may continue to rotate for a few minutes due to the static energy remaining in the thermoelectric units. This condition is normal and the fan should be permitted to cycle at will. The length of time that the unit operates is mainly due to the temperature within the camper or boat and the amount of food in the box. On a cool day, the unit will be off for longer periods than on. On a hot day, the unit may be on constantly; however, during the night the unit will be off for a good portion of the time.

THERMOSTAT SETTING

An adjustment screw is located in the center of the label appearing on the inside panel of the IceLess door. It can be turned with a standard screwdriver.

Due to changes in atmospheric pressures at differing altitudes, the operation of your IceLess will tend to run colder and longer at the higher altitudes. To conserve battery power and to maintain conventional icebox temperatures, we recommend turning the screw in a counterclockwise direction to the position that corresponds with the altitude at which it is operating.

If you choose not to turn the thermostat as suggested or if you turn the thermostat below the sea level designation, the icebox temperature will be colder and the amperage demand will increase (never above four amps per hour).

MAINTENANCE

The only required maintenance to keep your IceLess running efficiently is the removal of dust and or lint from the top of the fins contained within the door and immediately below the fan. Because of the air flow, dust will tend to accumulate over a period of time and can be picked out or blown out with the use of a high pressure air hose or with the reverse mode of your vacuum cleaner.

Heavy accumulation of dust and lint — if not removed — will impede air flow and cause your IceLess to work harder and longer to achieve the preset internal temperature.

SERVICE

In case of a problem with the IceLess icebox the following procedure is recommended:

1. Inspect all electrical connections. If possible, use a 12-volt trouble light to verify power is available at the icebox connection and an amp meter to determine that the IceLess is drawing four amps at the icebox.
2. Make sure the battery is charged. *Do not* connect the IceLess icebox to a battery without means of recharging the battery.
3. Write or phone the factory with a complete detailed description of the problem. *Do not* send the unit to the factory without authority.
4. If requested by the factory to return the unit, ship only the door. Be sure the door is well protected. Remember, freight companies are not responsible for damage due to poor packaging.

The fan motor may be replaced with a factory-supplied fan replacement kit. *Do not* attempt to replace it with a substitute motor or further damage may result. Fan motor replacement kits and detailed directions are available from our factory. **NOTE:** *Do not* attempt to take the door apart. It is completely sealed and any attempt to dismantle it may result in destroying the heat pump and your warranty.

Chapter Twenty

Insulation

Insulating most RVs after they have been built is virtually an impossible task, because insulating material properly goes between the inner and outer skins. Even in those few instances when inside walls can be unfastened with comparative ease, the overall job is much more extensive than we'll want to deal with here. In many instances, though, adding insulation to specific places is both easy and an excellent idea. Typical of these ''spot'' jobs are the areas behind cabinets that are left uninsulated by some manufacturers, and the walls which separate ovens from other storage facilities.

On a practical level, measuring the effectiveness of your rig's insulation is simple — you're either comfortable or you're not — and that's often the best test. On a more scientific basis, various indexes can describe how resistant a substance is to heat transfer, but the most familiar measurement in both residential and RV construction is the *R*-value. *R* stands for *thermal resistance*, and familiarity with the term (see accompanying box explanation) will make our discussion more meaningful.

20.01 UNDERSTANDING THE VARIETIES OF INSULATING MATERIAL.

The most common insulating material in RVs, and especially in travel trailers, is fiberglass batting. There are several ways to produce fiberous glass, and each technique yields fibers with different physical properties and different *R*-values. It is not necessary to understand these methods, but you should know that the ''blanket insulation'' best-suited to RVs is made by the flame-attenuation or flame-blowing process. Other grades made by the textile, long fiber and rotary processes are also available, but a higher density or greater thickness must be used to provide the same insulating value as the first type.

Because continuous vibration would encourage loose fiberglass to compact, RV insulation usually employs blankets wherein the fibers are glued between two stiff paper rolls. These blankets are thus cut to fit the spaces between the RV's framework, and then stapled to keep them in place.

One of the big advantages to fiberglass insulation is that it is extremely lightweight, easy to install and of proven insulating effectiveness. As long as it stays in place, it will provide the thermal resistance credited to it. But if the fastening should fail, the material will soundlessly fall down between the inner and outer skins of the rig, leaving an area with no insulation. Appropriately, technicians call this problem *fall-down*. (Even

---

HEAT LOSS DATA AND CALCULATIONS

In the United States the basic unit of heat is generally considered to be the British Thermal Unit or, as it is commonly called, a BTU.

BRITISH THERMAL UNIT (BTU) — the amount of heat required to increase the temperature of one pound of water one degree Fahrenheit.

The basic unit of heat flow: i.e., the amount of heat that will be transmitted through a unit of material in a given time, is known as the thermal conductivity of a material.

THERMAL CONDUCTIVITY (k) — BTU per (hour) (square foot) (Fahrenheit degree per inch of thickness) — the amount of heat expressed in BTU that is transmitted through one-square-foot of material *one-inch thick* during a period of one hour when there is a difference of temperature of one Fahrenheit degree across the two surfaces of the material.

When thicknesses other than one inch are considered the term *thermal conductance* is used.

THERMAL CONDUCTANCE (C) — BTU per (hour) (square foot) (Fahrenheit degree) — the amount of heat expressed in BTU that is transmitted through one-square-foot of the material of a given thickness other than one inch during a period of one hour when there is a difference of temperature of one Fahrenheit degree across the two surfaces of the material.

When reference is made to a structure such as a wall which is composed of several different types of materials, air spaces, etc., the term *overall coefficient of heat transmission* is used. Unlike the ''k'' factor or the ''C'' factor where the heat flow is measured from surface to surface of a solid material, this unit also takes into consideration the insulating value of the air films formed on the surfaces of the materials.

OVERALL COEFFICIENT OF HEAT TRANSMISSION (U) — BTU per (hour) (square foot) (Fahrenheit degree temperature difference between air on the inside and air on the outside of a wall, floor, roof or ceiling) — the amount of heat expressed in BTU that is transmitted through one-square-foot of a structure during a period of one hour when there is a difference in temperature of one Fahrenheit degree from the air on one side of the structure to the air on the other side of the structure.

To facilitate calculation, the unit **THERMAL RESISTANCE (R)** may be used. Its value is equal to the reciprocal of the above heat transfer factors. $R = thk/k$, $1/C$, $1/U$. Thermal resistances may be added arithmetically to give the overall resistance of a structure. When calculating heat loss problems, it is well to keep in mind that heat always travels from hot to cold, i.e., from a higher temperature to a lower temperature and the temperature drop across a material is directly proportional to the thermal resistance of that material.

(Courtesy of Johns-Manville Insulation Center)

APPROXIMATE COMPARATIVE R-VALUES

MATERIAL	THICKNESS	R
Fir, pine and similar		
softwood	¼	0.31
	¾	0.94
Plywood	¼	0.3
	⅜	0.5
Expanded polystyrene:		
Extruded	1	4.0
Moulded beads	1	3.85
Urethane foam	¾	3.93
	1½	8.82
Styrofoam	¾	3.93
	1½	7.89
Glass fiber:		
Textile	1	3.5
	1½	5.2
Flame-blown	1	3.6
	1½	5.4

well-installed blankets may fall a few inches, but this isn't serious.)

Because air is an excellent insulating material, fiberglass owes its effectiveness to the air entrapped within its complex web of fibers. You can quickly see that a fall-down problem would not only leave an uninsulated gap, but would compress the material toward the bottom of the rig and lower its value by forcing air out. This same decreased effectiveness would also be experienced if a manufacturer installed a three-inch thick blanket in a two-inch space. You could certainly say that you're using three inches of fiberglass with an R-value of 10.5, but its actual insulating abilities would be severely limited.

Plastic foam is another popular insulating material because it installs quickly, and when it hardens it actually contributes some structural strength to the rig's framework. Foam has a higher R-Factor than fiberglass, thus less of it is needed to achieve equivalent insulating effectiveness.

Some manufacturers have given up foam because it does have a fabrication problem which will also interest do-it-yourselfers. In a typical new installation, the skin is attached to the framework, then foam is sprayed into the pockets formed by the frame and skin (visualize doing this on a small scale with an aerosol can of shaving cream and you'll get the picture). Even electrical wiring and conduits are encased in the plastic. If the material isn't introduced by a skilled operator, though, too much can be sprayed in, necessitating hand-scraping to get rid of the excess; too little or uneven insulation could also inadvertently result.

Another critic says that when foam is inexpertly blown into a framework that has already been mounted on the vehicle chassis, it may settle be-

fore it hardens. If this should occur, you're left with the same problem as encountered in a minor fiberglass fall-down — i.e., an area which is devoid of insulation.

Some manufacturers who didn't care for spray-on foam application, but liked the material's qualities, have gone to polyurethane foam blocks. In this process the foam is pre-formed in a mold, allowed to set and then installed in the rig's framework. While the heat transfer ratings for the two materials are similar, pre-forming has limited application for consumers simply because you must first build your own form. You might want to hold this concept in mind, though, just in case it does fit a specific project.

Another type of plastic foam is called polystyrene bead board. The process entails expanding little plastic beads under heat and then fusing them together to form board material. This substance is lightweight and easy to use, but it has the disadvantage of being absorbent. Water is the nemesis of porous insulating material, because it forms an immediate pathway for heat transfer and effectively destroys the insulating qualities. (Fiberglass is also dramatically affected by water.) The criticism is strictly academic if the material is effectively isolated from contact with humid air or condensation, but when this can't be guaranteed there is a potential for problems.

The newest insulating material to hit the industry, extruded polystyrene, is chemically very similar to other plastics, but it has quite different properties. Dow Chemical Company is probably the largest supplier of this material, and markets it under the trade name of Styrofoam® (a name familiar to most people because of its use in inexpensive coolers, beverage cups, etc.).

The features of Styrofoam (and similar products) which interest RV manufacturers are its balance between high structural strength, low weight, good insulation, and complete moisture-resistance. Because its strength is more than just a slight improvement over other insulations, this material has given birth to an entirely new concept in RV construction — the sandwich panel.

There are two types of sandwich panels. In the Eastern-style application, a piece of extruded polystyrene board is bonded between equivalent-sized pieces of the RV's outer and interior skin. It is a lamination of individual wall components into one panel with solid insulation. The Western-style sandwich inserts an added layer of plywood between the insulation and the exterior skin. And some makers also add metal supports to the sandwich.

Sandwich panels can also be described as I-beams with lightweight cores, and the result is a sidewall with a creditable strength-to-weight ratio. This added strength means that less framework is needed in an RV, thus lowering overall weight and fuel consumption.

Honeycomb, a material named after its replication of the honeycomb made by bees, has been used in aerospace for many years, but is just now gaining popularity in RV construction. Beyond good insulating qualities, it has extraordinary strength and is very lightweight. The primary RV use for honeycomb thus far has been in sidewalls, tables and countertops.

Although sandwich panels are the most popular, especially in motorhome construction, all of the other materials we have discussed are still very much in use. In fact, some manufacturers use two or more types of insulators in the same vehicle. Mixing products in this manner often allows a manufacturing versatility which couldn't otherwise be achieved. The home installer can learn from this philosophy and match the insulating ma-terial to the specific job, regardless of what had been used through the rest of the rig.

20.02 VULNERABLE POINTS.

As in a residence, RVs also have inherently weak insulating points, with windows and vents leading the list. Proper ventilation is necessary, and needn't be extreme — but glass transmits heat rather well and may produce enormous losses. The best answer would be double thermal windows such as airplanes use; these inventions trap a layer of air between the panes and, as you recall, dead air is a prime insulator. The drawback to this equipment is its cost, and most manufacturers don't feel that customers would be willing to pay the tab. If you intend to spend much time in tem-perature extremes, you might look for a company that will fabricate some airtight extra frames and panes, but some RVers have effectively impro-vised with do-it-yourself thermal windows. Varia-tions of the technique outlined in Figure 1 will cer-tainly enhance your rig's cold-weather livability, and it should ease your condensation problems.

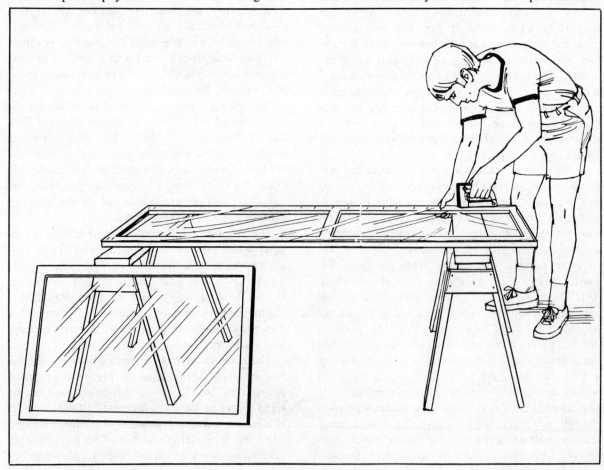

Figure 1.

20.03   INSTALLING INSULATION.

Aside from its commercial advantages and disadvantages, spray foam remains an interesting material for some install-it-yourself applications. Although you may have to hunt for a local source, spray foam is sold in small push-button containers that are ideal for small jobs where you want to seal-in wiring or pipes and provide insulation at the same time. Slightly larger quantities can be purchased from Dometic service centers. Professional services will also spray larger amounts of foam onto any portion of your rig, but an overall retrofitting would entail extensive removal and replacement of inside paneling (Figures 2 - 4).

CAUTION: Don't be tempted to pour spray foam into the spaces between walls. True, this application would enable you to insulate spots which can't be otherwise accessed. But the material expands slightly when it hardens and could thus damage the walls.

CAUTION: Some RVers are also spraying foam onto the underside of their rigs to create better insulation, but two states, Utah and Wyoming, won't allow this because they feel that a fire hazard would be created. (Most plastic insulating materials are flammable, some more than others, so RV construction standards require that these substances must always be covered.)

Another way that manufacturers use spray foam is to pre-form it in molds, then insert it into the appropriate places in the framework.

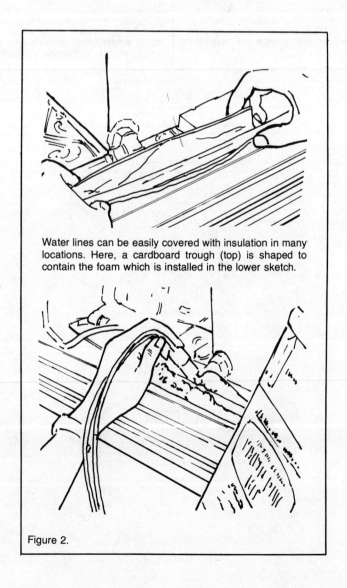

Water lines can be easily covered with insulation in many locations. Here, a cardboard trough (top) is shaped to contain the foam which is installed in the lower sketch.

Figure 2.

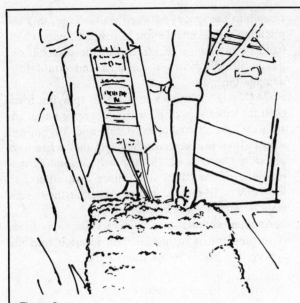

Figure 3.
Foam installed under the front seat shields the driver from heat while on the road.

Figure 4.
Foam is easily removed long after application, so don't worry if something is inadvertently covered.

Chapter Twenty-One

Condensation

Almost universally, RVers complain about moisture accumulating on the walls and windows of their rigs. The problem can become so acute that you think you're in a mobile steam room, and survival becomes an incessant mop-up operation.

21.01 HOW CONDENSATION FORMS.

At its root the problem is incurable, because the physics are inescapable — both your body and your activities (cooking, bathing, etc.) add moisture to the air. Because you've heated your rig, the interior air can absorb or hold this moisture in suspension (air's ability to retain water vapor increases as temperature increases). When this warm moist air contacts cold windows and aluminum frames, however, it looses its heat — and its ability to hold the water. This is how condensation forms. If the walls are also poorly insulated and thus cold, condensation will occur there, as well.

Few people really object to a little frost on the windows, and it may even be an occasion for impromptu Jack Frost artwork. But when water begins running down the walls, behind cabinets, across countertops and is finally absorbed into the carpeting, there's no denying that you're facing a real damage-producing force.

21.02 HOW TO FIGHT CONDENSATION.

Venting is always the first line of defense against insulation. Even though it's asking the heater to cycle more often, cracking open a roof vent to let moist air escape will definitely help the overall problem.

Some RV air-conditioners also contain heat strips, so the unit can be used as an air dehumidifier. If you're not facing a massive problem, this may be sufficient, because operating these units also helps circulate the air (moving air works against condensation). If your need is greater, as when several people are occupying a rig, outside temperatures are below zero and the wind is howling, you may also want to run a separate dehumidifier which can be purchased in small appliance stores. These measures will usually handle condensation in a well-made and well-insulated rig.

Condensation problems sometimes center around specific areas, and the nature of these usually imply their cure. In rigs where the beds are directly beneath windows, for instance, normal breathing during the night may moisturize the air sufficiently to create exaggerated condensation and runoffs. Venting may remedy this if you don't mind sleeping cooler, or you can try drawing the curtains and sacrificing the view for dryness. Another alternative is the thermal-type window described in Section 20.02.

Service managers also report that many condensation problems are exaggerated by unnoticed leaks in the coach where rain or external moisture has entered and been absorbed in out-of-the-way places. Often, they say, an inspection of nooks and crannies will reveal such a reservoir and the solution is obvious: locate and caulk the source.

The problem of condensation due to inadequate insulation is near-hopeless. You can't necessarily blame the manufacturer, because different rigs are designed for different temperature ranges. Unless you're willing to tear out your interior siding and reinsulate all around (and this isn't always possible), you're probably better off trading for a more appropriate rig.

An instance where you can blame the maker, however, occurs when you experience thermal shorts, or patterns of condensation on your interior walls. A thermal short is a break in the insulation occurring when, for instance, a metal or wood (yes, wood will conduct heat) stud directly contacts both the exterior and interior siding. In these cases, the stud forms a direct line for heat transfer to the outside, and you'll see the pattern of the rig's framework etched in water on inside walls.

If thermal shorts aren't widespread, you might accomplish first-aid. For instance, if there are just a few spots you may be able to pull out the panel and insert a thin non-conductor (foam, asbestos, etc.) to disrupt the heat transfer. In the case of metal screw heads which connect inside and outside through the metal framework, a small dab of colored or clear rubber compound may not disrupt the cosmetics of walls.

A more insidious type of condensation may go unnoticed because it occurs between the walls. If moist air enters the space between the inside and outside shell through loose seams, it can condense and saturate wood framework and absorbent insulation. When this happens, the insulation loses its effectiveness and encourages more condensation on the coach's interior walls, and the wood may begin to rot and weaken. In severe cases, you can detect this problem when condensation literally drips between the walls, or when insulation is obviously losing its effectiveness — but milder cases may escape notice until real trouble develops. Knowing how your rig is constructed will tell you whether or not there is even a possibility for this form of condensation, and you'll find that better manufacturers build in a vapor barrier to prevent it.

Here's advice that service personnel across the nation emphasize: If you *do* have an insulation or condensation problem, ask the manufacturer of your rig for assistance. They've often heard similar questions from others, and they have researched answers to most of them. Too many RVers, according to these experts, thrash around with guesses and well-meant advice from friends when a simple solution is available. So remember: A quality manufacturer is interested in your problems and anxious to be of service — and you should take full advantage of this urge to please.

Chapter Twenty-Two

Interior Care

Virtually every chapter in this manual has shown dirt to be second only to abuse as an RV equipment nemesis. So cleanliness should be your main weapon against the forces which gum-up, wear-down or paralyze your valuable machinery. What's more, the process of cleansing has the added advantage of forcing a minute visual inspection of your rig — and these are the times when you'll catch other problems while they're still in the embryo stage.

This section deals only with non-technical and generalized cleaning (mechanical care procedures for onboard equipment is treated elsewhere). Anyone who maintains a home already understands most of this material, as the techniques are identical. And, just as in the home, washing and vacuuming are the foundations of the cleanliness program.

22.01   CARPETING.

RV carpets deserve even more frequent vacuumings than their home counterparts because they generally receive more dirt. Sand and grit are especially harmful, as they work down into the piling and become tiny cutting edges which eventually sever fibers. It's obvious, then, that thorough vacuuming will substantially increase carpet longevity by removing the agents of destruction.

Spills on a carpet should be immediately cleaned before they have a chance to set. Your tools in most instances will be: (1) plenty of *clean* white cloths (diapers are great) and white paper toweling, (2) a solution of one tablespoon of non-alkaline household detergent per pint of warm water, (3) a good dry cleaning solvent which does not contain the dangerous compound carbon tetrachloride, (4) a solution of 1/3 white vinegar and 2/3 water, (5) club soda, (6) water and (7) a pile brush. You can usually follow these steps:

(1) Remove any solids in the spill with a spoon, spatula or fingers, then blot as much of the liquid as you can with paper towels or clean rags. (2) Apply small amounts of the cleansing agent recommended in Figure 1, working from the edges into the center. (Damage easily follows overwetting.) (3) Don't scrub, just remove the moisture by blotting, again from the outer edges toward the center if it's a large spill. (4) Rinse away the cleansing agent with a wet cloth, followed by more blotting. (5) When the carpet is blotted as dry as it will come, cover the area with clean cloths or toweling, then weigh these down so they will absorb more moisture and let it all remain undisturbed for six or more hours.

Dry or steam clean your carpets at least once a year, preferably more often. You can rent machines which make this an easy job.

As an extra-care measure, it's nice to have heavy-gauge plastic runners that can be laid down for special occasions such as wilderness camping or inclement weather. Long tacks are usually all you need to hold the plastic in place, although some people prefer using spring clips.

22.02   LINOLEUM.

There's very little to keeping linoleum floors sparkling. Simply vacuum-sweep and wet-mop with a good cleanser frequently, so dirt can't grind into the surface. Always keep a good protective coating of hard floor wax on the linoleum; it resists abrasion and makes regular cleaning infinitely easier.

22.03   WALLS, WINDOWS AND CEILINGS.

Walls windows and ceilings in most rigs are made of synthetic materials and usually just collect fingerprints, airborne dirt and grease. Keep these surfaces clean with a mild detergent-dampened cloth; cleanser labels usually suggest appropriate dilutions. Wood walls and trim must be periodically treated with a quality furniture polish, and fine woods such as teak will definitely benefit from regular applications of a preservative oil specifically designed for that wood.

Glass windows are easily cleansed with any commercial window product, or with your own solution of water, a dab of detergent and a small amount of ammonia. Because some synthetic interior walls may be sensitive to harsh chemicals, make sure that cleaning materials are applied sparingly and wiped away immediately.

Plastic windows are highly susceptible to scratching, so never use an abrasive cleanser. They will usually come clean with the solutions recommended above. When they begin clouding with age, you can try one of the clearing compounds sold in auto supply stores for restoring plastic sports car windows.

Screens are removable and can be hosed clean. (Soapy water and a soft brush will remove most stains.)

Ceilings receive a good coating of grease after months of cooking and living, so wipe them clean with a detergent solution. If your ceilings are made of acoustical tiling, be very gentle — and don't let the tiles get wet.

TYPE OF STAIN	TYPICAL EXAMPLES	TREATMENT
OILY MATERIAL	BUTTER, GREASE, HAND CREAM OIL, VASELINE, FURNITURE POLISH FRESH PAINT, VARNISH, GLASS WAX	Remove excess. Sponge with dry cleaning solution. Blot with clean, white cloth. Allow to dry. Sponge again with dry cleaner, if necessary. Use dry cleaner sparingly to avoid leaving ring. Brush up pile gently. Allow to dry.
FOODSTUFFS: GREASY FOODS ANIMAL MATTER BEVERAGES	COFFEE, TEA, MILK, CREAM ICE CREAM, CHOCOLATE, EGG GRAVY, MEAT JUICES, SAUCES SALAD DRESSING, VOMIT	Remove excess. Sponge with detergent solution. Take up excess solution with clean dry cloth. Blot thoroughly. If necessary, sponge with dry cleaning solution to remove remaining spot. Blot thoroughly. Brush up pile gently. Allow to dry. (See 22.01.)
FOODSTUFFS: STARCHES AND SUGAR	CANDY, BANANAS, SOFT DRINKS ALCOHOLIC BEVERAGES, BEER WHITE SHOE POLISH	Remove excess. Sponge with detergent solution. Take up excess solution with clean dry cloth. Rinse and blot thoroughly. Repeat detergent solution, if necessary. Again take up excess solution, rinse and blot thoroughly. Brush up pile gently. Allow to dry. (See 22.01.)
STAINS	FRUIT AND BERRY STAINS EXCREMENT (feces), URINE WASHABLE INK ALKALINE SUBSTANCES	Remove excess. Sponge with detergent solution. Take up excess solution with clean dry cloth. Blot thoroughly and repeat detergent solution, if necessary. Rinse with solution of 1/3 white vinegar and 2/3 water. Blot thoroughly. Brush up pile gently. Allow to dry. (See 22.01.)
HEAVY GREASE GUMS	TAR, CHEWING GUM ASPHALT, CRAYON HEAVY GREASE	Remove excess. Sponge with dry cleaning solution. Follow with detergent solution, if necessary, blotting up excess solution with clean dry cloth. Repeat with dry cleaning solution. Blot thoroughly. Brush up pile gently. Allow to dry. (See 22.01.) Repeat entire procedure if necessary until all material is removed.
SPECIAL	MUD	Allow to dry. Scrape up excess. Vacuum thoroughly.
	PUPPY STAINS, FRESH	Apply club soda. Blot thoroughly. Brush up pile. Dry. (See 22.01.)
	BLOOD	Blot up excess. Sponge with plain cold water. Blot thoroughly. If necessary, then follow with treatment for Animal Matter as above.
	LIPSTICK, ROUGE, NAIL POLISH, RUST, DRIED PAINT, FURNITURE STAINS	These stains require special reagents or techniques to be used only by a professional cleaner.

Figure 1.

22.04 UPHOLSTERY AND DRAPES.

Upholstery and drapes are a difficult area to discuss because so many synthetic materials are used and each requires a different cleaning regimen. All will benefit from vacuuming and gentle shaking to free dirt — but some accept washing and others require dry cleaning. (The tags attached to these materials when they are new must give specific instructions.) If tags are missing, don't try to guess which materials are present — ask the manufacturer what you have and how to clean it. Once you know which synthetics are present, you'll also be able to buy appropriate spot-cleaning compounds in virtually any supermarket.

Vinyl, Naugahyde and other hard plastic coverings merely require wiping with a damp cloth. They can also be scrubbed with a soft-bristled brush and soap solution to remove heavy dirt spots. Again, supermarkets carry very effective vinyl cleaners.

22.05 TABLES AND COUNTERS.

Tables and counters in many rigs are made of an almost iron-like plastic that can withstand abrasive cleansers. But don't use these products unless you know the surface can take it. (If you can slice and chop food directly on the surface without hurting it, you can use an abrasive.) Any surface, though, will accept scrubbing with a plastic or fiber-bristled brush and a soapy solution. Commercial window cleansers that contain a small amount of grease-cutting ammonia are also useful.

Table legs shouldn't be scoured, as the customary aluminum or wood will scratch. Just wipe with the same cleansers mentioned above. A good layer of hard wax will also make subsequent removal of shoe scuffs and the like a much easier task.

22.06 REFRIGERATORS.

Most refrigerators require regular defrosting. To

do this, set the temperature regulator to *def* or *off* whenever ice begins to form around the coils, remove food, and be sure the drops are caught in a tray or are channeled to the outside. Remove shelves and drawers and wipe out the inside with a warm detergent or baking soda solution. Unlike home refrigerators, plastic shelves and drawers usually can't tolerate very hot water, so you shouldn't clean them in an automatic dishwasher. It's OK to use abrasives on the metal shelf parts — in fact, that's often the only way to remove hardened foods. If the refrigerator will stand unused for any time, be sure to prop the door open — bad odors will result if you don't. (As an extra precaution against odors, keep an open box of baking soda inside.)

Cleaning the burner area of the refrigerator is frequently neglected because it's accessed from the vehicle exterior. If you'll simply run the vacuum cleaner hose out a window and suck up all the dirt that has accumulated within the pilot and control compartment, you'll save many frustrating problems in the future.

22.07 RANGES AND RANGE HOODS.

Grease quickly cakes the insides of range hoods and, when thick enough, actually represents a fire hazard. Give this area a frequent wipe with a warm detergent solution and don't let the grease accumulate.

Chrome cleansers are also available and do an excellent job, but don't use abrasives as they may score the surface. If the fan has a filter, wash it in soapy water, dry thoroughly and replace. If the filter is in any way damaged, get a new one — they're cheap and easy to insert.

The range top can be similarly cleaned, and this chore can be made easy if you remember to wipe off all spills when they occur. A trick used by some homemakers is to line the drip pans beneath the burner with aluminum foil and simply replace the liner when it's dirty.

Burners themselves can be vacuumed whenever you do carpeting, as this prevents dirt from accumulating. If a burner does become clogged, the holes can often be cleaned by gently inserting a tooth pick and reaming out the orifice. Don't, however, use a metal reamer — as this can alter the precise diameter of the orifice.

Periodically unfasten the stove top, pull it off and clean underneath. It's amazing how much dirt can accumulate there.

22.08 OVENS.

The most important trick to having a spotless oven is to wipe away spills and splatters while they're still fresh. Once they bake and harden, spills become a real chore to remove.

Fresh spills are easily removed with a damp cloth. A good detergent solution, perhaps with a little ammonia added, makes the job even easier. Baked spills, though, usually require loosening with scouring pads or abrasive cleansers. The same oven cleaners used in home ovens are also useful in their RV counterparts. Likewise, racks can be cleaned with the same compounds.

Be careful to dry the oven walls and racks thoroughly, as they can rust. Use a towel and operate the unit on high bake for a few minutes to ensure total dryness.

Some ovens have a rough-textured lining that is intended to be at least partially self-cleaning. With these units, you'll still want to manually remove major spills, as the system just isn't designed to handle them effectively. Getting to them immediately makes for an easier job, but *don't* use scrapers or hard abrasives, as you'll damage the self-cleaning surface. For best results, you'll find that warm water with strong detergent and/or ammonia, sometimes assisted by a synthetic (not metal) bristled brush, will remove the spill and protect the surface. Dry the unit as suggested above.

22.09 FURNACE AND WATER HEATER.

The largest number of gas appliance problems stem from dirt buildup in the pilot area. Simply vacuuming the pilot compartment every time you vacuum the floors will save substantial trouble in this area.

Thermostats also have a space through which dust can enter; place the vacuum nozzle against this "crack" every so often and suck out some of that dirt — but don't open it for cleanings.

If either unit uses an air filter, check this for cleanliness. Most can be washed in warm water and mild detergent, air-dried and replaced. If they look at all worn, simply put in a new one. And don't forget to vacuum the furnace duct outlets.

22.10 WATER AND SANITATION SYSTEM.

Here's another area where just a little care and thought will prevent the majority of annoying on-the-road problems.

Other than maintenance such as cleaning filters,

etc., which are detailed in the appropriate chapters, remember that your drain pipes are continually receiving debris which can accumulate and create stoppages. The materials used in RVs aren't usually compatible with commercial drain cleaners, but a frequent tea kettle full of boiling water down each drain can be nearly as effective. Also, take off the drain covers occasionally and pick out the "stuff" that accumulates there.

Stainless sinks can be scoured with commercial cleansers (Comet, Ajax, etc.), as can porcelain toilet bowls. On metal, work in the direction of polish lines. With plastic sinks, shower walls and toilets, use only a mild acidic cleanser (many brands are sold in markets), as abrasives will scratch these surfaces. Shower floors, though, are an exception. Wax on all these surfaces is highly advisable, and you should check the condition of all caulking while you're cleaning.

Periodically (perhaps once each year), plastic toilets will benefit from partial dismantling and soaking in a manufacturer-approved cleanser. This eliminates any absorbed odors before they become noticeable. While you're doing this, be sure to inspect around the base of marine-type units to see that the connection with the floor is watertight and stable.

Chapter Twenty-Three

Exterior Care

It's an old observation, but nonetheless true, that an RV's outside appearance usually reflects the kind of care it receives on the inside. But exterior care is not all just show; most of the chores have a direct relationship to how serviceable the rig is over the years — and to how it retains its value.

23.01 EXTERIOR SURFACES.

Most rigs are made of aluminum or fiberglass, and many use both materials. These surfaces are quite durable, but they are prone to oxidation fading, pitting and scratching. The best prevention for all three problems is a substantial coating of hard wax (one of the many wax compounds which contain carnauba wax are suitable). It's best to apply waxes exactly as the instructions on the can dictate. Admittedly, most of these directions advise using a cleanser made by the same manufacturer, but go ahead and give them the extra business because you'll be the winner in the long run.

Small scratches are eliminated by washing and local waxing. Deeper scratches can be cosmetically improved with touch-up paint. If scratches have penetrated the skin, they should be promptly sealed to keep moisture out of inter-wall spaces.

Do your washing in the shade, because direct sun dries spots on the surface. Road tars can be removed with a little kerosene, as can tree sap and resin. These stains require buffing if not removed while they're wet.

If small areas of acrylic finish on aluminum surfaces are damaged, clean the acrylic away with lacquer solvent. To refinish, use an aluminum cleaner on the metal, then apply a new coating of acrylic lacquer. All these items are sold in trailer supply stores.

Don't eliminate your roof from this regimen simply because it's difficult to reach. Take the standard precautions (bare feet or deck shoes), and be sure that your roof is designed to hold your weight.

The several permanent coating products offer an interesting alternative to regular waxing. We've had little personal experience with these, but enthusiastic reports from RVers keep coming in.

23.02 CAULKING.

Aside from beautification and preservation, frequent washing and waxing forces you to inspect all external surfaces. Use this opportunity to check the caulking and seams on your rig. These junctures will deteriorate over time, and their failure allows damaging moisture to gather where it shouldn't go.

Pay special attention to the caulking around anything mounted on the roof (air-conditioners, etc.), as even gentle knocks from tree limbs can loosen them.

Caulking is very easily repaired by scraping out the old, dried and cracked compound and installing new. Directions on the package are specific, but don't try to apply new caulking on top of the old as it just won't work.

23.03 VENTS AND COMPARTMENTS.

Louvered compartment doors, compartment interiors and vent holes are typical accumulation points for dirt, spider webs and animal nests. Regular sweeping of these areas should be part of a monthly maintenance program for a rig in continuous use — and you should always make such inspections after an RV has remained idle for more than a week. It's also good practice to vacuum around equipment such as refrigerators, generators and anything else that is accessed from the exterior.

23.04 AWNINGS.

The key words for either cotton or vinyl awnings are "keep 'em clean." Dirty awnings promote both mildew and permanent staining. Both will respond well to gentle hosings and sun-drying before you pack them away. Be careful that the cotton types aren't stretched taut when you clean them, as they contract while drying. Also hose off your aluminum poles, especially when they have been exposed to salty air. As some cleaning compounds may damage vinyl awnings, stick to the ones recommended by the manufacturer. A soft brush and gentle strokes can be used to remove stubborn spots on both types.

23.05 LP-GAS TANKS.

LP-gas tanks are generally exposed to the elements and flying debris, so they should be cleaned off frequently and inspected for "dings" and chipped paint. If damage such as this is discovered, and it appears minor, give the area a thorough cleansing and touch it up with paint immediately. Exposed metal will eventually rust and ruin the tank. Major dents should be referred to an authorized service station, where they'll probably run a pressure test to be sure the tank can still tolerate operational conditions. In addition, be sure the regulator is clean; check the regulator vent holes to see that they are free of dirt; and thoroughly clean the hoses and hose connections.

23.06 MISCELLANEOUS CLEANING.

Finally, clean around all receptacles, trailer hook-up umbilical cords and hitch apparatus. On both trailers and motorhomes, hose off the undercarriage and inspect these vulnerable surfaces for damage. Radiator grills should be relieved of their insect collection. Even the engine can benefit from periodic removal of grease buildup. A commercial de-greasing compound should be purchased for this operation, or the vehicle should be taken to a professional steam cleaner.

Chapter Twenty-Four

Storing Your Rig

The consequences of improper RV storage, especially in the winter, range from ruined batteries to actual structural damage. Both climate and length of inactivity determine the risks involved, as well as the protection you'll need to give your rig. As you read through these procedures, you'll quickly see which steps don't fit your circumstances (for instance, several steps can be eliminated if the rig will simply be ''dry docked'' in a temperate climate). And realize, please, that the order of the steps simply makes the most sense to us and isn't meant to be inflexible.

24.01   CLEANING.

The best beginning is a complete inside-and-out cleaning and inspection. This may seem more like a springtime chore, but there are good reasons for doing it now. Road grime (a catchall phrase for a multitude of contaminants), acidic insect bodies and the chemical pollutants in rain and snow will eventually pit or discolor most RV skins. A thorough cleansing, followed by a thick coat of hard wax, will yield a brand-new looking vehicle when you finally hose off the remnants of winter.

As long as you're seeing the skin in such detail, this is the ideal time to check the caulking in seams and moldings. Any portion which shows signs of hardening and deterioration should be re-caulked. Also, notice the condition of door and compartment seals, tighten all exterior screws, and see that vents and stacks are secure and watertight. Remember that insects and animals would like the vents and orifices around an RV for winter homes, so be sure to cover them all securely. And while you're on the roof doing this, clean or replace the air-conditioner filters. (And don't forget to drain the water from evaporator-type air coolers.)

Thoroughly clean the interior, wax appropriate surfaces, take dry cell batteries out of appliances and put a dab of petroleum jelly on the contacts (Figure 1). Sort through everything and remove foods and liquids which could freeze. Give the refrigerator a thorough cleaning and prop the door open. Finally, remove drapes and linens that are likely to mildew in damp air, then cover the windows with aluminum foil, reflective side out. (This would also be a good time to send your drapes, slipcovers and the like to the dry cleaners.)

If you have an awning, unfurl it to be certain it is completely clean and *dry*. It will last much longer if you keep it dry throughout the winter — by either storing it inside or totally protecting it with heavy-gauge plastic. If you choose the latter,

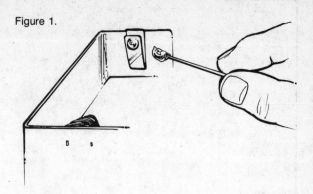

Figure 1.

though, make absolutely sure that the wrapping is waterproof.

24.02   PROTECTING THE LP-GAS SYSTEM.

Protecting the LP-gas system often presents unseen problems in that many dealers sell a mixture of propane and butane and seldom know what the proportions are. This is all right for general operations, but butane won't vaporize below 32 degrees F. while propane's lower limit is minus 44 degrees F. (If you bought your supply in the same area you live in, you're probably OK.) Additionally, no matter how much your LPG dealer protests the idea, the chance that water can contaminate his gas supply is quite high. Add this to typical consumer habits, such as leaving empty LPG cylinders open in moist climates, and you can almost bet there is some water in your system — and that it will freeze when the temperature drops. Potential damage can be circumvented by having a dealer inject a drying agent such as methanol into your tank, and running this through the system and out each appliance. Don't forget to turn all gas supply valves off after purging the lines, then carefully inspect the tank and repair any chipped spots (they will rust and weaken the walls). Finally, wrap the regulators so rain can't accumulate and freeze.

24.03   DRAINING WATER AND SANITATION SYSTEMS.

Preparing the water and sanitation system is simple if you know which type you have (demand or air pressure) and know where the drains are located. Simplistically, a pump that functions synchronously with the opening and closing of a faucet indicates a demand system, while one that runs at odd times is an air compressor. (See Section 11.01 for a complete explanation of both types.) Drains are typically located both at the water heater and near the lowest points in the water system (Figure 2); your owner's manual will

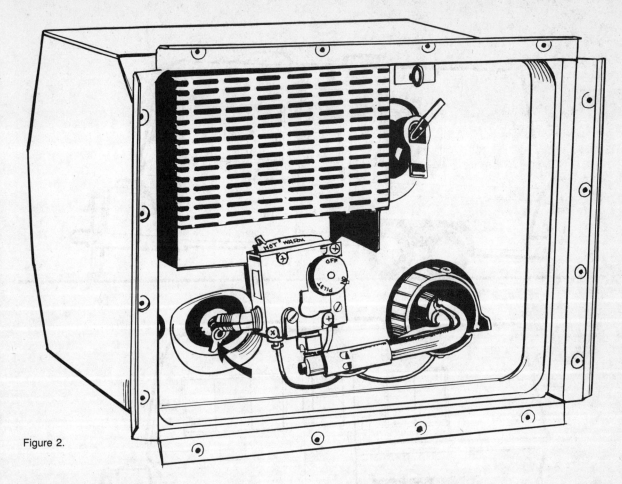

Figure 2.

indicate exact locations.

If you have a demand system, empty it by opening all drains and faucets with the pump switch on. As the system begins to run dry, operate the toilet-flushing mechanism until no more water appears, then do the same with sprays and shower heads — extending their hoses downward so that water will drain out (Figure 3). CAUTION: Switch the pump off as soon as the reservoir is empty, because some pumps will suffer permanent damage if operated dry.

Remove water remaining in the pump by disconnecting the input and outlet hoses (Section 11.12) and then either switching *on* briefly or turning the pump by hand. Empty and clean the in-line strainer (Section 11.08) and reconnect the hoses. If your system uses an accumulator tank (Section 11.06), disassemble and drain it, too. With a trailer, you can "squeeze" out more last drops by using the hitch jack to first elevate and then lower the front end (Figure 3).

With an air pressure system, turn the compressor off and open the water heater and line drains (the water heater may have an air release valve on top which will facilitate draining; otherwise, open the nearest hot water faucet). When water no longer appears at the drains, operate the trailer hitch jack as above.

Now close all the drain valves, and partially repressurize the tank. Open the hot water heater drain valve again. Close it if no more water appears, and begin opening the hot water outlets in your rig one-by-one, until water no longer flows from each. You may have to repressurize the tank before moving from one faucet to the next, but you don't need a full load of air. (Operate the electric supply manually to prevent the compressor from running continuously.) Repeat this procedure with cold water outlets, and be sure to empty the toilet, shower and spray hoses as suggested above.

24.04 DRAINING THE HOLDING TANK.

With both demand and air pressure systems, the next step is to drain the holding tanks. Partially refill both black and gray water tanks, add approved cleansing chemicals, and drive for a few miles to allow the contents to slosh and dislodge any solidified matter clinging to the tank walls. Drain again and flush with clear water. Carefully clean all hoses and lay them straight on an incline to they can completely dry before being stored.

Figure 3.

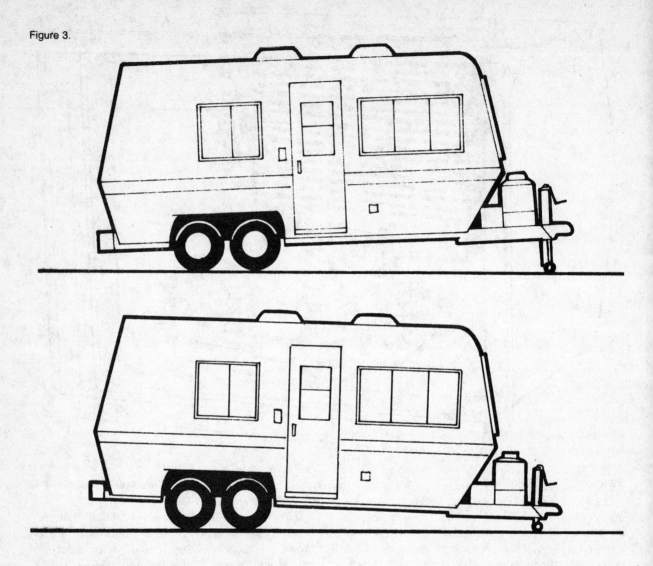

24.05 THE BENEFITS OF ANTIFREEZE.

This is the point where the old-fashioned method of winterizing stops, because no matter how careful you are, it's always possible that some water remains in an obscure corner and will later freeze and cause damage. The modern technique prevents this possibility by injecting antifreeze into both water and sanitation systems.

Antifreeze compounds should be approved for potable water systems, and several brands fit this description. The EPA (Environmental Protection Agency) registration number on these products simply means that the solution meets certain standards and will leave your system sanitized at the end of winter. An EPA number is not a guarantee of efficiency, quality or "goodness." Read the directions carefully for details about diluting for specific temperatures. (CAUTION: Regular automobile antifreeze compounds should not be used because they may be poisonous, and can also damage tanks, lines, hoses and pump seals.)

24.06 PROTECTING WATER FILTERS.

Before injecting antifreeze into the system, you have a decision to make regarding your water purifier. Some people simply ignore the device, flush it out in the spring and continue using it. The danger with this practice is that antifreeze is more viscous than water and could clog some filter cartridges. Also, some parts of the cartridge may still freeze and be harmed. One suggestion is that you save the old filter cartridge in place (some devices won't even function without a cartridge) and install a fresh one when you're ready to travel again. Some RVers keep an old filter on hand specifically for winterizing, thus saving the existing cartridge for actual operation. One word of caution, though: If you do remove a cartridge which you intend to use again, wrap it so that it is completely airtight and keep it in a cold (not freezing) place. Cartridges which are exposed to the air can easily pick up spores.

24.07 INSTALLING ANTIFREEZE.

There are several ways to inject antifreeze into your system. One is simply to put enough chemical in the reservoir to fill both the water heater and all the lines. But water heaters can hold upwards of six gallons and filling it is both pointless and expensive. Alternatively, you can disconnect the input and output lines at the heater and tie them together, effectively bypassing the heater and leaving it dry. (Bypass devices can be purchased at RV supply houses or you can easily do this yourself with a short hose terminating in fittings which are compatible with your heater.)

Alternatively, you can fill hot water lines by backpumping antifreeze through the lines from faucets and showers. This eliminates the need to either bypass or fill the water heater.

Backpumping requires a simple pump device sold in most RV supply stores. Start with the hot water outlet farthest along the line from your heater and, with the heater drain valve open, pump antifreeze into the line until it begins to run out of the heater. (You may need a second person to watch the drain while you pump.) Close that outlet and move to the next farthest faucet. Repeat the process until all hot water outlets have been backpumped.

Cold water lines can be protected simply by pouring some antifreeze into your reservoir. Experience will tell you how much chemical is necessary, but start with a gallon and be prepared to add more if necessary. (With a demand system you can either pour directly into the reservoir or run a hose from the jug of antifreeze to the input side of the pump — see Figure 4). Turn on the pump (or pressurize the tank) and open the farthest outlet. When the distinctive color of the antifreeze appears, let about one cup run down the drain, close the valve and move to the next nearest faucet, repeating until all outlets have produced antifreeze. And while you're at it, don't forget toilets, showers and sprays. (Some people prefer to simply remove toilets, shower heads and sprays from the rig.)

The purpose of seemingly wasting antifreeze down the drain is to force fresh water out of the trap beneath each sink and replace it with chemical. Don't forget to drain this small amount of water from the gray water tank. (You won't need your hose, just collect it in a bucket.) There is no trap beneath the toilet, so the antifreeze will pass directly into the black water tank and may remain there.

An alternative to actually handling the antifreeze compound is offered by the Prevent-A-Freeze system which adds a reservoir of antifreeze in your water line (Figure 5). The antifreeze is injected into the lines when a button inside the coach is pushed.

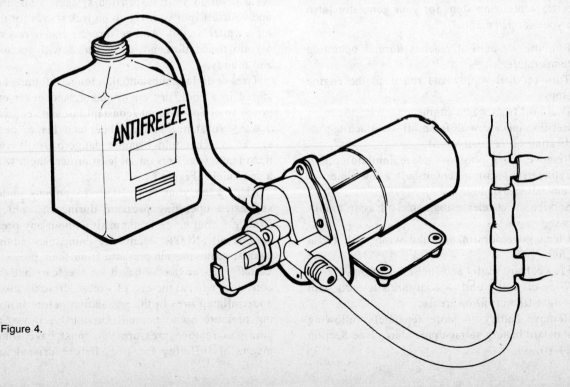

Figure 4.

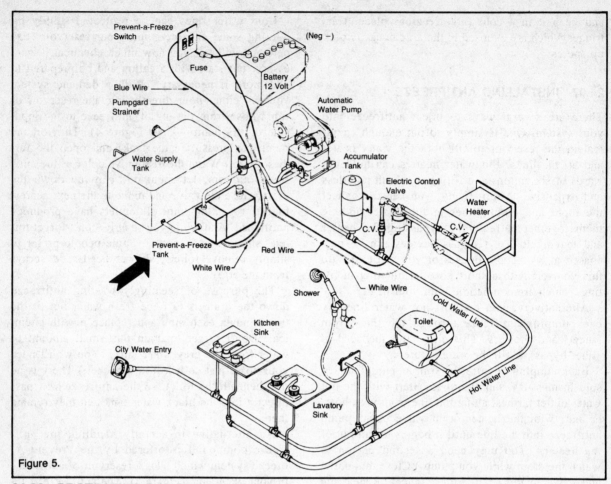

Figure 5.

24.08   PROTECTING THE GENERATOR.

Service technicians at Onan offer the following specific winterizing steps for your generator (also see your service manual):

- Run the set until it reaches normal operating temperature.
- Turn off fuel supply and run until the engine stops.
- Drain oil from warm engine.
- Refill crankcase with fresh oil — attach tag indicating oil viscosity used.
- Remove spark plugs — place inhibitor oil in cylinder(s) — rotate crankshaft a few times — reinstall spark plugs.
- Service air cleaner using same oil as in crankcase.
- Clean governor linkage and wrap with clean cloth.
- Plug exhaust outlet and fuel inlet fitting.
- Wipe off entire unit — coat turnable parts with a light film of oil or grease.
- Remove battery — store separately following standard battery storage procedures (see Section 24.10).

24.09   STORING TIRES.

As a favor to your suspension system, your tires and yourself, put your rig up on jack stands for the long winter's vigil. And be sure the stands rest on a solid foundation, not earth which will get soft and muddy.

Tires will last substantially longer if they are stored in a cool, dry environment, and never exposed to direct sunlight (constant hot sun removes a waxy substance in the rubber and leaves deep cracks which could become dangerous). If you must leave your tires on, at least protect them with a sun shield (Figure 6).

Also, keep your tires 10 to 15 pounds under suggested operating pressure during off-vehicle storage — but *never* let them sit without any pressure at all. NOTE: Many tire companies advise against removing air pressure from their product. Usually this advice is based on the fear that the consumer will, at the end of winter, drive on those underinflated tires to the gas station before bringing pressure up to normal. Obviously, if you're going to remove pressure you must have some means of inflating the tires before driving on

Figure 6.

them. One of the many 12-volt inflation devices would be handy for that purpose.

You should also know that tire pressure will decrease approximately one pound per square-inch for each 10-degree drop in temperature. But rather than trying to predict the weather, your best advice is to check the tire pressure throughout the winter and add air as needed.

24.10 STORING THE BATTERY.

A fully-charged battery will resist freezing down to minus 71 degrees F., but as the battery loses charge so does its resistance to freezing (e.g., at 1/2 charge it will freeze at zero degrees F.). If the battery electrolyte (the liquid in the battery) does freeze, it expands and pops the pellets of active material out of the cell plates.

RVers are sometimes advised to remove their battery and store it inside, but remember that heat causes a loss of charge (e.g., at 80 degrees it will lose roughly one percent charge per day) and a battery which remains in any state of discharge for a period of time loses its ability to regain full power. It's obviously a better idea for unused batteries to be brought to full charge and full electrolyte capacity and then stored in a deep freezer. This suggests that if your rig is parked in continuously freezing weather, you can simply disconnect the battery and let it sit in the vehicle. But if you do this, check it at least every 60 days with a hydrometer and bring it to full charge if necessary.

Maintenance-free batteries will retain their charge roughly six to eight times longer than a conventional battery, but be sure to check them periodically, too.

24.11 WINTERIZING THE VEHICLE.

Motorhomes and vans have one additional dimension — the engine. Accordingly, now is the time to have repairs made so that the rig goes into storage in good condition. Next, give the rig its regular servicing (change the oil, install a new oil filter and air cleaner, etc.), and top off the gas tank so there is less room for condensation and rust. Don't forget to antifreeze the vehicle's cooling system, remove the spark plugs, pour a little oil into the cylinders, then replace the plugs and hand-tighten.

24.12 PARK OR DRIVE?

Where you leave your rig is an important consideration. Make sure that it isn't under bird roosts or trees that will drip sap. In the absence of a garage or carport, some people drape a cover over the body (a porous fabric will let condensation evaporate).

If your storage is in a damp climate, you may benefit from the old yachtsman's trick of leaving one or two low-wattage bulbs burning inside; their heat may be just enough to keep the interior dry.

If you can't thoroughly winterize your RV, the next best idea is to set a regular schedule of driving it. Failing that, at least run the engine for 20 minutes and move it a few feet to change tire position. Most sources suggest this once every three weeks, but we prefer a more frequent schedule just to be on the safe side. (When the rig is to be driven, you'll obviously omit steps such as tire deflation, battery removal, spark plug loosening, etc.)

But no matter how you store it, don't let an RV

sit through a whole winter without a few inspections, both exterior and interior. Catching leaks and problems in their initial stages is defintely to your benefit.

24.13 COMING OUT OF STORAGE.

Spring is the season when owners of winterized RVs collect a huge dividend — if they conscientiously performed all the winterization procedures outlined in the previous chapter. If they didn't? Well, instead of a dividend they're bound to collect a few big bills.

The probability is quite high that if you put your vehicle to rest in top condition it will emerge dirty but healthy. The first step, then, is cleansing. A good soapy water solution and some elbow grease should take care of this matter. As you wash, look carefully and try to detect any skin damage which should be rectified. Sometimes little rust spots will need steel-wooling, or perhaps even a dab of naval jelly for the tough spots. (While you're about it, make a note of these spots for added protection next winter.) Any cracks or deteriorated caulking should also be fixed now.

Pay attention to vents and openings — including the vehicle's grille — for accumulation of dirt, leaves and even animal nests. Check underneath for these same things, too.

The key word through the whole procedure of ''spring shakedown'' is *look*. Remembering Murphy's Law — ''anything which can go wrong will go wrong'' — inspect the rig thoroughly with your eyes. The little things caught now won't become big later.

Interior cleaning should be minimal: dusting, vacuuming and replacing the things you took out last fall. Don't forget to vacuum the burner areas of your furnace, hot water heaters, refrigerator and air-conditioner vents.

24.14 RESTORING BRAKES, WHEELS AND TIRES.

For obvious reasons, the brake system is very important to check. If you've stored the tires and wheels indoors, this is the best time to inspect the linings and trailer brake magnets. After remounting the wheels, be sure to adjust the brakes (see Chapter 2 for a detailed explanation of brake servicing). Also, check all hydraulic brake lines running from a trailer to the tow vehicle.

Before removing the jack stands that supported the RV all winter, bring tires up to normal operating inflation. Then check them thoroughly for signs of cracking or any kind of damage. (As your rig is still elevated, you'll want to rotate your wheels now, too.) Some RVers also use this opportunity to apply one of the several rubber preservative compounds; tire companies won't recommend them, but neither will they advise against them, and from our experience they seem to do a good job.

Don't forget to check trailer brake functioning via both the breakaway switch and the tow vehicle's activation system. And don't neglect the safety chain and coupling mechanism on both the trailer and tow vehicle.

24.15 RESTORING THE VEHICLE.

Using the proper wrench, tighten your spark plugs and make sure the engine compartment is in top shape. Clean out any dirt, check the oil, brake fluid, coolant, power steering and windshield washer fluid-levels. Have a mechanic check for condensation in the oil system. Reinstall the battery and be sure it's still in top condition with a full load of electrolyte.

Now is also a good time for changing lubrication and performing any other regular service recommended in your vehicle manual.

Reinstall the awning and check for both security and functionality of the mountings and mechanisms.

On trailers, check the lubrication on the load-equalizers and jack assembly. On campers, check the external hardware for both integrity and functioning, lubricating as necessary.

24.16 REACTIVATING THE WATER AND SANITATION SYSTEMS.

If you filled the water and sanitation systems with antifreeze last fall, it's not necessary to drain it as you did for winterizing. Simply purge the antifreeze out by flushing several times with fresh water and let it collect in the holding tanks.

After you're satisfied that the antifreeze has been forced out, refill the freshwater tank and chlorinate. Pump this mixture through the system, opening each dispensing outlet until you can smell the chlorine, and you're through. Be sure to reinstall your water filter or cartridge before using the water for drinking.

Check toilets, shower heads and any water-consuming appliances for correct operation. If you used a water heater bypass in the winterization process, reconnect the heater in the functioning manner now. Finally, check everywhere for water leaks.

24.17 RESTORING THE LP-GAS SYSTEM.

Visually scan all the gas lines and test connections before turning on the gas at the main shutoff valve. Then, with the gas supply on, test the whole system for leaks. If you have a leak detector installed (Section 14.07) this is simple. If not, use the old soapy-water method (Section 14.09).

When you're positive that there are no leaks, operate each gas-burning appliance independently to check for proper functioning (see the Troubleshooting Section in the appropriate chapters of this manual for any appliance which doesn't run perfectly).

Give the LP-gas tanks a visual inspection for dents or signs of rust. Rust will obviously weaken the tank walls and should be taken seriously (Section 14.13). Also, have a technician check the gas regulator to be sure it's supplying the correct pressure.

24.18 RECONNECTING THE ELECTRICAL SYSTEM.

If you have an auxiliary battery for the 12-volt system, check this out now. Before switching on the power, inspect the electrical lines for soundness, paying special attention to attachment and connection points. Then, with the power on, individually operate everything that functions on 12-volt electricity. Also, test items which run off the vehicle's main battery, like exterior running and operating lights. It's a good added precaution to test the 12-volt supply from both batteries with a voltmeter, as appliances can be hurt by asking them to run on low voltage.

If you also have a 115 VAC electrical system, give it the same performance and metering tests.

24.19 AWAKENING THE GENERATOR.

Generators require a special routine for properly returning to service. This sequence is suggested by Onan for a unit which has been properly winterized:

- Remove the cover and all protective wrappings. Wipe off the oil film from all exposed engine parts. Remove the plug from the exhaust outlet.

- Visually inspect the unit for any damage. Check to be sure the carburetor and governor linkage are free. Remove the generator belt band and check to be sure the brushes work freely in their holders.

- Check the tag to ensure oil of the proper brand and grade has been installed. Check the oil level.

- Install the battery (be sure battery is fully charged), observing proper polarity.

- Remove spark plugs, clean and gap. Turn the engine over by hand several times. Reinstall spark plugs.

- Turn on fuel, disconnect electric fuel pump lead (and electric fuel solenoid shutoff lead, if unit is so equipped). Jumper the fuel pump and electric fuel solenoid shutoff leads to the battery to prime the unit. Use the hand-primer lever on units with mechanical pumps. Reconnect the leads.

- Remove all load and start the generator set at the unit. Initial start may be slow, due to oil or rust inhibitor in the cylinders. Excessive smoke and rough operation will occur until the oil or rust inhibitor is burned off.

- Apply a 50% load after the set runs smooth. Allow the generator set to warm up (one hour) with the load connected. Check speed and voltage.

- Unit is now ready for service.

24.20 THE TEST RUN.

When you're positive that everything has been restored to operational order, the final step is to take a short shakedown cruise. Be very gentle and slow at first: Try the brakes at slow speeds, listen for unusual sounds and test the turning and general functioning of the vehicle in a cautious manner. The rig has been sleeping a long time; give it a chance to stretch slow and easy just like you do in the morning.

RV REPAIR AND MAINTENANCE LOG

DATE	TYPE OF SERVICE	COST	COMMENTS

DATE	TYPE OF SERVICE	COST	COMMENTS

DATE	TYPE OF SERVICE	COST	COMMENTS

DATE	TYPE OF SERVICE	COST	COMMENTS

DATE	TYPE OF SERVICE	COST	COMMENTS

DATE	TYPE OF SERVICE	COST	COMMENTS

DATE	TYPE OF SERVICE	COST	COMMENTS

DATE	TYPE OF SERVICE	COST	COMMENTS